CANADA'S
CHANGING
GEOGRAPHY

A Selection of Readings Edited by

+ICDN

Library of Congress Catalog Card No. 66-23337

11290

2   3   4   5   71   70   69   68
PRINTED AND BOUND IN CANADA

Contents

INTRODUCTION 4

LIST OF CONTRIBUTORS 6

PART I—THE ECUMENE **7**

1 The Canadian Ecumene–Inhabited and Uninhabited Areas
    Roman T. Gajda 8

PART II—OCCUPANCE **14**

2 The Indian Occupance of Huronia, 1600—1650
    Conrad E. Heidenreich 15

3 Some Remarks on the Seigneurial Geography of Early Canada
    R. Cole Harris 30

4 The Agricultural Background of Settlement in Eastern Nova Scotia
    R. Louis Gentilcore 34

5 Western Canada in 1886
    John H. Warkentin 56

PART III—THE LAND CHANGES **83**

6 Agricultural Regions of Southern Ontario in 1880 and 1951
    Lloyd G. Reeds 84

7 Settlement Migration in Central Bonavista Bay, Newfoundland
    C. Grant Head 92

8 New Light From Labrador-Ungava
    F. Kenneth Hare 111

9 The Future Colonization of Northern Canada
    Trevor Lloyd 130

PART IV—INDUSTRY AND CITIES **138**

10 The Spatial Organization of the Iron and Steel Industry in Canada
    Donald Kerr 139

11 The Location of United States Subsidiaries in Southern Ontario
    D. Michael Ray 149

12 The Growth of Toronto
    Donald Kerr and Jacob Spelt 163

13 Industrial Development in the Vancouver Area
    P. D. McGovern 182

14 Large Urban Places in the Prairie Provinces–Their Development and Location
    Karl Lenz 199

PART V—CANADIAN REGIONALISM **212**

15 Canadian Regionalism in Life and Letters
    J. Wreford Watson 213

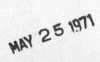

Introduction

The articles in this volume were chosen with two objectives in mind. First, they provide an introduction to the geography of Canada as seen by Canadian geographers. Each selection is the work of a professional geographer whose research has been focussed, in significant measure, on Canada. The bulk of the material has been reprinted from geographical literature. Some has been revised by its authors. One selection was translated from the German original. Four articles appear in print for the first time.

The second purpose of the collection is to emphasize the significance of change in Canada's geography. We are a young country and the study of our geography is still in its infancy. Nevertheless, changes have been extensive and their effects dramatic. It seems appropriate to take stock of what's been happening.

Among the main concerns of the geographer are distribution and areal differences. These have very limited meaning without reference to change. In the words of Ackerman, "Any fundamental understanding of distribution must probe the character and operation of the processes which produce the change".[1] Material for this collection has been chosen to convey some of the variety and the extent of change in Canada's geography, and to indicate the ways in which it has occurred.

In its short history, Canada has been confronted with tremendous developmental difficulties. Occupance was a heroic struggle against continental conditions and physical obstacles. The result has been a new geography, shaped by cultural processes. Foremost among these has been settlement—the movement of people, their establishment on the land and their transformation of it through the economic, political and technological means at their disposal. The articles in this volume have been arranged in sections, representing different aspects of settlement, beginning with early occupance and culminating in the complex geography of cities.

To set the stage, some excerpts from Gajda's "The Canadian Ecumene" are presented. The accomplishments of man in this country need to be put in spatial perspective. The map of the Canadian ecumene does this. Dramatically, it tells us that the effectively settled parts of the country are a very small, almost insignificant, part of the whole. But the map is misleading. What is more important is what has happened in these settled parts, the kind of transformation that has taken place within them, and the ways in which various peoples have initiated the changes. In its ecumene, Canada exhibits a maturity of development that contrasts sharply with conditions in the virtually untouched areas beyond.

The articles in Section II provide examples of early occupance and its accomplishments. Heidenreich examines a segment of the human geography of aboriginal Canada. Reconstructing the salient features of Huronia before 1650, he establishes the main components of the settlement pattern, the factors in its distribution and the effect of occupance on the land. Next to the aboriginal populations, the oldest Canadian stock is of French origin. Before 1760, its settlement created a unique geography, well described in professional literature.[2] But Harris looks at early Canada in a new way. He claims that its seigneurial system was irrelevant to the development of a distinctive human geography. In the article on Nova Scotia, attention is directed to another ethnic group, the Highland Scots. The background to their settlement and its role in a new land are examined. The resultant geography is reconstructed and its conditions traced through subsequent periods. Warkentin's subject is Western Canada, at a critical stage in its development, when many of the forces that produced its present geography began to operate effectively. His division of the area into regions is based on the extent and character of settlement and the land use prevailing in 1886.

In Section III, Canadian development is carried to modern times. Four faces of change are presented, each associated with one of Canada's primary economic activities. Reeds compares the agricultural geography of southern Ontario in 1880 and 1951, emphasizing the increasing concentration on more productive land with changes in technology and economic conditions. Head takes us to a very different part of Canada, to an area of Newfoundland where livelihood is tied not to the land but to the sea. Even here, however, the land changes; whole settlements have migrated, in response to a new set of social and economic conditions. The awakening of the huge wilderness of Labrador-Ungava is the subject of the next article. Not only does Hare unfold its story of past and potential economic achievements but he also establishes its physical basis in a step-by-step account of how the geographer explores a new area. Beyond the exploited areas of Labrador-Ungava and its other Canadian counterparts, stretches the barren immensity of the North, the bulk of uninhabited Canada, where man's impact has been minimal. What are its prospects for the future? Is man likely to change its geography any more than he has in the past? Lloyd addresses himself to these questions and draws some sobering conclusions.

Striking though they may be, the developments examined in Section III pale beside those that have taken place in the heart of the ecumene. We have become a predominantly urban country. Urbanization and industrialization dominate our geography. It is here that man's ability to establish new forms on the land reaches a climax. The way in which geographers have examined these changes is indicated in the articles in Section IV. Kerr's summary of the iron and steel industry stresses its main features of distribution and relates them to a number of locational factors. Ray applies quantitative techniques to an important aspect of Canadian industry, developing a general concept of industrial location to help explain the distribution of United States subsidiary plants in southern Ontario. In a more localized study, Kerr and Spelt examine the growth of Toronto with particular reference to its manufacturing and its role as a financial, trading and service centre. The development of these functions is related to market, labour supply and transportation facilities. McGovern's study of Vancouver is primarily concerned with industrial changes and illustrates the type of detailed analysis applicable to this aspect of urban growth. The next article deals with development and patterns on a completely different scale. Lenz reconstructs a geographic panorama through time, summarizing the main features of urban change in the Prairie Provinces from the beginning of urbanization to the present.

No attempt has been made in this volume to emphasize regional geography. At the same time, many of the articles contain material that is indispensable to this type of study. Regional differences in Canada are so well marked that they are the best reflection we have of the important changes that have taken place in our geography. Accordingly, the collection is brought to a close with an essay on Canadian regionalism. Watson presents the personality of each major region in geographic terms, heightening his portrayals with selections from the literature of that region. Regionalism embraces both diversification and interdependence. As we celebrate the centennial of Confederation, it is pertinent to reflect that Canada's changing geography, which obviously contributes to diversity, may well be an element in strengthening unity.

Any collection of articles derives its major strength from the material that has been used. Special thanks, therefore, are due to the authors who so graciously allowed the inclusion of their published or unpublished works. I am also grateful to Mary Buckley for assistance in typing and to Wolfe Darnel for the translation of the Lenz article.

R. L. G.

*

FOOTNOTES

1. E. A. Ackerman, *Geography as a Fundamental Research Discipline,* Department of Geography, Research Paper, No. 53 (University of Chicago, 1958), p. 18.
2. Two examples are Pierre Deffontaines, "Le Rang, Type de Peuplement Rural du Canada Français," *Cahiers de Géographie de Québec,* No. 5 (1953), pp. 3-32 and M. Derruau, "A l'Origine du Rang Canadien," *Cahiers de Géographie,* Nouvelle Série, No. 1 (1956), pp. 39–48.

*

LIST OF CONTRIBUTORS

GAJDA, ROMAN T.   6
Research Geographer, Geographical Branch, Department of Mines and Technical Surveys, Ottawa.

GENTILCORE, R. LOUIS   32
Associate Professor of Geography, McMaster University, Hamilton.

HARE, F. KENNETH   109
Master of Birkbeck College, London; formerly Professor of Geography, King's College, London and McGill University, Montreal.

HARRIS, R. COLE   28
Assistant Professor of Geography, University of Toronto.

HEAD, GRANT C.   90
Ph.D. Candidate, Department of Geography, University of Wisconsin, Madison, Wisconsin.

HEIDENREICH, CONRAD E.   13
Ph.D. Candidate, McMaster University; formerly instructor in Geography, York University, Toronto.

KERR, DONALD   137
Professor of Geography, University of Toronto.

LENZ, KARL   197
Professor, Geographisches Institut, Technische Hochschule, Hannover (Germany).

LLOYD, TREVOR   128
Professor of Geography, McGill University.

MCGOVERN, PETER D.   180
Assistant Chief Planner, Livingston New Town, Scotland; formerly with the Lower Mainland Regional Planning Board of British Columbia.

RAY, D. MICHAEL   147
Research Geographer, Spartan Air Services Limited, Ottawa.

REEDS, LLOYD G.   82
Professor of Geography, McMaster University.

SPELT, JACOB   161
Professor of Geography, University of Toronto.

WARKENTIN, JOHN H.   54
Associate Professor of Geography, York University.

WATSON, J. WREFORD   211
Professor of Geography, University of Edinburgh.

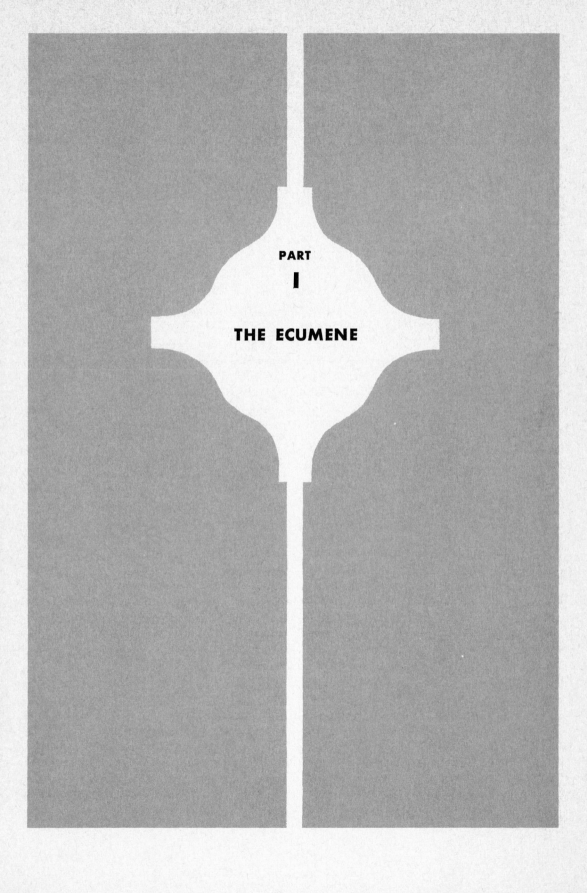

PART

I

THE ECUMENE

1

The Canadian Ecumene – Inhabited and Uninhabited Areas*

ROMAN T. GAJDA

* *From* Geographical Bulletin, *No. 15 (1960), pp. 5-18. Excerpts reprinted by permission of the Queen's Printer. Revised by the author.*

That part of Canada which is settled and effectively utilized represents a relatively small strip along the U.S. border. To the north the land is either sparsely inhabited or uninhabited; here, only scattered areas have as yet been developed economically, but nevertheless, this area is of increasing strategic and economic importance.

Although a need has existed for factual data on the Canadian ecumene,[1] until recently no studies have been made to delineate these areas, or to establish a classification applicable to types found in Canada. Jefferson's study was mainly concerned with the problem of population distribution in southern Canada.[2] Since 1934, there has been considerable population growth, settlement has spread, and tremendous development has taken place in northern areas of the country. This preliminary study attempts to differentiate between the various types of ecumene, and to map the characteristic zones, irrespective of political divisions.

The original plotting of occupied and unoccupied areas was done on large scale topographic maps ranging in scale from 1 : 50,000 to 8 miles to 1 inch. The townships or municipalities have been used as unit areas. Where necessary, the enumeration areas of these divisions were used.

The data enumerated by the census were localized and rearranged to obtain a detailed distribution of population. This was accomplished by using visitation records prepared by enumerators, and analyzing recent large-scale topographic maps. Additional information, particularly with regard to land utilization, was obtained through analysis of airphotos, from published works and through interviews with people familiar with the areas in question. This refinement of geographic procedure enabled the writer to map inhabited and uninhabited land across Canada. The results were transferred to a 35-miles-to-1-inch base map on which the occupied and unoccupied areas were measured by planimeter. Very small areas that could not be measured precisely were attributed nominal values. Finally, for the purpose of this paper the information has been further generalized.

Canada's enormous area of 3,560,000 square miles contains a population of 18,238,300 according to the 1961 Census of Canada. This gives a density of only 5.1 persons per square mile. Even if the 1,458,800 square miles of the sparsely populated or totally uninhabited areas of the Yukon and the Northwest Territories are excluded, the density increases only to 8.7 persons per

TABLE I
AREA OF ECUMENE AND REAL POPULATION DENSITY

Province	Land area in sq. miles	Ecumene in sq. miles	Per cent	Population*	Density of population	
					p.sq.m. of total area	p.sq.m. of ecumene
Newfoundland	143,045	9,400	6.6	457,853	3.2	48.7
P. E. I	2,184	2,184	100	104,629	47.9	47.9
Nova Scotia	20,402	11,000	53.9	737,007	36.1	67.0
New Brunswick	27,835	17,400	62.5	597,936	21.5	34.4
Quebec	523,860	65,900	12.6	5,259,211	10.0	79.8
Ontario	344,092	65,700	19.1	6,236,092	18.1	94.9
Manitoba	211,775	36,640	17.3	921,686	4.4	25.2
Saskatchewan	220,182	103,700	47.1	925,181	4.2	8.9
Alberta	248,800	74,720	30.0	1,331,944	5.4	17.8
British Columbia	359,279	31,600	8.8	1,629,082	4.5	51.6
Canada excl. of the Territories	2,101,454	418,244	19.9	18,200,621	8.7	43.5
Yukon Territory	205,346	1,979	0.9	14,628	0.07	7.4
Northwest Territory	1,253,438	4,144	0.3	22,998	0.02	5.5
Canada	3,560,238	424,367	11.9	18,238,247	5.1	43.1

*Census of Canada, 1961, Introductory Report, Vol. I

square mile. However, large empty areas are still included in this calculation. The real density of population is much greater. According to the writer's research, the utilized land in Canada amounts to 418,000 square miles excluding the territories, or to 424,000 square miles if the territories are included. Therefore, the real density of population amounts to 43.5 or 43.1 persons per square mile, respectively, a figure comparatively high for a young country. The above table gives further details with reference to the provinces and territories.

The greater part of the ecumene comprises a strip of land in the south whose core coincides with the area of farm lands and the dense populous zone. (Fig. 1) To the north, beyond this strip and the fringe of settlement, the ecumene has a different characteristic as no appreciable use of land is connected with agriculture. In place of the familiar southern landscape of rural and urban settlement with its continuous and integrated transportation and communication systems, the north is an area where the marks of cultural environment are discontinuous, absent, or found only in narrow connective strings or patches. There are, nonetheless, enclaves of the familiar rural and urban landscape and vestiges of man's former occupation in the form of cut-over forest and abandoned mines. This region contains within its boundaries all of the Yukon and Northwest Territories and large parts of every province with the exception of the Maritime Provinces. Broadly speaking, there are actually two Canadas: Northern Canada, which involves an immense area of over three million square miles or about six-sevenths of Canada's land area on which less than 2 per cent of the nation's population lives; and Southern Canada, an area of less than half a million square miles but occupied by more than 98 per cent of the population.

On the basis of the distribution population, types of settlements and the resource complexes, four different zones have been delineated (Figure 1.)

*

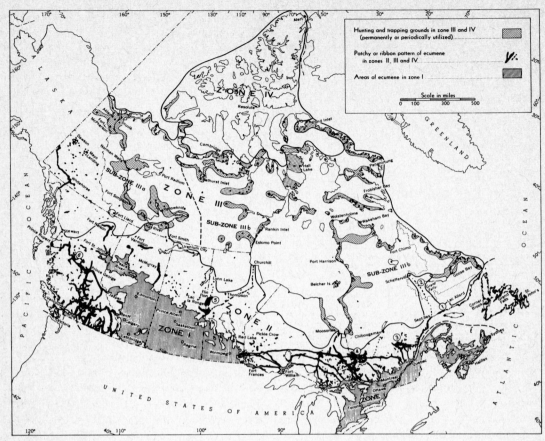

FIG. 1. The Canadian Ecumene

*

ZONE I

Zone I, in the south, is densely populated and shows utilized agricultural land, although not comparable with the absolute density figures of many European countries. The narrow strip of utilized and populated land is not continuous, but is divided into segments of widths varying from several miles in the eastern part of the country to 600 miles in the Prairie Provinces. The Maritime Provinces are separated from Quebec by the sparsely populated and isolated zone of Gaspé Peninsula, whereas the Prairie Provinces and the St. Lawrence Lowlands are separated by a belt of Canadian Shield 900 miles wide. Finally, the Pacific coast is cut off from the agricultural plains by the thinly-populated Rocky Mountains area and the interior plateaux.

Most notable in this zone is the large extension of the ecumene in the west, that of the Peace River region where the cultivation of grain crops and starchy roots has been established for over 30 years.[3] This most northerly extension is very promising economically as it lies entirely within the high potential oil and gas-bearing area. Because of this favorable resource complex this area is likely to extend farther north in the foreseeable future.

The entire zone is not static and changes occur slowly over periods of time with further clearing of forested land. However, most of the good agricultural land within the populous zone has already been taken up.

ZONE II

Zone II is semi-populated and has a completely different settlement pattern from Zone I. The population pattern and land utilization in Zone II, extending from Newfoundland to British Columbia either follows railways, roads and coastlines in a strip-like fashion, or is found in small patches. It embraces a large part of the belt crossed by the transcontinental railways and branch lines, several of which spur deeply to the north providing important transportation routes to mining and lumbering communities. Here the population spreads northward in small groups, although the amount of land in farms is either negligible or non-existent. Several of these enclaves of the ecumene serviced by railway lines are important. In the far eastern part of the zone, a small enclave is located in the Allard Lake area, a titanium mining community. The second one extends deeply into the north as far as Schefferville, an iron ore mining centre. Associated with it to the south are the recent mining developments of the iron belt in the Wabush Lake, Mount Reed and Mount Wright region, and the hydro-electric power site at Grand Falls, Newfoundland. The third large enclave is located in the Lake St. John-Saguenay River area and is associated with the presence of good soil deposited in relatively inhospitable surroundings on the Canadian Shield. Excellent power resources of the Saguenay River offer good opportunities for the extension of this ecumene to the east; the mining activities in the Chibougamau copper area allow for its extension in a northwesterly direction. The fourth large extension toward the north

is in the Clay Belt. This area is typical of pioneer farm land and the development of agriculture has met with varying success. The gold fields of the Porcupine area have greatly contributed to the development of the region.

The God's Lake enclave in northern Manitoba is associated with a mineralized zone, but development here is proceeding very slowly. The fifth enclave lies in the prairies and is associated exclusively with the zinc and nickel mining field of Flin Flon and the more recent development of the copper-nickel mines in the Lynn Lake region. Land utilization in the southern part of this enclave is associated with the agricultural development in the area of The Pas, an important communication centre. Finally in the extreme west, on the Pacific side of the Cordillera, strips of land between Prince Rupert and Prince George, particularly along Skeena River, are cultivated with acreages mostly in tame hay or in grain crops. The strip-like pattern of land utilization in southern British Columbia reflects the varying topography and terrain conditions. The development of land in this area is restricted by the mountainous character of the region, with elevations of over 3,000 feet.

Of interest is the penetration into this zone of railways to Hudson Bay at Moosonee and at Churchill, the largest harbor in Northern Canada, and by the Mackenzie Highway to the Hay River settlement on the shores of Great Slave Lake which marks its most northerly extension.

ZONE III

This sparsely populated and comparatively little utilized zone contains within its boundaries the bulk of Canada's land area. It stretches far north to approximately 70° N.

latitude, and from the Alaska border in the west to Baffin Bay, Davis Strait and Labrador Sea in the east. This zone may be divided into two sub-zones: a western area that is more settled and better developed (sub-zone IIIA); and the central and eastern area which is mostly inhabited by Eskimos, and where there has been little exploration or economic development.

In this zone modern mining communities have been superimposed upon an original background of native Indian and Eskimo settlements that were based on a hunting economy. The characteristic patchy appearance of utilized land is confined as a rule to areas occupied by groups of people whose livelihood depends on mining, lumbering, hunting, trapping, fishing, or fur trading. In addition there are personnel servicing land for water routes and airfields, scientific stations and other research and defence establishments. The settlements, of course, reflect those economic activities. There are approximately 200 settlements in this zone, ranging in size from Yellowknife and Whitehorse, with populations of approximately 5000, to tiny communities of 5 to 25 people.

*

ZONE IV

The last and most northerly zone, consisting mainly of the Arctic Archipelago, is virtually empty. The land is totally unused and is uninhabited, with the exception of one Eskimo settlement in Arctic Bay and a few meteorological stations or police posts, where a number of Eskimo families gather.

*

THE DEVELOPMENT OF THE ECUMENE

In Southern Canada (Zone I), the development of agriculture was the basis for the exploitation of other components in the resource complex and was responsible for the establishment of the ecumene; in the Canadian North (Zones II, III and IV), it is apparent that the exploitation of mineral resources is often the basis for the exploitation of other resources, and consequently the development of settlements. The fact that the non-mineral resources are discontinuous or thinly spread restricts the type of exploitation that would absorb the cost of transportation to distant markets. Metallic minerals, and oil and gas, on the other hand, having a high value in comparison to weight, and being generally in demand on the world market, can better bear the relatively high transportation costs imposed by the vast area of the north. In general the richness of the non-mineral resources decreases with higher latitudes, which means that the farther the non-mineral resources are from national or world markets, the poorer are the economic returns. With the mineral resources, however, this does not hold to such an extent. It is possible that a very remote deposit can be rich enough to merit the development of transportation for its exploitation. This has indeed been the case with all the remote, exploited deposits, such as at Yellowknife, Lynn Lake or Schefferville.

The development of a mineral deposit creates a settlement in which there are essential community services. It also creates a market for other local resources which would otherwise not be developed. The mining belt of northern Ontario and western Quebec is a very good example of the exploitation of local resources for the local market supplied by the mining development.

However, in the clay belts adjoining the Porcupine gold mining field, agricultural products, particularly dairy products, cannot compete in other than local markets. The mines supply a considerable market for forest products, chiefly pit props and rough lumber, and there are industries ancillary to mining, such as foundries. Most of the inhabitants of this region, except those engaged in the logging industry, are employees of the mines or are supported by the mining industry. The local logging industry is, for the most part, independent of the mining industry. This is possible because a large part of the area is in the Ottawa River drainage basin, permitting cheap transportation of logs to the south, and because the area is traversed by intercontinental rail lines, whose existence is for the most part independent of local resources. Despite these incidental features, the mining belt of northern Ontario and western Quebec is a good example of the exploitation of a northern resource complex based on the primary exploitation of minerals.

It follows that the commercial exploitation of the resources of the north are to a considerable degree dependent on the development of transportation. On this factor depends further expansion of the ecumene.

In Zone I, the resource complex consists of agriculture, minerals, water power, wildlife and some forest. In Zone II, the resource complex includes commercial forest, water power, minerals, discontinuous areas of soils suitable for some agriculture, domestic and non-domestic grazing, commercial and sporting fresh-water fish, game and fur-bearing animals.

In Zone III, the complex is composed of some soil suitable for limited agriculture, mostly garden produce and some domestic grazing; commercial forests, game animals and fish, fur-bearing animals, some water power and inorganic and organic minerals, chiefly oil. In Subzone IIIA this complex is more intensified, whereas in Subzone IIIB its intensity diminishes considerably with minerals being the dominant resource.

In Zone IV, the resource complex consists of some soils suitable for non-domestic grazing; some fur-bearing animals, primarily white fox, coastal animals, such as seals, whales, walrus, and polar bear, some fish, oil, and minerals. There is no agriculture, forest or water-power. This zone cannot support human life, and the scientific posts and other stations are supplied from outside.

*

FOOTNOTES

1. In this study *"ecumene"* refers to land where man has made his permanent home and to all *work areas* which are considered occupied and utilized for agricultural or any other economic purposes.

2. M. Jefferson, "The Problem of the Ecumene," *Geografiska Annaler,* Vol. 16 (1934), p. 461.

3. M. K. Bennett, "The Isoline of Ninety Frost Free Days in Canada," *Economic Geography,* Vol. 35, (1), (1959), p. 48.

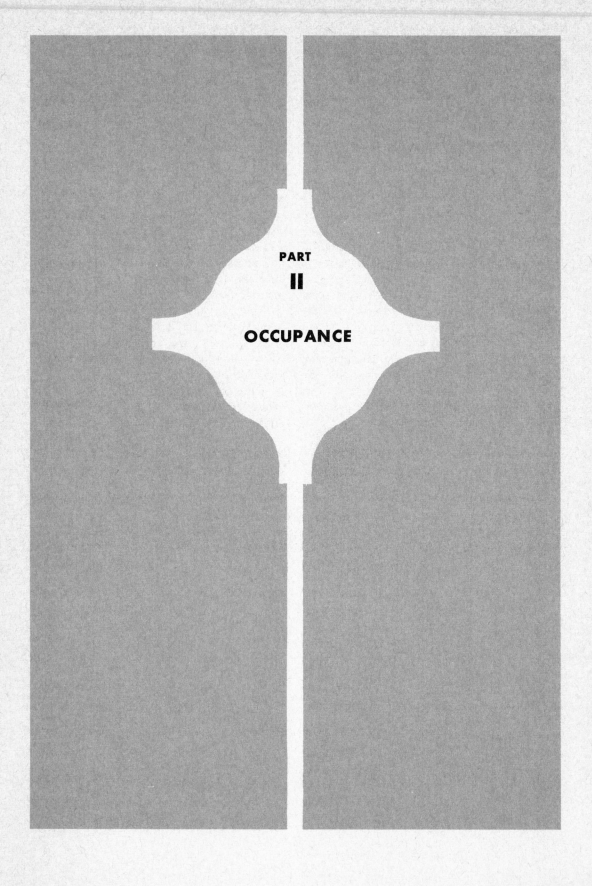

PART

II

OCCUPANCE

2

The Indian Occupance of Huronia, 1600-1650[*]

CONRAD E. HEIDENREICH

[*] *From* The Canadian Geographer, *VII* (3)
(1963), *pp. 131-144. Revised by the author.*

The Hurons, or Wendats as they called themselves, hold an extremely important position in the early development of this country. By about 1600, they occupied the northern part of Simcoe County (Fig. 1), and were engaged in a lively trade with the Petun and Neutrals to the south, and the Algonquins to the north. With the Algonquins, they were also allied in a war against the powerful Iroquois Confederacy located south of Lake Ontario.

When Champlain arrived on the scene, the Quebec and Montreal areas were under Algonquin control. Because he needed the co-operation of the local Indians in the fur trade and their guidance in exploring the Great Lakes system, he was obliged to commit France to the Huron-Algonquin alliance against the Iroquois. The Hurons, in turn, rapidly adapted their trade network to become the middlemen between the French and their old trading partners the Petun, Neutrals and Algonquins. This position they jealously guarded. Huron control of the route to the northern fur country led the Iroquois, once they had run out of furs in their own territory, to eliminate them. But until 1650, the Hurons held the key to the French fur trade, and the key to French success in Canada.

Like the other Indians of the eastern United States and Canada south of the "Shield", the Hurons practiced a shifting type of agriculture, derived about three-quarters of their diet from agricultural produce, and lived in compact, semi-permanent villages. This paper deals with the human geography of the Hurons prior to the great disasters of the late 1630's and 1640's.

*

POPULATION, MIGRATION PATTERNS AND DISTRIBUTION OF VILLAGE SITES

During their visit to the Hurons, both Champlain[1] (1615) and Sagard[2] (1623) estimated that there were about 30,000 people living in 18 to 25 villages in what is now the northern part of Simcoe County, Ontario (Huronia). According to Le Jeune this figure was still about the same in 1636[3] but, as a result of war and disease, had declined to between 10,000 to 12,000 by 1639.[4] In 1649, the population of the once crowded

15

Huronia consisted of about 6,000 starving refugees on Christian Island.[5] Famine, disease and the ever present Iroquois armies had taken a dreadful toll. Some had managed to escape to the Erie, Petun and Neutral Nations, but most decided to stay with the Jesuit Fathers. By the spring of 1650, winter famine had further reduced the Christian Island group to a mere 300 men, women and children.[6] In that year, this remnant left Huronia with the missionary fathers for the comparative safety of Quebec.

Figure 1 shows the distribution of Huron village sites in Simcoe County. One of the outstanding patterns is the concentration of historic sites in the northern portion of the County. The percentage of historic to prehistoric sites ranges from a high of 80 and 75 in Medonte and Tay to a low of 17 and 14 in Innisfil and Tecumseth (Table I). It appears, then, that a north-

TABLE I

PERCENTAGE OF SITES CONTAINING FRENCH
TRADE MATERIAL

Township	Percentage
Medonte	80
Tay	75
Orillia	66
Tiny	51
Oro	35
Nottawasaga	35
Vespra	27
West Gwillimbury	20
Innisfil	17
Flos	16
Tecumseth	14

ward shift of the Huron population had taken place in late prehistoric and in historic times. This shift must have been gradual at first but later accelerated under strong Iroquois pressure. Since Champlain, Sagard, and the Jesuits did not mention Huron villages south of Kempenfelt Bay, one can assume that the historic villages in that area had received their trade material and been abandoned before Champlain's arrival in Huronia in 1615. This is entirely possible, because Champlain relates as early as 1603 that the Algonquins were trading French goods to the Hurons ("the good Iro-

quois").[7] French merchants were trading in the Tadoussac area with the Algonquins by 1600, so it is almost certain that some trade goods had reached Huronia before the turn of the century. The Hurons themselves did not come to trade with the French until June 1611, two years after their joint raid against the Iroquois with Champlain and some Algonquins, and four years before Champlain visited them.[8] At one time the Hurons certainly occupied a greater area. Champlain, for instance, relates that within their memory the Hurons lived further to the south and to the east, near the Kawartha Lakes.[9] A slow migration from the south and the east into Huronia as suggested by historical records, seems to be supported by archaeological evidence based on the distribution of pottery traits.[10,11,12] Such a migration pattern could also account for the fact that the Hurons were composed of four clans who, according to the stories they told Le Jeune, arrived in Huronia separately, and not too long before 1600.[13]

The problem of Huron migrations is by no means solved. Ridley suggests a uniform late prehistoric Huron population in the area between Toronto and Georgian Bay, which gradually withdrew north into historic Huronia.[14]

Which theory of Huron migration patterns is correct, is difficult to say. One can probably not answer this question with finality until more reliable dating techniques have been devised. At any rate, the Hurons at one time did occupy other areas, and did move further north in late prehistoric and historic times. With shifting cultivation some migration is necessary. But it must be kept in mind that this particular migration was in only one direction—north, away from the Iroquois. As has been suggested by some authors, closer trade relations with the Algonquins may have played a part in this northward movement,[15] but it is unlikely that an agricultural people would move toward a nomadic one. The reverse is usually true. The principal reason for this movement, as the Hurons themselves often said, was unquestionably the attacks of roving bands of

Iroquois, who were not only better warriors, but were also better organized than the Hurons. During pre-Champlain times, villages on the southern fringe of Huronia had to be abandoned. As this process continued the southernmost villages were, as a rule, more heavily fortified.[16] During historic times Huronia shrank further into itself, culminating in a last refuge on Christian Island. The driving motives behind the Iroquois were the age old rancours of inter-tribal warfare and the prospects of eliminating the Hurons as rivals in the fur trade.[17] The possession of a greater number of guns and better methods of warfare finally tipped the scale permanently in favour of the Iroquois. In Champlain's time, the French did not trade guns to their allies because they never quite trusted them. The few guns that the Indians did obtain were either captured or obtained through illegal trading activities at the mouth of the St. Lawrence.[18] Later, some firearms were traded to the Christian converts among the Hurons and Algonquins, but never in the numbers that

the Dutch and English traded them to the Iroquois.[19] The latter not only traded guns at considerably lower prices, but also instructed the Iroquois on how to use them effectively in warfare. Father Jogues' letter from Iroquois captivity is a vivid testimonial to the rapaciousness of the traders and of this whole unfortunate period.[20]

Rev. A. E. Jones made an attempt in 1908 to discover the distribution of French mission sites in Huronia[21], an extremely difficult if not impossible task. Only the sites of Ste. Marie I and II are absolutely certain, because French fortifications had been excavated. Some of Jones' work must be revised to take account of more recent work such as Jury's location for St. Ignace II, MacIlwraith's location for Cahiagué and Kidd's location for Ossossané. The only available sources are the written descriptions and a few early maps.[22] Unfortunately, archaeology in Huronia has not progressed far enough to make positive identifications of all sites, and it is by no means certain that such identifications can be made.

*

THE PHYSICAL SITE OF HURON VILLAGES

When investigating Huron village sites one is soon struck by several features that they have in common: (1) they are *sometimes* on hills, old shorelines, meander spurs or some other type of eminence; (2) they are *almost always* on fairly sandy soil with good drainage; (3) they are *always* handy to a good water supply. The last point is so invariable that one may state with certainty that today's dry valleys (where village sites occur) held water during Huron occupation.

Sagard states that they chose a site with care, "that it shall adjoin some good stream, on a spot slightly elevated and surrounded by a natural moat if possible."[23] There is no doubt that a water supply was of major importance. As a matter of fact, some villages had springs issuing on the site itself, as Champlain relates of an Onondaga village he unsuccessfully attacked.[24] Houghton, in

his studies of the Iroquois, also noticed a strong predilection for defensible sites with spring water, but says that lakes and navigable streams were generally avoided because they formed avenues for invading armies.[25] This does not seem to have been the case in Huronia, where sites can be found on navigable streams wherever there are high banks for defence and well-drained soils.

Next in importance to a water supply were the natural defences of hillside locations, as is well exemplified by historic sites such as Jones' St. Joseph II and MacIlwraith's Cahiagué. The direct relation between village sites and the post glacial Lake Algonquin terraces during the historic period (Figures 1 and 2), was partly due to the springs which issued along these terraces, but in part also because these old shorelines provided excellent defensive sites. The prehistoric sites are also situated at springs but with much less regard to defensible hills. A glance at a map of their distribution in conjunction with field studies amply demonstrates that many had no natural defences; indeed, they were often placed on sites that, for defence, seem vastly inferior to a site a few hundred yards away. Champlain noticed that only six of the eighteen villages he visited were fortified.[26] Now of what use is it to place a village on a rise and leave it without a palisade? We know that with the increasing frequency of Iroquois attacks during the later historic period, defensible sites with palisades became more important, and the Hurons tended to move from the smaller to the larger villages. My contention, therefore, is that before this period only the largest villages or those that had the best

natural defenses were fortified, and that many sites were located on hillsides simply because of a water supply and well-drained soils.

Sandy soils and good drainage both within the village and in the surrounding land were also important prerequisites for village sites. Sandy soils are easily worked for primitive cultivation, and good drainage within a village has obvious advantages. Simcoe County is almost ideal for sites of this type. The large dissected ridges which lie in the County are composed mainly of varved clays and bouldery till overlain with sands and sandy loams (Figures 1 and 2). Such physical characteristics, therefore, provided many spring lines, good drainage, and defensible positions in Huron times.

*

THE VILLAGE PATTERN

Archaeology has revealed that the palisades surrounding a village were usually composed of a double or triple row of staggered posts. Historical descriptions vary slightly and so, I believe, did the construction of palisades. Sagard's description of a Huron palisade is fairly typical: "They are in three rows, interlaced into one another and reinforced within by large thick pieces of bark to a height of eight or nine feet, and at the bottom there are great trunks of trees placed lengthwise resting on short forks made from tree trunks."[27] Both Champlain and Sagard noticed galleries furnished with stones for hurling and water for extinguishing fires. Iroquois fortifications were similar, but according to Champlain "much stronger than the villages of the Hurons and others."[28]

During the latter part of the 1640's the Jesuits, being very conscious of the obvious defects in the Indian palisades, became anxious that the Hurons build their fortifications like those of the French, in a regular manner with bastions at the corners. Du Creux[29]

and Garnier[30] relate that the Hurons began to fortify La Rochelle (Ossossané) in such a way, although archaeology has as yet not confirmed this. Only Ste. Marie I and II show strong French fortifications.

Only a few villages have been dug sufficiently to let us know much about the overall village pattern. W. Jury's Forget site near Wyebridge shows a double row of palisades closely following the brink of the steeper slopes. Within the site most of the houses point northwest to southeast, the direction of the prevailing winds in that area. The same is more or less true of the houses excavated at Cahiagué, a village with a triple palisade. Although it seems logical that bark houses would be oriented in this way, for protection from strong winds which might blow them down, not enough is really known to permit positive statements. Historical documents are mute on this point.

Huron houses have been similarly described by all explorers and missionaries from Cartier to Brébeuf. Champlain's description is one of the best:

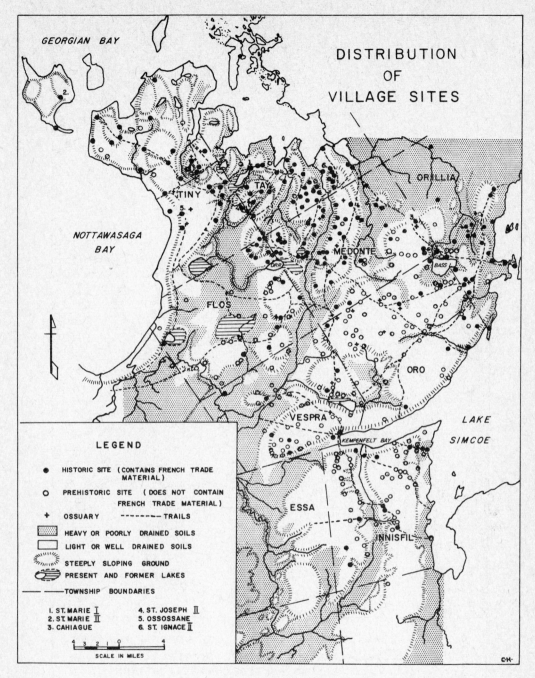

FIG. 1. This map shows three of the principal characteristics of Huron village sites:
1) *Their proximity to steeply sloping land;*
2) *Their coincidence with light or well drained soils;*
3) *The predominance of historic sites in the northern townships.*

Claims for completeness or absolute accuracy cannot be made, since all Huron sites in the area may not have been discovered yet, and some prehistoric sites may turn out to be historic after further investigation. However, the overall patterns are essentially correct. (Compiled from A. F. Hunter, A. E. Jones and others).

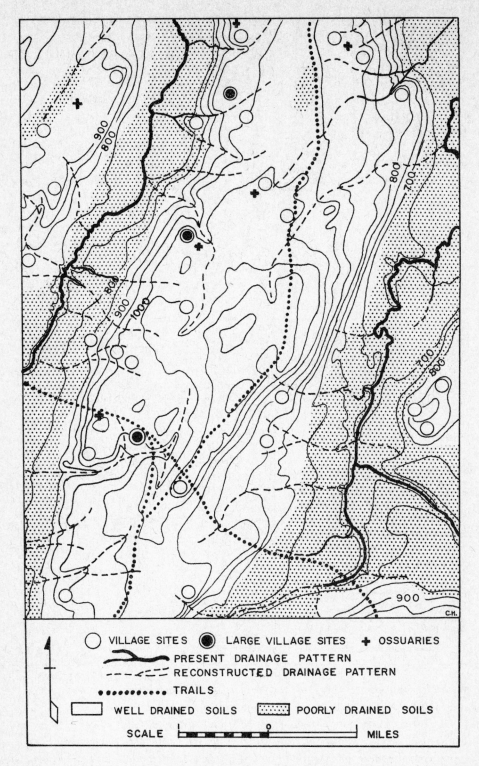

Legend:
○ VILLAGE SITES   ◉ LARGE VILLAGE SITES   + OSSUARIES

PRESENT DRAINAGE PATTERN
RECONSTRUCTED DRAINAGE PATTERN
•••••••• TRAILS
▭ WELL DRAINED SOILS   ▦ POORLY DRAINED SOILS

SCALE |————0————| MILES

FIG. 2. This map shows the relation of slope, drainage pattern and soils to Huron village sites on the Mount St. Louis Ridge, Medonte Township. (Compiled from A. F. Hunter and field work by the author).

Their lodges are fashioned like bowers or arbours, covered with tree-bark, twenty-five or thirty fathoms long more or less, and six wide, leaving in the middle a passage from ten to twelve feet wide which runs from one end to the other. On both sides is a sort of platform, four feet in height, on which they sleep in the summer to escape the annoyance of fleas of which they have many, and in winter they lie beneath mats near the fire in order to be warmer than on the top of the platform. They gather a supply of dry wood and fill their cabins with it, to burn in winter, and at the end of these cabins is a space where they keep their Indian corn, which they put in great casks, made of tree bark, in the middle of their lodge Pieces of wood are suspended on which they put their clothes, provisions and other things for fear of mice which are in great numbers. In one such cabin there will be twelve fires, which make twenty-four households, and there is smoke in good earnest, causing many to have great eye troubles, to which they are subject, even to the end of their lives losing their sight; for there is no window nor opening except in the roof of their cabins by which the smoke can escape.[31]

The number of fireplaces and families varied with the size of the lodge. According to archaeological investigations the average longhouse was about thirty feet wide and 120 feet long. Most varied in length between 90 and 150 feet. The largest lodge ever excavated was at Woodbridge, Ontario, measuring 28 by 174 feet. If one can judge from the confusing array of postholes at Cahiagué, the exterior walls of the longhouse were composed of a double row and in places a triple row of staggered posts. There may have been storage areas at either end with storage pits and hearths scattered the length of the longhouse. Doors were at either end of the structure, which was rounded at its extremities and not square as is shown in Champlain's drawings.

The favourite building material was cedar, one reason why "whole villages are sometimes consumed" by fire.[32] According to the

Relations, these fires were a frequent occurrence and often contributed to widespread famine. In 1635, for instance, because of drought, the harvest was poor; in addition, three villages burned down and with them all surplus grain.[33] To diminish the effect of fires, houses were usually spaced up to four or five yards apart.

The number of lodges per site varied widely (Table II). Cahiagué was the largest village in Huronia during Champlain's visit, and was thought to have later split into two.[34] One can, therefore, tentatively assume that this may represent the maximum village size.

TABLE II

Site	No. of Houses	Size of Site (acres)	Houses per Acre
Miller	5	1	5
Forget	12	2½	5
Woodbridge	14	2½	5½
Cahiagué	200	25	8

Cartier, who visited Hochelaga on the present site of Montreal in 1535, described that village as having an "open square between the houses (some fifty), about a stone's throw or thereabouts in width each way."[35] Since the Indians of the Hochelaga area were at that time one of the Iroquois groups and may even have been Hurons, it would be interesting if archaeology could find support for such a statement. An anonymous Dutch traveller who visited the Mohawks and Oneidas in December 1634 also observed some regularity in the village pattern: "There stood thirty-six houses, in rows like streets, so that we could pass nicely."[36] None of the Iroquois or Huron villages that have been excavated so far show either "open squares" or "streets."

More is known about the position of the garbage dumps (middens), which, until recently, have been the principal interest of archaeologists. Garbage was simply dumped over the palisade, or in any other convenient place. Most middens are found along the edge of the ravine immediately beyond the palisade. Occasionally garbage may have been dumped in the village proper as is reported for Cahiagué,[37] but this must have been rare because no other occurrences have been reported.

Another aspect of the village pattern was the cemetery. About every eight to twelve years all the villages within a clan or district decided to bury their dead. This event was a great occasion for ceremony and was described by Brébeuf as "a picture of what Hell must be like."[38] The deceased were taken from temporary graves, cleansed of all flesh, and reinterred in a large communal grave. A. F. Hunter described several of these "bone pits," some of which contained over five hundred skulls.[39] Occasionally, various villages held their own "Feast of the Dead,"[40] but it is safe to assume that not every village had a cemetery connected with it. Most ossuaries have been found anywhere up to a mile from a village site, although with present dating techniques it is virtually impossible to say if village and ossuary were contemporary.

The villages across Huronia were strung together by a network of trails. The exact location of these is not known. Hunter was in the area early enough to map Indian trails as they existed when the first European settlers entered the area. But these may have been the trails of Algonquin hunters who moved into Huronia some time after the Huron dispersion. Of Hunter's trails, the most likely one to have existed in Huron times is the one running from the "Narrows" of Lake Couchiching to Fesserton and from there along Georgian Bay to Midland. This is roughly the route of the present Highway No. 12, and may have been the trail followed by Champlain when he went from Carhagouha in Tiny Township to Cahiagué and from there to the "Narrows" of Lake Couchiching. In general, Hunter's trails follow high ground wherever possible, only descending to the wet lowlands to cross a stream.

*

THE LAND

The methods employed for land clearing were more or less typical of all shifting cultivators. The trees were cut down about two or three feet above the ground, a matter "very troublesome for them, since they have no proper tools."[41] Before the arrival of iron trade axes, stone adzes and axes were used. After the tree was cut down, the branches were removed, piled against the stump, and burned. In the course of time even the roots would be pulled out. Trees that were too big to be cut down had their branches cut off, were then girdled to kill them, and later burned. After these operations the ground was thoroughly cleared of bushes and weeds, the refuse was burned, and planting begun.

This was an immense job, and it must have taken several years of clearing before a new site was occupied. The introduction of the iron axe was revolutionary, and was for many years the most popular trade item with the

Hurons. Hunter reports that the iron axes found in Simcoe County in the late nineteenth century numbered in the thousands. They were turned up so frequently that scrap iron dealers used to make regular stops at the farmsteads.[42]

The type of land cleared usually consisted of sandy, well-drained soils, that were easily worked. Champlain noticed this and commented: "To speak the truth, the soil seems to me a little sandy, but is none the less good for that type of grain (corn)."[43] Du Creux[44] and Sagard[45] made similar statements. Le Jeune states that the soils were usually so droughty that the crops might fail if there was no rain for three days.[46] This is an exaggeration but shows that there was a problem.

The soil types preferred by the Hurons seem to have been almost exclusively Vasey sandy loams and Tioga loamy sands.[47] Both of these soils are well drained with a low moisture holding capacity and have developed on sandy tills or on sandy outwash deposits. The Vasey series is moderately stony and the Tioga series generally stone free. Both soil types are low in potassium, nitrogen and phosphorous. Because the Tioga loamy sands have a finer texture they are very susceptible to erosion. The natural vegetation on both soils is maple, beech and oak, with some poplar, birch and elm. Much of this land, once cultivated by the Hurons and lately by white settlers, has now been abandoned or given over to reforestation. This is particularly well illustrated by the Tioga loamy sands along the township boundary of Medonte and Oro, between Craighurst and Coulson. During Huron times a substantial string of settlements existed there, while today only a few farms still operate in the same area. About 45 per cent of this land has now been reforested. A strong factor in the abandonment of this land was the drop in the water table, subsequent to the clearing of the forest. During Huron times a series of springs and small streams issued in the area. These springs were still there in 1889[48] but are non-existent today. With the total clearing of the forest, the water table must have dropped at least fifteen to thirty feet through these porous soils. This may also have happened during Huron times, and could be one of the reasons why prehistoric but not historic sites are found in the "Dry Hills of Oro." That the water table in Simcoe County was at a higher level during the seventeenth century has been established through the excavations at Ste. Marie.[49] The bottom of a channel running from the Wye river into the fort is at a level of 585 feet while the level of the Wye (1941) was at 578 feet above mean sea level (A.M.S.L.). In order to float a canoe in the channel, the water of the Wye must have stood at about 588 feet A.M.S.L. or ten feet higher. This implies that the levels of Georgian Bay and Lake Huron and consequently the water table of surrounding lands were higher during Huron times.

The extent of cleared land at the time of Champlain's arrival is difficult if not impossible to estimate. There are many lyrical descriptions: "The country is fine and pleasant, for the most part cleared, shaped like Brittany,"[50] or "They do not have cattle, but have in their country good pastures in abundance."[51] The latter refers to abandoned corn fields. Popham estimated that in order to feed a population of 30,000 Indians about 390,000 bushels of corn were needed annually which could be grown on about 23,300 acres under the methods employed by the Hurons.[52] In addition to this acreage, there were large areas of abandoned land, in "meadows and fields." All in all, anywhere from 20 to 30 per cent of the land in Simcoe County could have been cleared of forest at any one time. Since only the well drained, sandy uplands of the northern part of the County were occupied in historic times, these must have been almost totally cleared, which may well account for Champlain's statements.

We have a slightly better idea of how large the corn fields could have been in relation to the size of the village. Sagard relates that he frequently got lost in them, "more than in the meadows and forest."[53] In 1779 an Iroquois village, (containing forty houses and some sixty acres of corn[54]), on the Chemung river in New York State, was destroyed. In the same area another village, comprising seventy dwellings and about two hundred acres, was also destroyed. During Denonville's campaigns in 1687 against the Seneca of the "Finger Lakes" area, the five villages destroyed contained an estimated 350,000 bushels of standing corn and 50,000 bushels of dried corn.[55] Similarily, in 1696, Frontenac had destroyed corn extending about a league-and-a-half to two leagues (roughly four to five miles) from an Onondaga fort.[56] These examples are Iroquois villages, but the Huron ones were very similar. One can, therefore, imagine the vast fields that must have extended around a village the size of Cahiagué with its two hundred longhouses. Since there were usually two families per fireplace and three to four fireplaces per longhouse, and assuming at least three members to a family, a village such as Cahiagué could have contained 4,000 to 5,000 people.[57] Taking Popham's estimate that one acre of corn supported about one-and-a-half persons, the extent of Cahiagué's corn fields might well have been about 2,600 to 3,200 acres.[58] Although the above is only an estimate, the larger figure is probably closer to the truth, because, quite apart from seed, the Hurons strove to create a large surplus for trade and lean years.[59]

*

THE ECONOMY

The Hurons were a society in which families held land by right of occupation and retained the rights to that land until it was abandoned. All uncleared land was common property and any group could clear as much as it wished.[60] After harvest, corn was stored in large communal bins within the longhouse and in private caches hidden in the ground. Through social pressure the well-to-do were forced to share with the needy and lazy; thus a great part of the corn that was grown became communal property. Many events, such as house building, gathering of firewood, land clearing, hunting and so forth, were semi-communal affairs. The members of one extended kinship group, usually all in one longhouse, co-operated with one another. In larger affairs such as moving a village or war, the whole community would work in unison.

Agricultural methods were, to say the least, primitive. The digging stick was the main tool and the hoe was unknown except in a very rudimentary form. There was only a vague idea that fertilization might improve the soil or that burning was contributing anything to agriculture except to get rid of unwanted brush and weeds. The Hurons did, however, know the importance of removing weeds and of carefully choosing seed according to the type of corn wanted. Surprisingly, they also knew that seed could be germinated in the warmth of the lodge when soaked in water or placed in a bed of bark and water.[61] Except for land clearing, the women naturally did all the agricultural work.

Sagard described one method of planting corn:

...at distances a pace apart they dig round holes or pits. In each of these they sow nine

or ten grains of maize, which they have first picked out, sorted, and soaked in water for a few days, and so they keep on until they have sown enough to provide for two or three years.[62]

On the Saco river, among the Almouchiquois, Champlain described a method of planting in little hillocks.[63] Lafitau later drew a picture of this method, but does not tell the reader which Indian group he was describing. A. F. Hunter, as well as many farmers, claim to have seen large acreages of these "corn hills" when the land of Huronia was settled during the last century.[64] By implication then, the Hurons may have used two methods of planting corn, in hillocks or simply by poking a little hole into the ground and dropping seeds into it

Crop rotation was apparently unknown, for "every year they sow corn thus in the same holes or spots, which they freshen with their little wooden spade."[65] According to Sagard, Champlain, Du Creux, the Jesuits, and others, lack of crop rotation and lack of manure were responsible for rapid soil exhaustion and were therefore contributory factors in the abandonment and movement of villages. Sagard summed up by stating that: "...the land becomes so exhausted that their corn can no longer be grown on it in the usual perfection for lack of manure; because they do not understand cultivating the ground nor putting the seed anywhere else than in the same holes."[66]

Lescarbot among the Almouchiquois[67] and Hennepin among the Seneca, found that these Indians "manured a great deal of ground for sowing their Indian corn in."[68] This practice had evidently not spread north to the Hurons and it is not known whether the other Indians really understood what they were doing. In 1858 the Chippewas on Beausoleil Island in Matchedash Bay (previously Huron territory) were still working their land in the traditional way, for the Indian Affairs Commsision of that year reports: "...after a single crop, the clear sharp sand appears in the top, obliging them to seek fresh land, or commence new clearings."[69]

Corn provided about three-quarters of the Huron diet. The other main cultivated food plants were red beans, squash and some sunflowers. These crops were planted either in separate fields, or more often mixed together in one. The corn stalks have been described as growing "as high as a man," yielding, "two or three ears, each ear yielding a hundred, two hundred, sometimes four hundred grains."[70] Judging from carbonized corn cobs excavated at Huron sites, four hundred kernels on one cob seems like a gross exaggeration. Sagard's first estimate of one hundred kernels is probably close to the truth. Yields were reported to be higher in Huronia than in Quebec, with the grain ripening "in four months, or in three, in places."[71]

Waugh records that five varieties of corn (Zea Mays) were grown depending on their use.[72] Lima beans, kidney beans, and Scarlet Runner beans twined around the corn stalk and formed an important addition to the otherwise monotonous Huron diet. Peas were introduced by the French, but some of Ontario's wild varieties, eaten but not cultivated by the Indians, were close enough to the European kind to fool Sagard at first sight.[73] Wild rice was apparently not grown by the Hurons, but was well known to the Algonquins who made some attempts to cultivate it. The Sunflower (Helianthus Sp.) is mentioned by Champlain as being grown for hair and body oil. This may be the Jerusalem Artichoke (Helianthus tuberosus) which Sagard says the Hurons prized.[74] Squash and its relatives, the pumpkin, cucumber, and melon, were very important. At times they formed a major part of the diet, and many early writers mention them as a welcome addition to the ubiquitous and tasteless corn gruel.

To the dismay of Sagard, the Hurons were inveterate smokers. He recognized that smoking was habit forming, and suggested that it acted like a laxative. It appears that the Hurons grew little tobacco (Nicotiana rustica) of their own, for tobacco was a major article of trade from the Petun (Tobaccos) and the Neutrals who lived to the south of the Hurons. Since tobacco is very sensitive to frosts and needs a long growing season, northern Simcoe County was probably too marginal climatically for such a crop. The Neutral territory on the north shore of Lake Erie, and the Petun lands on the lake plain below the Collingwood hills are both better suited for tobacco growing.

Additional foods were gathered in the forest, including cherries, plums, raspberries, various nuts, leeks and the mayapple which Champlain describes as "of very good flavour."[75] Grapes grew in abundance and were eaten but not fermented. The Indians had no knowledge of alcoholic beverages.

Vegetable foods were plentiful but some game animals may not have been.[76] Huronia was heavily settled and much hunted. Judging from archaeological sites, the Virginia deer and the beaver were the most hunted animals. Both are reported by Sagard to have been more plentiful outside of Huronia.[77] Hunting expeditions frequently went outside the occupied areas, and at times meat and furs had to be obtained from the Algonquins for corn. A general scarcity of meat in the Indian diet is frequently mentioned by Sagard and the Jesuits, although by their accounts, except for deer, moose and the beaver, game was apparently plentiful.

Fish seem to have been considerably more important than meat, and every traveller mentions both their abundance and the Indian's numerous ways of catching them. Regular fishing expeditions were undertaken to Lake Huron and Lake Simcoe. Archaeological evidence shows that the "Narrows" of Lake Couchiching, as Champlain mentioned, were a favourite fishing spot.[78] Fish were caught in nets, weirs and on the line, and were then immediately cleaned and dried, or sometimes, in the case of whitefish, reduced to oil.[79]

There were no domesticated animals except the dog, which was occasionally eaten at ceremonials. Champlain makes a reference to bears, "which they fatten and kept for two or three years, for their usual feasts."[80] Although the bear could by no means be considered a domesticated animal, the practice of keeping them in cages for special occasions seems to have been fairly widespread because it is also reported for the Iroquois.[81] It is interesting that Sagard considered the turkey an easy animal to domesticate but "the savages did not want to take the trouble."[82] The fact that domestication of animals was possible probably never occurred to the Hurons, although in all fairness it must be said that the turkey was really the only animal in the area that offered any chances for domestication.

Much of what the Hurons gathered in the forest had to be supplemented by trade from the Algonquins. Besides meat, fish and especially furs were regularily exchanged for corn. Although the Hurons considered the Algonquins inferior, they became increasingly dependent on them for furs to trade to the French. It has been suggested that the Algonquins in turn became dependent on the Hurons for corn.[83] Father Le Jeune went so far as to describe Huronia as "the granary of most of the Algonquins."[84] Although this seems a bit far fetched, it does illustrate the reality of active trade between the two groups, a trade pattern which had been in existence for some time before the arrival of the French.

*

THE MOVEMENT OF VILLAGES

Champlain tells us that "they sometimes change their village site after ten, twenty or thirty years, and move it one, two or three leagues from the former spot."[85] According to Father Brébeuf this happens "when there is no longer sufficient wood for their fires or when the land, long tilled, produces scanty crops."[86] Other references, too numerous to mention here, confirm these statements.

Due to the construction of their lodges, smoke had to be kept at a minimum. Since only dry wood from a few species was used, the Huron women often had to undertake long trips to obtain it.[87] Wood was collected during March and April before foliation, and stored in and about the lodge for winter. Large logs were left to rot in the woods because the Hurons did not have the tools to cut them up. Champlain also gives a hint as to the importance of firewood in his statement that, upon marriage, "each woman and girl is bound to carry a load of wood to the bride for her supply."[88] When the fuel supply became too distant the village was moved.

The other reason for the movement of villages often given by the early travellers, was soil exhaustion. It is fruitless to argue whether the wood supply or soils were more important; a deficiency in either would be sufficient reason to move.

It is doubtful that the Hurons obtained as many as "ten to thirty crops" from one parcel of land, especially on the sandy soils of Simcoe County. Probably, land adequate for the first couple of years was cleared around a new village site and then, after a few years, and every succeeding year, more land was cleared to keep pace with a diminishing return from the original fields. Then, after ten years or so, the productive fields might be located too far from the village for easy communication, and the village would be shifted. Because corn places heavy demands on soil, it is almost certain that sandy unmanured soils could not produce a crop after four to six years of constant tillage.

Population pressure may have been a minor reason for shifting a village or splitting it in two, although it is doubtful if there was any large natural increase in the Huron population in prehistoric or historic times. Du Creux refers to a high infant mortality rate among the Algonquins, due to cold winters and the poor health (on account of overwork) of the mothers.[89] There must have been similar conditions, though not as extreme, among the Hurons, because a large proportion of the skeletal material excavated from Huron ossuaries is that of young children or infants.[90] If population pressure existed, it is more likely that it was due to refugees from the Iroquois wars. This is certainly true of the latter part of the Indian occupation of Huronia.

Hunter thought that "the incredible foulness" of the villages after years of occupation may have been cause enough for their abandonment.[91] The domestic habits of the Hurons were filthy enough, but all refuse was usually cleared out of the village, as archaeology has shown. If this was a reason for moving a village, it could not have been as important as exhausted soils and insufficient wood.

The number of occupied villages in Huronia at any one time has been variously reported as between 18 (Champlain in 1615) and 25 (Sagard in 1623), while Brébeuf estimated 20 in 1636. By 1909 Hunter had found approximately 400 in Simcoe County alone, of which 120 had French trade material in them. The historic villages, therefore, must have shifted about six times between 1600 and 1650. If Hunter's "small camps" and the historic villages south of Kempenfelt Bay are eliminated, and the fact that large villages were often split in two is taken into consideration, we would come to the tentative conclusion that villages shifted about every ten to twelve years. Although this estimate is extremely rough, it agrees fairly well with the written records.

There is some evidence to suggest that, in Huronia at least, once a site was abandoned, it was never actively re-occupied. Archaeology has not uncovered different occupational levels in the sense that it has in classical archaeology. The reason for this is unknown, but several theories may be put forth. First, Huronia is not lacking in attractive sites; there are an enormous number to choose from. Secondly, the Hurons had been slowly moving north into new territory and may never have settled long enough in any one area to be forced to re-occupy old sites. Whether there were religious reasons as well is an open question. Fires and the Iroquois wars were often major causes for shifts in village sites.

Three to four years in advance of a move, the new site would be selected by the men and clearing begun. This done, the village was pulled down and re-erected on the new site, or completely abandoned and a new one built. As Champlain mentioned, this move was never too far—just far enough to allow access to new soil and supplies of firewood. The missionaries often lamented this semi-nomadic existence, knowing that only a settled life could lead to a higher culture.

*

EPILOGUE

The year 1650 marked the end of the Huron occupance of northern Simcoe County. Eight years later Radisson passed along the shores of the Penetanguishene peninsula and relates that Indian fields were still visible, but that the land was deserted.[92] Du Creux's map of the "Regionis Huronum", published in 1660, describes the area as "hodie desertae". This map was drawn from information supplied by Jesuits living in Huronia before 1650, and is therefore remarkably good. On later maps, Huronia becomes hazier, until on the early 18th century maps, if Huronia is mentioned at all, it is usually marked in the wrong place. Thus Huronia as a geographic area became all but completely forgotten. Slowly the corn fields reverted back to forest. Iroquois and Algonquin groups hunted in the area, but the land was not cleared again until Irish, English, Scottish and French Canadian settlers arrived in the early nineteenth century.

*

FOOTNOTES

1. H. P. Biggar, ed., *The Works of Samuel de Champlain,* 6 Vols. and maps (Toronto: The Champlain, Society, 1922-36), Vol. 3, p. 122.
2. G. M. Wrong, ed., *Sagard: The Long Journey to the Country of the Hurons* (Toronto: The Champlain Society, 1939), p. 92.
3. R. G. Thwaites, ed., *The Jesuit Relations and Allied Documents, 1610-1791,* 73 Vols. (New York: Pageant Book Co., 1959), Vol. 8, p. 313.
4. *Ibid.,* Vol. 17, p. 223.
5. *Ibid.,* Vol. 35, p. 87.
6. *Ibid.,* Vol. 35, p. 199.
7. Biggar, *op. cit.,* Vol. 1, p. 164.
8. *Ibid.,* Vol. 2, p. 186.
9. *Ibid.,* Vol. 3, p. 59.
10. R. S. MacNeish, *Iroquois Pottery Types,* Canada, Department of Resources and Development, National Museum Bulletin No. 124, Anthropological Series, No. 31 (Ottawa, 1952).
11. J. N. Emerson, "Problems of Huron Origins," *Anthropologica,* Vol. 3, No. 2 (1961), p. 181.
12. J. N. Emerson, "A Rejoinder upon the MacNeish-Emerson Theory," *Pennsylvania Archeologist,* Vol. 29 (August, 1959), pp. 3-12.
13. Thwaites, *op. cit.,* Vol. 16, p. 227.
14. F. Ridley, "The Huron and Lalonde Occupations of Ontario," *American Antiquity,* Vol. 27 (1952), pp. 197-210.
15. B. G. Trigger, "The Historic Location of the Hurons," *Ontario History,* Vol. 54, No. 2 (1962), pp. 137-148.
16. Wrong, *loc. cit.*
17. G. T. Hunt, *The Wars of the Iroquois* (University of Wisconsin Press, Madison, 1960).
18. Biggar, *op. cit.,* Vol. 5, p. 3.
19. Hunt, *op. cit.,* Appendix A and B, pp. 165, 175.
20. Thwaites, *op. cit.,* Vol. 24, p. 295.
21. A. E. Jones, *Old Huronia,* Fifth Annual Report of the Ontario Bureau of Archives (Toronto, 1908).
22. See collection in the Map Division, Public Archives, Ottawa.
23. Wrong, *loc. cit.*
24. Biggar, *op. cit.,* Vol. 3, p. 70.
25. F. Houghton, "The Characteristics of Iroquois Village Sites in New York State," *American Anthropology,* Vol. 18 (1916), pp. 508-520.
26. Biggar, *op. cit.,* Vol. 3, p. 122. In Vol. 4, p. 301, he says eight were fortified.
27. Wrong, *op. cit.,* p. 91.
28. Biggar, *op. cit.,* Vol. 3, p. 70.
29. J. B. Conacher, ed., *Du Creux: The History of Canada or New France,* 2 Vols. (Toronto: The Champlain Society, 1951-52), p. 198.
30. Jones, *op. cit.,* p. 306.
31. Biggar, *op. cit.,* Vol. 3, pp. 122-124.
32. Conacher, *op. cit.,* p. 102.
33. Thwaites, *op. cit.,* Vol. 8, p. 35.
34. Wrong, *op. cit.,* p. 92.
35. H. P. Biggar, ed., *The Voyages of Jacques Cartier,* Publications of the Public Archives of Canada, No. 2 (Ottawa, 1924).
36. J. F. Jameson, ed., *Narratives of New Netherlands 1609–1664* (New York: Scribner's and Sons, 1909), p. 141.
37. M. M. Thomson, *Excavating Ontario History,* Division of Extension, Royal Ontario Museum (Toronto, 1948), p. 14.
38. Conacher, *op. cit.,* p. 130.
39. A. F. Hunter, *Notes on Village Sites of the Huron Indians.* A collection of all Hunter's published reports. Appendix to the Report of the Minister of Education, Toronto, 1899 (Tiny Twp.), 1900-1911 (Tay Twp.), 1902 (Medonte Twp.), 1903 (Oro Twp.), 1904 (North and South Orillia), 1906 (Flos and Vespra Twps.).
40. Conacher, *op. cit.,* p. 126.
41. Wrong, *op. cit.,* p. 103.
42. Hunter, *op. cit.,* Medonte Report, p. 73.
43. Biggar, *Works of Champlain,* Vol. 3, p. 51.
44. Conacher, *op. cit.,* p. 194.
45. Wrong, *op. cit.,* p. 91.
46. Thwaites, *op. cit.,* Vol. 10, p. 35.
47. Research Branch, Canada Department of Agriculture, and the Ontario Agricultural College: *Report No. 29, Soil Survey of Simcoe County* (Guelph, 1962).
48. Hunter, *op. cit.,* Oro Report, pp. 165-167.
49. K. E. Kidd, *The Excavation of Ste. Marie I* (Toronto: University of Toronto Press, 1949), pp. 84-86.
50. Biggar, *Works of Champlain,* Vol. 3, p. 122.
51. *Ibid.,* p. 130.

52. R. E. Popham, "Late Huron Occupation of Ontario: An Archaeological Survey of Innisfil Township," *Ontario History,* Vol. 42, No. 2, (1950), p. 87.

53. Wrong, *op. cit.,* p. 104.

54. F. W. Waugh, *Iroquois Food and Food Preparation,* Mem. 86, Anthropological Series, No. 12, Geol. Survey Can. (Ottawa, 1916), p. 4.

55. W. J. Eccles, *Canada Under Louis XIV, 1663-1701* (Toronto: McClelland and Stewart Limited, 1964), p. 153.

56. Waugh, *loc. cit.*

57. T. F. MacIlwraith, "Archaeological Work in Huronia, 1946," *Canadian Historical Review,* Vol. 27 (December, 1946), pp. 394-401.

58. Yield is estimated to be about 20 to 25 bushels per acre (Popham). Huron need was about two pounds of shelled corn a day. There are 56 pounds of shelled corn to the bushel.

59. Wrong, *op. cit.,* p. 103.

60. *Ibid.*

61. J. F. Lafitau, *Moeurs des Sauvages Ameriquains* (Paris, 1724), pp. 76-78.

62. Wrong, *loc. cit.*

63. Biggar, *Works of Champlain,* Vol. 1, pp. 327-328.

64. Hunter, *op. cit.,* Medonte Report, p. 85; Tay Report, p. 77; Tiny Report, p. 7ff.

65. Wrong, *op. cit.,* p. 104.

66. *Ibid.,* p. 93.

67. W. L. Grant and H. P. Biggar, ed., *Marc Lescarbot: The History of New France,* 3 Vols. (Toronto: The Champlain Society, 1911), Vol. 3, p. 248.

68. R. G. Thwaites, ed., *Hennepin: A New Discovery of a Vast Country in America,* 2 Vols. (Chicago: McClurg and Co., 1903), Vol. 1, p. 46.

69. F. B. Murray, ed., *Muskoka and Haliburton, 1615-1875,* a collection of documents (Toronto: The Champlain Society, 1963), p. 121.

70. Wrong, *op. cit.,* p. 104.

71. *Idem.*

72. Waugh, *op. cit.,* pp. 72-75.

73. Wrong, *op. cit.,* p. 90.

74. *Ibid.,* p. 239.

75. Biggar, *Works of Champlain,* Vol. 3, p. 51.

76. Waugh, *op. cit.,* p. 131.

77. Wrong, *op. cit.,* pp. 225, 232.

78. Thwaites, *Jesuit Relations,* Vol. 5, p. 298.

79. Wrong, *op. cit.,* p. 186.

80. Biggar, *Works of Champlain,* Vol. 3, p. 130.

81. Jameson, *op. cit.,* p. 143.

82. Wrong, *op. cit.,* p. 220.

83. Trigger, *op. cit.,* p. 144.

84. Thwaites, *Jesuit Relations,* Vol. 8, p. 115.

85. Biggar, *Works of Champlain,* Vol. 3, p. 124. The league varies in length, and it is not clear which league was used by Champlain, Sagard or the Jesuits. About 2.5 miles seems to be the most reasonable estimate. For a full discussion see Jones, *Old Huronia,* p. 114, or Thwaites, *Jesuit Relations,* Vol. 34, p. 249.

86. Thwaites, *Jesuit Relations,* Vol. 11, p. 7.

87. Wrong, *op. cit.,* p. 94.

88. Biggar, *Works of Champlain,* Vol. 3, p. 157.

89. Conacher, *op. cit.,* p. 85.

90. Thomson, *op. cit.,* p. 20.

91. A. F. Hunter, *A History of Simcoe County* (Barrie: Barrie County Council, 1909), p. 4.

92. A. T. Adams, ed., *The Explorations of Pierre Esprit Radisson* (Minneapolis: Ross and Haines Inc., 1961), pp. 86-87.

3

Some Remarks on the Seigneurial Geography of Early Canada*

R. C. HARRIS

* From a paper read to the Canadian Association of Geographers, Vancouver, June 1965. Printed by permission of the author.

This short article is a report on some of the results of a geographical investigation of the seigneurial system in Canada before 1760. In seventeenth century France, the seigneurial system or French feudalism was probably effete and anachronistic, but many historians have insisted that in Canada the system became a framework for colonization and a vital buttress of social and economic development. A picture of beneficent seigneurs and happy, dependent habitants is common in the historical literature and is part of many English—as well as French-speaking Canadians' image of old Quebec. Because this myth about the seigneurial system can elicit strong and often conflicting popular responses in contemporary Canada, it is important to examine carefully the evidence on which it rests.

This examination has been made in a detailed study of the seigneurial geography of Canada before 1760.[1] The study has been based on the assumption that if the seigneurial system were an important factor in the development of early Canada, then many of the patterns of settlement, land use, and trade along the lower St. Lawrence during the French regime would have reflected the seigneurial mould. The study, then, was an examination of much of the basic geography of Canada during the French regime in an attempt to provide evidence relevant to the understanding of the Canadian seigneurial system. Because the habitants were an illiterate class, and because the relationship between habitants and seigneurs is fundamental to an understanding of the seigneurial system, the geographical evidence is probably all that is available.

At the onset of this study, a series of maps was constructed showing the size, shape and distribution of seigneuries at different periods during the French regime. During the proprietary years from 1627–1663, the Company of New France conceded seigneuries of many basic shapes, and the size of its grants ranged from two or three to a thousand or more square miles, a variety which suggests that the Company had little interest in its seigneurial grants and no firm policy regarding their concession. During Talon's intendancy (1665–1672), seigneurial land grants were rarely more than fifteen to twenty square miles, for both the Intendant and his monarch were convinced that the many large concessions made by the Company had retarded the development of the colony. After 1672 the size of seigneurial grants expanded steadily, in spite of continuing royal insistence on small concessions, until, by the end of the French regime, some concessions were almost as large as the largest granted during the proprietary period. This increase in the size of seigneurial concessions in the face of opposing royal pressure reflects two fundamental characteristics of Canadian seigneurialism. First, because of the size of Canadian families, seigneuries were usually subdivided after the first generation into many smaller units. A map of land controlled by individual seigneurs often shows many more subdivisions than a map of original seigneurial concessions, and suggests that seigneurial control had been rapidly diluted among many co-seigneurs. Second, because settlers would take land only along or near the river, and because seigneurial dues were so low in Canada, (to cover his expenses for mill construction and maintenance, a seigneur needed approximately forty families in his seigneurie), a seigneur required several miles of river frontage before he could hope to profit eventually from his seigneurie. Officials conceded larger seigneuries in an attempt to make them potentially profitable and to induce seigneurs to attend to the development of their land.

Maps were then drawn to show the distribution of population along the lower St. Lawrence at different dates, and the population change between these dates. This series of maps shows a steady expansion of settlement outward along the St. Lawrence from Montreal and Quebec, and, before 1700, some isolated pockets of settlement along the routes of the fur trade. Only here and there do the maps reveal a change in population density across a seigneurial boundary; in short, they do not suggest that the seigneurs played an important role in the spread of settlement along the lower St. Lawrence. When it is remembered that a seigneur needed forty families in his seigneurie before he could begin to profit from it, that there was never a large enough population in early Canada to permit the establishment of forty or more families in most seigneuries, that seigneurial control and revenue were often subdivided among many co-seigneurs, that throughout most of the French regime the only possible recruits for the settlement of a seigneurie were habitants from another sei-

gneurie, and that the individual seigneurs had almost nothing to offer these habitants to induce them to move, the reasons for the seigneurs' indifference to colonization are clear. Their role was usually that of land agent. They granted land to habitants who requested it.

Within seigneuries throughout the French regime the characteristic shape of a concession of land or *roture* was a strip of land a mile or more deep and 150–200 yards in width. These long, thin rectangles, conceded at right angles to river or road, gave each farm direct access to an important transportation route. They permitted a man to live on his own land and yet to be close to neighbours, they were easily surveyed, and they divided the natural meadows along the river among many individuals. In early Canada, the strip farm and associated line, or shoe-string village, was an alternative to the compact village, but why the latter settlements did not appear is one of the most intriguing puzzles in the geography of New France. There were no compact agricultural villages in Canada before 1700, and only six at the end of the French regime, although their establishment had repeatedly been urged by the crown, royal officials in Canada, the Church, and some of the seigneurs. In 1665, Talon laid out three villages just north of Quebec, but most of the original habitants quickly sold their plots, and Charlesbourg, the most important of the proposed villages did not appear on the land until well into the eighteenth century. Apparently, villages did not emerge in the seventeenth century because the habitants would not live in them. Habitants who had lived in villages in France may have associated village life with the close control of seigneur and curé, and they may have sought to avoid this control in Canada. Moreover, habitants who participated illegally in the fur trade, often in direct competition with their seigneur, would be courting trouble if they settled in villages where their movements could be relatively easily scrutinized. By the eighteenth century, memories of France had faded; Canadian seigneurs had proved to be anything but domineering, and the relative importance of the fur trade had declined. However, the settlement pattern which had been established in the seventeenth century was not altered because there was little economic reason to change.

This settlement pattern had not developed within a seigneurial framework. Line villages spread along the river and the roads and crossed seigneurial boundaries without a break. Trunk roads made travel between nearby seigneuries as easy as that within a single seigneurie. Occasionally, parish and seigneurie were the same spatial unit, but more often they were not. There were several parishes in the largest and most densely settled seigneuries, and several seigneuries within a parish in sparsely settled areas. The church was seldom located on the seigneur's domain, and frequently church, manor house, and grist mill were well separated. None of these patterns provide any evidence for the existence of a social and economic bond between the seigneurs and their habitants.

Additional information about the habitants comes from a variety of sources. An examination of the deeds of sale of *rotures* reveals a rapid turnover of land, particularly in the early years, and an active speculation in land. The habitants' activity in the fur trade, the fishery and forests, and on the farm, also suggests a quest for economic gain. Prices for different types of farm products and farm output were closely correlated. Although no habitants were wealthy, a great many lived in ample stone houses, employed one or two domestics and a hired hand, and purchased French luxury items, such as good quality cloth and wine. The Canadian farmer was at least as well off as his New England counterpart, and, judging by his accomplishments, as energetic. His standard of living was often higher than that of his seigneur.

This summary of a great deal of geographical evidence is sufficient to suggest certain conclusions. The seigneurial system was altogether irrelevant to the development of the distinctive human geography of Canada during the French regime. Had there been no seigneurs and had all the *rotures* in Canada been held directly from the king and conceded by his officials, patterns of settlement, land use, and trade in the colony would have been little different. Perhaps a seigneurial title was an important status symbol and entrée to a commission in the army, and certainly the legal base of the seigneurial system in Canada still emphasized the position of the seigneur. In fact, however, the bond between seigneur and habitant had evaporated; thus, the seigneurial system was largely unrelated to the social and economic development of early Canada.

The seigneurial system collapsed in Canada, in part, because seigneurs, who could not profit from subdivided and sparsely settled seigneuries, had no incentive to develop their holdings and, in part, because the habitant did not need a seigneur. His seigneur could not protect him against Indian attacks, and the habitant, who could fend for himself for months in the fur country, seldom needed a seigneur's protection on his farm along the lower St. Lawrence. The seigneur knew no more and often a good deal less than the habitant about the problems associated with clearing, planting and fishing. Considered at another level, the system collapsed because two basic conditions of its French existence had been transformed. Whereas land was scarce and labour plentiful in France, the opposite was true in Canada. A totally uncleared seigneurie of one hundred or more square miles could be bought for the price of a cow or two. Because land was worth so little, a system which attempted to create a landed aristocracy in Canada was completely incongruous. Moreover, the seigneurial system, a system of social and economic organization and control, depended on a manageable peasantry. A controlled peasantry was possible in France but not in Canada where the habitants were scattered along the St. Lawrence for several hundred miles, and where the complete freedom of the fur trade was always an accessible alternative to farming. The Canadian habitants were a vigorous and independent people. They created a way of life which was no longer French and, in the process, cast aside a French social and economic system which was ill-adapted to the conditions of the New World and in sharp conflict with the mentality which emerged there.

Although the seigneurial system was little more than a legal skeleton at the time of the conquest, in the ninety years between the conquest and the abolition of the seigneurial system, the skeleton may have acquired some flesh. In these later years the population and, consequently, seigneurial revenues were increasing rapidly. Moreover, when the Intendant was replaced by English officials who were ignorant of French law, the seigneurs began to interpret French customary law to their advantage and to raise their seigneurial charges. On the other hand, the value of labour was declining and as land became scarce along the lower St. Lawrence, farms became steadily smaller. The fur trade, the traditional outlet from the lower St. Lawrence, supported ever smaller percentages of the Canadian population. In short, the position of the seigneur may have been improving and that of the habitant deteriorating. A domineering seigneurial élite and a dependent habitant class may have developed; but, had this been the case much would have changed since the days of the French regime.

Frederick Jackson Turner's concept of the frontier is relevant to an understanding of early Canada, in the sense that an European institution had come to Canada, had been found wanting in a new environment, and had been superceded, in fact, if not in law, by a way of life which was no longer French. And yet, an advancing frontier, free land to the west, safety valves, and isolation—the staples of Turner's argument—are misleading in the early Canadian context. Canadian settlement during the French regime did not advance westward; nor was free land to the west as important as free land within seigneuries along the lower St. Lawrence. The routes to the fur country, or to New England were not safety valves, for there would have been no explosion without them, but their existence made the habitants more independent than they would otherwise have been. At the official level in Canada, close contacts with France were maintained throughout the French regime, and the Intendant, as the king's representative, was a constant watchdog on seigneurial pretentions. When the Intendant was removed, that is, when contact with France was broken, the seigneur's position was strengthened and the seigneurial system began to acquire some French characteristics. In this instance, Turner's stress on the role of isolation is reversed. On the other hand, the Canadian evidence does support Turner's picture of a mobile and independent frontier society. Canada was not an unruly colony, but the traditional authorities in France—the crown, the church, and the seigneur—had been enormously weakened.

For the old myth about the seigneurial system during the French regime, I would substitute a picture of vigorous habitants who prospered on their farms along the lower St. Lawrence, and who lived much as they chose. This picture supports neither the French-Canadian nationalist who has found in the influence of the seigneurial system and the church, the pillars of an unique North American colony, nor the English critic who has derided the habitants' commercial indifference and insouciance. It is a picture of a society whose character two and more centuries ago, adumbrates some of the turbulence in contemporary Quebec.

*

FOOTNOTES

1 R. C. Harris, *The Seigneurial System in Early Canada: A Geographical Study* (University of Wisconsin Press, 1966).

4

The Agricultural Background of Settlement in Eastern Nova Scotia*

R. LOUIS GENTILCORE

* From Annals of the Association of American Geographers, *Vol. 46, No. 2 (1956), pp. 378–404. Revised by the author.*

Located in a section of the country generally recognized as marginal for commercial agriculture, Antigonish County, Nova Scotia, points up in a remarkable way many of the agricultural problems of its province and the surrounding Maritime area. The most apparent of these include the emphasis upon subsistence and part-time farming, the high degree of farm abandonment, the need to purchase large quantities of feed grains and commercial fertilizer, and an unfavorable situation with respect to markets.

Following confederation, agriculture in Antigonish and in the rest of Nova Scotia expanded to a peak in the decade 1881–91. Then, as the general movement toward specialization gained momentum, the rural economy of self-sufficiency began to break down. Small rural industries moved to urban centers; poor land went out of production and good land was hard pressed to meet competition from newly developed parts of the continent. Rural population declined, the number of farms declined, and the area in farmland and cropland declined.

Nowhere in Nova Scotia is this decline more marked than in Antigonish County. Between 1891 and 1951 the total population declined from 18,060 to 11,971, the number of farms from 2,710 to 1,164, and the area in improved land from 142,588 to 34,934 acres.[1] The declines in acreage and production of the principal crops—hay, oats and potatoes—have not been as marked because they have been accompanied by increased yields per acre as production kept moving to the better lands. There has also been a steady decline in all classes of livestock, although the proportion of sheep has remained higher here than elsewhere in the province.

Basically this decline was part of the much larger economic picture in which the dominant force was continental expansion in Canada and the United States. But Antigonish, more than any other part of mainland Nova Scotia, found itself unable to adjust to changing agricultural conditions. Physical handicaps—a short growing season, occasional summer drought and rugged topography—and the economic handicap of lack of ready markets undoubtedly contributed to the decline. But these are difficulties shared by the rest of the Maritime area. Where the county stands unique is in the high proportion of its land area that was occupied in the period of early settlement. Seventy-three percent of the county was in farms in 1881, a proportion higher than in any other county in the province. The high proportion of land occupied meant a high proportion of subsequent abandonment. A basic factor in both occupation and abandonment was the agricultural background of the settlers, a background that has colored developments in eastern Nova Scotia to the present day. It is with this background and its significance that this paper is concerned.

*

ORIGIN OF SETTLERS

The first actual settlements were those of the Acadian French in 1768, returning after their expulsion from Nova Scotia and taking up land at Tracadie, Pomquet, and Havre-au-Bouche on the mainland, and at Cheticamp and Arichat on Cape Breton Island.[2] Sixteen years later the first settlement was made by the English with the arrival at Antigonish Harbour of a number of officers and men of the Nova Scotia regiment. These were followed in 1795 and 1796 by the arrival of a small number of Scottish Highlanders who, with a few disbanded Highland soldiers, were located by the government along the north shore of Antigonish and adjacent Pictou. The Highland trickle became a stream with arrivals in 1800, 1805, and 1810. The enumeration of 1827 listed a population in Upper Sydney (now Antigonish) of 7,724.[3] A check of the names on the enumeration rolls reveals that more than two-thirds were Scottish. If the eastern township of Tracadie with its Acadian French is excluded, the proportion is more than 80 percent. More strikingly, the Scottish were almost entirely Roman Catholics, and thus definitely Highlanders. The proportion of non-Catholics among them was a little over 10 percent.

Where did these Scottish Highlanders come from? Some indication is provided by place names in the county. The exiled Scots, newly arrived in a strange land, liberally sprinkled it with names of home (Fig. 1). Arisaig, Moidart, Knoydart, Lochaber, Keppoch, Strathglass and many others recalled districts and villages in the Scottish Highlands and, more precisely, sections in the county of Inverness.

Written records bearing on emigration yield little. "Nothing can be more difficult to trace," writes Cowan, "than the movements of peoples who, leaving no written records themselves, sail from a land which affords a harbour to almost every estate and who arrive in a country where the lack of a well-regulated land system permits the newcomer to take up his abode in an uncharted wilderness."[4] Neither their going nor their coming was set down. The commercially rewarding emigrant trade was usually carried out under conditions of great risks to the passenger. Ships were overcrowded; there were no medical facilities on board and usually not sufficient food. Understandably, ship operators and others engaged in the trade were as eager as possible to escape detection.

Some pertinent data for the years 1801, 1802, and 1803 are supplied by Brown[5] who provides a list of vessels carrying emigrants from the Highlands to Nova Scotia, together with total passengers aboard, origin of the settlers (by districts and estates), and, occasionally, ports of landing. The statement, however, is far short of the actual emigrants for, as noted by a House of Commons committee of the time, "A very extensive tract of coasts is not included from whence many vessels sailed and also because even on the coast which is included . . . many vessels are believed to have sailed from unfrequented Bays and Creeks which have entirely eluded inquiry."[6] Defective as the account must be it does specify vessels and places of origin and is useful for corroboration.

The basic source of information for the origin of the settlers is Rankin's genealogies.[7] These provide a complete list of important family names with occasional notes as to place of origin and dates and places of arrival. This information together with that on the enumeration rolls of 1827 makes it possi-

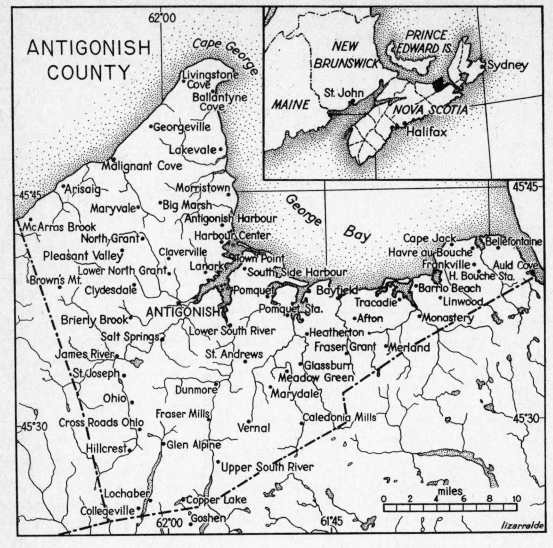

FIG. 1 Antigonish County, Nova Scotia Location and place names.

ble to determine where the Highlanders came from in Scotland and where they settled in Antigonish. The material cited previously, and scattered Scottish comments to be noted later, confirm the picture.

The bulk of the Scots were MacDonalds and Chisholms, family names accounting for approximately 41 percent of the total Scottish names in the 1827 census. The Mac-Donalds (of Clanranald and Keppoch) came from the districts of Moidart, Knoydart, Arisaig, Eigg, along the west coast and from Glenroy and Glenspean in Lochaber

(Fig. 2). The Chisholms came almost entirely from Strathglass in the eastern part of Inverness. Families of fishermen, MacNeills, Livingstones, and Ballantynes, came from the Island of Barra. Camerons and MacMillans came from Lochaber, and Gillis families came from Morar. These are the important family names. Others could be mentioned, but they are minor and reveal no new places of origin. Antigonish was settled by Highland Scots from the districts of Inverness-shire listed above.

Occupance

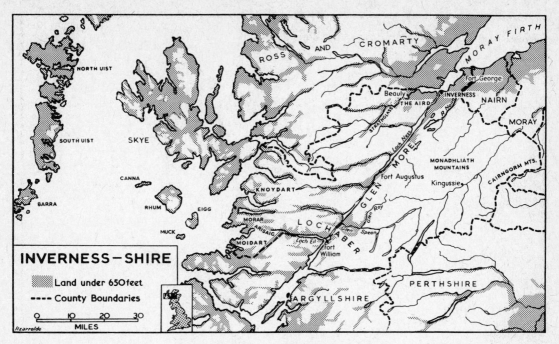

FIG. 2. Inverness-shire, Scotland.

INVERNESS-SHIRE

In many ways Inverness-shire epitomizes the characteristics of the Scottish Highlands. It occupies a central position on the dissected plateau of schist, gneiss, and other metamorphic rocks typical of the Highland country. The southwest-northeast alignment produced by the Caledonian mountain building finds its best expression here in the valley of Glen More. Rejuvenation following peneplanation has left many glens, steep slopes, lakes and waterfalls. Glaciation has resulted in over-deepened valleys, numerous morainic piles, and valley floors covered with drift.

Inverness is dominated by hills, mountains and highland (Fig. 2). The only extensive areas under 650 feet (200 meters) elevation occur along some of the streams and in the northeast around Moray Firth where a lowland plain has developed on the shales and sandstones of the Old Red Sandstone formation. Activity has always been concentrated in these lower areas. It was the valleys that fostered and promoted the Highland clan system and later provided the best land for a booming sheep industry. And it is in some of these valleys today that an attempt is being made to revitalize the Highlands by converting the flatlands to ranches.

The traditional climatic contrast drawn in the Highlands is that between a mild and humid western side and a dry and continental eastern side. However, this is mountain country and averages mean little, especially with respect to temperatures. Precipitation does vary markedly from west (over 60 inches; in some places over 100 inches) to east (24 to 26 inches). Rain days "number 250 to 260 per year in the west and are much less numerous in the east."[8] Too much rain, rain during planting and rain during the harvest, has always been prominently cited as the chief foe of the Highland farmer. Robertson describes a common harvesting procedure in the county in which oats were set up in single sheaves, pointing out that "the season is so rainy in most places that by this method alone can the crop be saved."[9] The situation was further aggravated by the failure of tenants to provide even the barest drainage facilities. Handley uses the wet cli-

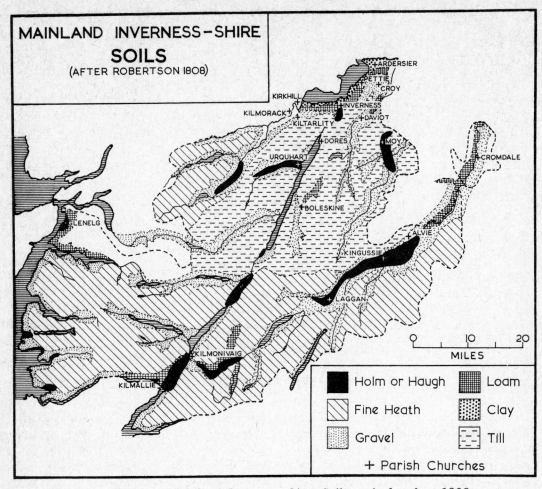

MAINLAND INVERNESS-SHIRE
SOILS
(AFTER ROBERTSON 1808)

Legend:
- Holm or Haugh
- Fine Heath
- Gravel
- Loam
- Clay
- Till
- + Parish Churches

MILES 0 10 20

FIG. 3. *Mainland Inverness-shire. Soils and churches, 1808*

mate to help explain the general listlessness and laziness of Highland farmers noted by English travelers in the eighteenth century.[10]

Because of the excessive moisture and low temperatures, soil cover is generally peaty. On Robertson's soil map (Fig. 3) the most productive soils, as he saw them in 1808, appear as *holm* (or *haugh*) and *loam*. The holm is alluvial soil found in places subject to periodic flooding. Loam, a term which Robertson applied to any place where the land was fairly productive without the presence of clay, is the most fertile and at the same time the most restricted of the county soils. The extent of both of these alluvial soils is limited because of the steep gradients of most of the streams. As a result, extensive areas of sand and gravel have been the most common

legacy of flood waters. The bulk of the county is classed as till, divided on the basis of cover into *till* and *fine heath*. The former apparently includes all steep and stony land more or less barren of vegetation, mountains and hills that were "gloomy, black and sterile." Where the till was covered with a mixture of grass and heath or where the heath was short and fine the designation fine heath is used. Robertson had high hopes for the fine heath of the county, maintaining that "the industry of man will banish heath and introduce verdure upon any spot."[11] Such achievement never came to pass, but portions of the fine heath have continued as important pasture lands from Robertson's day to the present.

AGRICULTURE

Generally speaking, Highland agriculture in the late eighteenth century still possessed many of the features of early Scottish farming from which the Lowland counties had already emerged. "The feudal system has been abolished," wrote Selkirk, "but the customs that arose out of it are not forgotten."[12] The open field system prevailed. Farmers lived in small groups of dwellings and cultivated a number of non-contiguous strips. The division of land into strips, usually separated by lower, marshy tracts not suitable for cultivation, was known as "runrig" and was accompanied by the infield-outfield layout of farms. The infield, or area closest to the dwellings, received most of the manure and was continuously cropped. The outfields farther away were manured only during summer and autumn when cattle were kept in folds over night. The fields were then cropped as long as the land could produce any grain. Beyond the outfield lay waste, moor or hill land, usually held in common and used for pasture.[13]

Land in the county was most commonly held under *tacksmen* or gentlemen farmers, part of the legacy of the period of Highland clans. As the chiefs of the clans turned from war to more peaceful pursuits, certain cadets of the family were given leases of large tracts of land. Out of these they carved domains for themselves with the help of tenant labor and tenant production for rent.[14]

The Highlander was not an outstanding farmer. He had always been a soldier and the sword came more naturally to his hands than the plow or the spade. "The conditions of his life, not to speak of the character of the soil, prevented him giving much attention to the tillage of his fields."[15] Robertson lamented that the "greater part by far of the county is in the hands of persons exceedingly ignorant of the modern improvements in respect of tillage . . . crooked ridges . . . obstructions to the plough in every field . . . the furrows turned over in a clumsy manner . . . with every other sign of ignorance and inattention."[16]

The most common grain crop was oats, "universally a gray-bearded or black oat, little better than the seed of a good rye grass."[17] But even the best variety of oats tended to degenerate and take on a grey or black appearance under the effect of the wet Highland climate. Barley ranked next to oats. This again was a variety peculiar to the Highlands, generally known as Scottish *bere* (or *bear*) or *bigg*. It required a shorter growing season than ordinary barley and produced a better crop on poor land and in wet weather.[18] Hay was not cultivated as a crop but was obtained as bog hay from poorly drained, uncultivated land.

The potato was extensively cultivated by the end of the eighteenth century and recognized as the food crop without equal. It had been strongly promoted in Inverness and other counties by the Commissioners of the Annexed Estates who issued detailed instructions and offered premiums "for Raising and Preserving Potatoes . . . observing that there is almost every year a scarcity of meal and other provisions in the wilder portions of the Highlands."[19] Robertson noted with satisfaction that "every householder from the highest to the lowest order of his family has potatoes for his family."[20]

The chief, and in most cases the only, commercial product of the Highlands, were black cattle, fed on hill pastures in the summer and on whatever else could be spared during the rest of the year. Sheep numbers were greatly increasing in the county at the end of the eighteenth century, Robertson noting an increase from 25,000 to 50,000 in the period 1794 to 1804. The old indigenous sheep, which was small, fine-wooled, and all white, was still common, and so was the Linton or blackfaced breed. And stocks of Cheviot sheep, introduced by the sheep farmers from the south who had taken up cleared lands, were becoming important. Next to hogs, against which Highlanders had a strong traditional prejudice, horses probably received the least attention of all livestock. They were raised in large numbers and were generally inferior animals because of starvation diets on which they had to subsist. Numbers declined sharply as more sheep were introduced and took up greater shares of the hill pastures.

Apparently in most districts all livestock pastured together and there was little attempt to watch that the animals did not stray. As a result there was virtually no control over breeding. The Rules and Articles of the Commissioners for Managing the Annexed Estates contains a provision that "all and each of the tenants shall be obliged to herd their horses, black cattle, sheep and other bestial, in the winter as well as the summer, under the penalty of one-half a merk Scots [approximately seven shillings] for each beast found upon a neighbor's ground or farm."[21]

*

STRATHGLASS

The portion of the Highlands known as Strathglass in the eighteenth century included the valleys of the Grass and Beauly rivers (Fig. 2). It formed part of the two Church of Scotland parishes of Kilmorack and Kiltarlity, the former on the north side of the river, the latter on the south side (Fig. 3).

The valley is one of the simplest and most clear-cut glens in the Highlands with a remarkably flat floor and an abrupt rise to the hills on either side. Robertson wrote of it as "all either hill or a dead flat of land formed by water."[22] Unfortunately, the soil on the flat is largely sand and gravel and, as described in a later report, "thin and light [and] very difficult to trench . . . from the number of stones."[23] Under such conditions a great deal of labor and heavy applications of lime and manure were a prerequisite to successful crop production. It is no surprise, then, that cultivated crops were a minor part of the agriculture.

It was just to the east of Strathglass that the first Inverness-shire agriculturists, the monks of Beauly, tilled the land and planted crops. English travelers commonly noted the beauty and fertility of the area around the monastery. But although the *Aird*, as it was known, might have been an object lesson to part of Strathglass, it had no effect upon agriculture there. Apparently there was no contact between the two areas. Then, too, the poor soils in the *Strath,* compared to the more arable land associated with the old red sandstone formation in the Aird, were a definite handicap.

On the maps of the Roy Survey of Scotland some indication of the land utilization of the area appears.[24] The concentration of activity on the flats of the river is apparent, along with the arrangement of fields. All of the fields are small, a fact that was looked upon by more than one of the parish writers as a great disadvantage.[25] There is no evidence of enclosure. The villages or clusters of houses are named and the extent of woodland is shown. The river flats seemed to have been devoted largely to pasture. One writer observes that "in this Strath . . . is a great deal of good pasture for black cattle, sheep, and goats. South . . . is very high ground all covered with heath and only fit for pasturing sheep and goats."[26] The writer for Kilmorack declared that "it is impossible to ascertain the number of cattle," adding that a "great number" were annually sold for the south of Scotland and English markets.[27] The same author points up the importance of potatoes. "Within these 20 years," he writes, "the Laird of Chisholm's tenants in the height of Strathglass were in the constant practice of purchasing yearly oat meal, but during the 12 or 14 years past they have paid so much attention to their potatoe [sic] crop that they are not under the necessity of laying out £5 in the year for meal."[28]

Sheep were not important in the parishes

before 1800. There is no mention of sheep farms in the Old Statistical Account. By the time of the New Statistical Account, however, the situation had changed. The Kiltarlity author writes of the "considerable extent" of sheep farming and describes the woods which provided winter shelter as "abounding in sheep walks."[29] Even today the aspect of the glen is predominantly pastoral. But the sheep ranch has given way to the cattle ranch, with sheep relegated to the steep hillsides. The small amount of land in crops bears out the soundness of similar land use in the Strath over 150 years ago.

*

LOCHABER

Lochaber lies on the other side of the "divide" from Strathglass, the divide between the dry east and the humid west. This is the rougher side of Britain with steeper slopes, more numerous streams, and smaller fields and farms. "The most mountainous parish perhaps in the kingdom" is the description in one report.[30] Pennant notes that "Lochaber had been a den of thieves and as long as they had their waters, their torrents and their bogs in a state of nature, they made their excursions, could plunder and retreat with their booty in full security."[31]

With the break-up of the clan system Lochaber became an important cattle producer. In his tour of 1769 Pennant observed the importance of cattle in Lochaber noting that the district alone sent out more than 3,000 head annually. There were also few sheep at this time, but their numbers were being rapidly increased. "There is scarce any arable land," he notes, "for the extensive wet which reigns here almost totally prevents the growth of corn. . . . The inhabitants of this district are therefore obliged, for their support, to import 6,000 bolls [36,000 bushels] of oatmeal annually."[32] By the end of the eighteenth century sheep farming had become the dominant industry. Their numbers in the parish of Kilmonivaig in 1796 were set down as 50,000, compared to 1,500 black cattle and 500 horses.[33] By 1842, sheep had increased to over 100,000.

Most of the Antigonish emigrants from Lochaber came from the valleys of Glenroy and Glenspean in the parish of Kilmonivaig, one of the few Highland parishes whose population was more than one-half Roman Catholic.[34] These glens contain large areas of flat land, mostly holm and loam (Fig. 3) which apparently were neglected. "In Glenspean alone," writes the Kilmonivaig author in 1842, "there are upwards of 40,000 acres of excellent soil, which by the application of skill and capital could be brought into cultivation."[35] He goes on to blame absentee landlords, poor management and lack of inducements for the small amount of cultivation. Today the same glens are still marked by a lack of cultivation. The crofters who live here are not farmers. Most of them work in nearby Fort William and raise a few sheep and keep a cow or two as a supplementary activity. Movement out of the area is heavy. The population in Roybridge Parish declined from 1,000 in 1870 to less than 300 in 1950.

*

THE WEST COUNTRY

The western districts of Knoydart, Morar, Arisaig, and Moidart,[36] now as in the eighteenth century, are the loneliest and most isolated on the county mainland. To the ever-present rugged topography of mountains, hills and high moors must be added such features as the long distance from main centers, the deep penetrations of sea lochs effectively preventing land movement, and one of the most disagreeable climates in northwest Europe. Excessive precipitation is repeatedly mentioned as a cause for crop failure. Deluges of rain, followed by floods might postpone harvests until November. The destruction wrought might then render the crop useless. "Such quantities of rain follow," writes one author, "and at all seasons, that an agriculturist might calculate on losing almost every fourth crop."[37] No wonder that, in the words of Hunt, "the pulse of life beats but feebly, activity of any sort, agriculture or otherwise, being at a discount."[38]

Again the raising of livestock was the chief activity in the eighteenth century. The practice of going to the *shealing,* that is, moving to the hills beyond the inhabited areas for pasture, was still important. It is mentioned for Knoydart and Morar in 1774,[39] and was probably common in the other districts as well. Robertson describes the procedure.[40] Every year in June after the crop was sown and the peat cut for fuel, whole families would move to the far-off hill pastures. Here they would live simply, subsisting on milk from herds and a bit of meal and moving from place to place as the pasture was used up. Occasionally some member of the family would return to the farm in the lowlands to hoe the potatoes, weed the crop and collect fuel. This type of nomadic herding persisted until the end of the century when the pastures were withdrawn from the farmers and let to shepherds.

The Catholic proportion of the population was higher here than in any other part of the Highlands from which emigrants left for Nova Scotia. In 1798, out of the total population of 1,990 in Moidart, Arisaig, and

South Morar, 1,896 were Catholic.[41] The population was scattered in small hamlets on flat land near the sea. Occasional mention is made of small areas of light or gravelly soil yielding oats, barley and potatoes. In contrast to Strathglass there seems to have been very little natural meadow because of the need to utilize the small amount of flat land for tillage. In some parts of Moidart cultivation was practiced on land so rocky and broken that neither horse nor plow could be used, and the only implement for turning up the soil was the *caschrom,* a clumsy heavy spade with a crooked handle. In contrast, on the more level land seven or eight horses might be employed. This extravagant use of stock seems to have been general in the whole county. In many places eight oxen were yoked to one plow. "Inconceivable," snorts Robertson. "It might with equal propriety [be] 80."[42]

The same Robertson refutes the charge that West Coast Highlanders were lazy and poor workers, by pointing to their efforts in making composts for their potato crop. In Moidart the compost was a common sight outside the cottage door. It was made up of moss, dung, seaweed and berries. The material from the sea was carried up from the shore on people's backs up slopes too steep to be negotiated by horses.

Today, the west country is largely a land of small crofters, dependent as their eighteenth century forebears had been on cattle, hay and potatoes. But this is not enough to provide a living for most of them. There is little outside labor available, as in Glenspean and Glenroy. There are, however, two other sources of income, government agricultural subsidies and an increasing summer tourist industry. In common with the preceding sections of the county, population is declining.

*

BARRA AND EIGG

The island of Barra (Fig. 2) was one of the holdings of Roderick MacNeill at the

time that its inhabitants were leaving in large numbers for eastern Nova Scotia. Many of

Occupance

these emigrants were fishermen or boatmen, and references to their ability on the sea provide one of the few examples of praise bestowed upon anyone in the West Highlands and islands. "The fishermen of Barray," writes MacDonald, "are the most active and prosperous now to be found in the Hebrides."[43]

MacDonald divides Barra into four main physical divisions. It is significant that he relates each to the dominant agricultural activity, the raising of black cattle. The first division is that of mountains and valleys, about one-fifth of the island, of limited use for grazing,[44] but valuable for the kelp which collected in its sea inlets. The *machir,* or sand wastes, one-tenth of the island, provided grass in the summer, but was more important as the source of sea shells used as manure throughout the island. A third division, designated as "grass and arable" occupied another tenth of the island, near the western shore, and it was here that most of the habitations were located; a disadvantage was its poor drainage in the wet season. The rest of the island was *montich,* a covering of deep moss over gravel, clay or granite, not productive, but a source of fuel and a place of shelter for cattle.

The most important activity and one carried on to the detriment of both agriculture and fishing was the manufacture of kelp. Barra was a kelp estate and kelp was king throughout the summer season when the inhabitants might have been attending to farming or fishing. The value of kelp as a commercial crop also meant that the use of seaweed for agriculture was greatly restricted. Kelp manufacture was also important on the mainland in the districts of Knoydart to Moidart and although it began to decline after 1823, with the abolition of the tax on Spanish barilla, it was important in Barra as late as 1840, at which time it was still regarded as an obstacle to farming.[45]

Kelp manufacture was also the mainstay on the small island of Eigg. The rearing of horses, cattle and sheep on pastures of heath and coarse grass was the other important activity. Wool and horses were occasionally exported to Uist in exchange for meal. Local grain was scarce; it had to be sent to Arisaig to be ground, a difficult and expensive voyage as there was no regular communication with the mainland.[46] There was not much emphasis upon fishing, probably because the islanders could not afford the equipment. Consequently, the ever-present potato crop had to provide almost the entire means of subsistence.

*

AGRICULTURE AND EMIGRATION

On the basis of the foregoing descriptions and associated remarks in the references cited, it is possible to see certain relationships between agriculture and emigration in these sections of Inverness. The emigrants were farmers whose main activity had been the raising of cattle. But the cattle were inferior, small and rangy, because of the lack of feed. It is apparent that most tenants kept too many cattle. As a result, pastures were overstocked in the summer and it was necessary to plow even the stoniest and poorest lands in an effort to supply enough fodder to keep the cattle from perishing in the winter. The result was half-starved cattle and crops that in many instances were little better than weeds.

Of the crops raised, potatoes received the most attention and were always the most heavily manured. In most instances, oats and/or barley followed and depended upon what was left of this manure. This was the sum total of rotation practiced. Hay was everywhere a natural crop, bog hay from poorly drained meadow lands. Composts varied a good deal, but usually left much to be desired. The best heaps seem to have been in the West Country where seaweed could be used. Here, too, shells provided lime. Elsewhere the application of lime in any form was rare.

A good deal of the blame for the low state of agriculture lay with the land owners who took a large part of the production in high rents, but did nothing to encourage improvement or to increase the fertility of the soil, which after all belonged to them. They also demanded service, either on their own farms or in kelp manufacture, in conflict with the tenants' own labor requirements.

In the late eighteenth century this old order of subsistence farming with cattle as the main rent-paying commodity was being replaced throughout the Highlands by large-scale commercial sheep farming. The change had made considerable progress in Inverness by 1790. It brought with it a complete upheaval of agriculture. Sheep farming meant an introduction into the Highlands of a south country "store-master" with south country shepherds, sheep and dogs. Even the old Highland sheep were swept away. They were too small, too unprofitable, and of too many varieties to play a part in the new system.[47]

The emigrants to Antigonish were involved in this upheaval and were carried by it across the Atlantic. They brought with them none of the "new ways" because these were not part of their tradition. They were farmers of the old order, "black cattle and potato men," forced out, as they and later generations of Highlanders saw it, by sheep:

*The sheep with the brocket faces that have
    made confusion in all the world
Turning our country to desert and putting
    up the rents of our lands.*[48]

The bulk of migration to Antigonish took place in the period 1790 to 1810, the years of the peak migration from the Highlands. The extent of the movement was viewed with sufficient alarm to bring about the appointment of a House of Commons committee to survey the Highlands and ascertain the causes of migration. The most powerful cause the committee found was "the converting of large districts into extensive sheep walks. This ... requires much fewer people to manage the same tract of country."[49] Another observation of the committee was that income from the sale of black cattle had facilitated migration by enabling farmers and former tenants to bear the costs involved.

The great migrations from Strathglass followed the clearances from the Chisholm lands in 1801. In Lochaber, sheep were "a strong temptation to proprietors who value money more than men. ... They require a smaller number of hands than black cattle, can graze in places where they did not venture and yield a great produce."[50] Some attempts were made by proprietors to let lands for sheep farms among former tenants, but there was no enthusiasm for the idea from either side and it met with failure.

The West Country and the Islands witnessed the largest emigrations and here some population figures, faulty though they may be, are available. The population of Moidart in 1798 is given as 712 compared to a figure of "over 1200" eight years before. The number of emigrants to America "by whole families and of all ages" in 1790 and 1791 for the district is listed as 250. For Arisaig and South Morar the figure is 322.[51] From the small island of Eigg 176 individuals left in 1788 and 1790.[52] Sheep are again regarded as the main reason for movement, but other causes "contributing to the evil" are also mentioned—"high rents . . . the increase of population and the flattering accounts received from friends in America."[53]

One of the most comprehensive views of the causes of migration was taken by a reporter for the Society for the Propagation of Christian Knowledge in 1791. He attributed the blame not only to sheep, but also to the whole range of agricultural conditions then prevalent in the Highlands. These included:

The conversion of small into great farms to the exclusion of the inferior order of tenants ... the prejudice against granting leases of a sufficient length to encourage the tenants to improve their farms.... The ignorance with which some landowners raise rents, while they furnish neither the means nor the instruction as to the manner by which the tenants may be enabled to pay them . . . the non-resistance of the proprietors and their . . . total want of attention to their people.

"At the same time," he concludes, "the great and most universally operating cause of emigration is that in comparison of [*sic*] the means of subsistence which they afford these countries are greatly overstocked with people."[54] Adam, writing well over a century later, came to the same conclusion: "The real cause of Highland distress and Highland emigration in the late eighteenth century is to be found in circumstances . . . entirely apart from the introduction of sheep. Briefly the Highland population was over-running its resources and unless positive preventive mea-

sures were taken emigration or migration on a large scale was inevitable."[55]

The relating of population to resources raises a delicate question. It is obvious that the handicaps of a wet, fickle climate, poverty of soil, lack of shelter and sheer remoteness restricted the ability of these sections of the Highlands to support large numbers of people. It should be just as obvious that most areas were not producing anywhere near their full capacity in crop, stock and pasture. Common to all areas was the absence of more intensive forms of production which could compensate in part for the small size of the holdings. This is still a problem in the Highlands.[56] It is also a problem in eastern Nova Scotia.

*

EARLY SETTLEMENT IN ANTIGONISH

The major period of settlement in Antigonish was between 1790 and 1810, although there are records of Highland Scots in the county as early as 1780, and immigration continued into the 1830's. Martell presents no evidence of Scottish migration into Antigonish between 1815 and 1838, but his compilation is based only on what is available from shipping records.[57]

The period before 1815 is significant because it was a time when nothing was being done officially to induce settlement. The strongest advocates of immigration were "neither those interested in the defense of the colonies nor in the general advancement of their prosperity. They were . . . men personally interested—merchants, ship owners, and land speculators."[58] At this time too (more precisely from 1790 to 1808) land grants in Nova Scotia were forbidden, following a period during which they had been given away. The prohibition meant little, however, and was circumvented by one means or another, most commonly by squatting.

By 1827 nearly all the land suitable for settlement had been taken up (Fig. 4). In

his quest for land for emigrants, Cockburn could find little in Sydney County.[59] The whole county (now the two counties of Antigonish and Guysborough) was reported to contain 120,000 acres of "good vacant land well situated for settlement," but this was scattered in several tracts and its quality was generally over-rated. The best land for settlement, as it had been in the homeland of the settlers and as it remains today in Antigonish, was the flood plains and lower terraces along the main streams, especially those converging on the town of Dorchester (now Antigonish). These lands were known as "interval" (or intervale) lands because they presented open spots or "intervals" in the forest.[60] They possessed a double advantage. They did not require clearing and they were of above-average fertility. It is significant that the town of Dorchester was first known as Antigonish Interval. Further, the most common place names associated with early settlement were those of Rivers and Brooks—Lower and Upper South River, James River, West River, Brierly Brook and others (Fig. 1).

The boundless forest was a new and

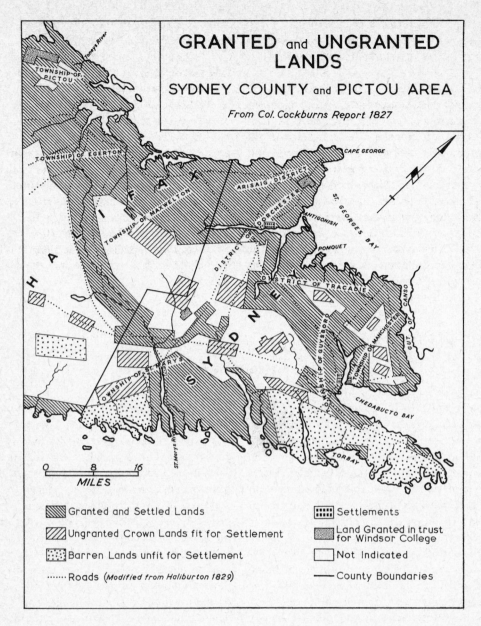

GRANTED and UNGRANTED LANDS

SYDNEY COUNTY and PICTOU AREA

From Col. Cockburns Report 1827

Granted and Settled Lands

Ungranted Crown Lands fit for Settlement

Barren Lands unfit for Settlement

······ Roads *(Modified from Haliburton 1829)*

Settlements

Land Granted in trust for Windsor College

Not Indicated

—— County Boundaries

0   8   16
MILES

FIG. 4. *Sydney County and Pictou Area, Nova Scotia. Granted and ungranted lands, 1827*

strange sight to the Highlander and he must have viewed it with fear and dismay. "An emigrant set down in such a scene," wrote Selkirk of his Highland settlers on Prince Edward Island, "feels almost the helplessness of a child. He has a new set of ideas to acquire." The result was that "abandoned to their own exertions," the Highlanders rarely avoided "involving themselves in inextricable difficulties."[61]

But the Highlanders were hardy pioneers. They knew how to endure hardships and how to live with a minimum of comfort. They had been bred to this type of life and the forest, once cleared, proved more of a blessing than a curse. It provided the logs to build houses and material for the construction of carts and implements. On land newly cleared by fire the wood ashes provided potash for an abundant first crop. This, together with the

Occupance

TABLE I

AGRICULTURAL PRODUCTION IN ANTIGONISH
COUNTY, 1827; 1881, 1891; AND 1941, 1951

Agricultural item	1827[a]	1881, 1891[b]	1941, 1951[b]
Total population	7,724	17,087	11,258
Total number of farmers	883	2,622	1,294
Total acreage improved[c]	30,257	135,174	39,622
Acreage improved per farm	36.5	51.5	30.5
Production per farm:			
Wheat, bushels	19.8	12.9	4.5
Oats, bushels		54.1	116.6
Barley,[d] bushels		4.2	11.0
Potatoes, bushels	273.6	116.8	78.8
Other roots, bushels	—[e]	13.0	52.1
Hay, tons	11.9	15.0	20.4
Livestock, number per farm:			
Cattle	12.3	9.3	8.2
Horses	0.7	1.4	1.6
Sheep	20.6	10.4	12.3
Swine	6.4	1.2	1.3
Poultry	—[e]	14.0[f]	42.0

a Data adapted from "Statistical Return of the Upper District of the County of Sydney, 1827," *Report P A.N.S* (Halifax, 1939), Appendix B.

b Data adapted from Census of Canada, averaged for the two census years. Data for 1961 is not comparable because of changes introduced in the enumeration.

c For 1827 and 1881, 1891 (not 1941, 1951) includes non-tillable land used for pasture.

d Enumerated with oats in 1827; includes mixed grain for 1941, 1951.

e Not available.

f Data for 1891 only

cheapness of the land, encouraged rapid clearing, in some cases carried on to excess. The amount of cleared land per farmer in 1827 was 36.5 acres, a figure actually larger than that of improved land per farmer in 1941 and 1951 (Table I).

The timber also turned Highlanders away from the land. Between 1812 and 1819 considerable quantities of large timber were exported from the area between Antigonish and Pomquet and when this declined Antigonish continued to provide sawed lumber shingles and staves for the Halifax and Newfoundland market.[62] But Highlanders knew little of lumber and made poor woodsmen. More often than not their earnings failed to cover expenses and in the process their lands were neglected. But in the Highlands tradition, carried from Scotland to Nova Scotia and still very much in evidence in both places, farming was regarded as a last resort. If other activities were available, be they fighting or kelp manufacture in the old country or lumbering in the new, agriculture was forsaken.

The failure of these activities or the lack of others forced a return to the land.

By 1827 the economy of the county revolved around the export of horses, cattle, sheep, grain, butter and pork. The emphasis clearly was upon livestock activity, something that came much more easily to the Highlander than the cultivation of land. The conditions of the times—the demand for meat, especially by the armed services during and after the War of 1812 and the availability of cheap flour from the United States—promoted a livestock economy into which the Highlander could very easily fit.

Great efforts were made to discourage the emphasis on livestock that was prevalent throughout most of the province and to promote in its stead cultivation of the land and the raising of wheat. The administration of Lord Dalhousie was anxious to make the colony independent of American flour, but the feelings of some writers of the day went even deeper. John Young was one of these.[63] Constantly he sought to demonstrate to the

TABLE II

AGRICULTURAL PRODUCTION PER FARMER, ANTIGONISH COUNTY AND DISTRICTS, 1827[a]

Product	County	Arisaig	Dorchester	St. Andrews	Tracadie
Wheat, bushels	19.8	24.1	19.3	18.2	17.6
Other grains, bushels	34.4	30.5	36.8	26.0	44.1
Potatoes, bushels	273.6	248.9	308.0	246.3	291.0
Hay, tons	11.9	8.9	13.9	9.9	15.0
Livestock, number per farm:					
Cattle	12.3	11.2	13.6	11.4	12.8
Horses	0.7	0.7	0.5	0.9	0.7
Sheep	20.6	18.7	20.0	19.6	24.1
Swine	6.4	6.3	6.2	5.1	8.1

a Data adapted from Statistical Return, 1827.

new settlers that they could profitably grow wheat, that the country was adapted for something better than pasture, that grazing was a poor activity "compatible with indolence, stupidity and a gross ignorance of all principle."[64] He could understand the emphasis on stock back in the Highlands, where excessive moisture in the summer and fall limited crop production. But here the climate was different. It was "infinitely superior... and could ripen productions that scarcely lived under glass in Scotland." The dry fall should have been a special inducement. "During the whole autumn from the beginning of September to that of December, we are blessed with a delightful tract of weather —the sky serene and unclouded, the roads dry—and the plough may be in perpetual motion."[65]

The number of stock in the county was high, even for a pioneer land. Each farm averaged more than 12 cattle and 20 sheep (Table I), numbers which have since significantly declined. Even the number of hogs was fairly high although this was even more of a temporary situation. Again, as they had in Inverness-shire, farmers tried to keep too much stock and their means were not sufficient to keep them in good condition. Livestock numbers in the Scottish parts of the county differ very little from those in the district of Tracadie, occupied largely by Acadian French (Table II). However, considerable differences do exist in the matter of

forage for the stock, notably "other grain" and hay. The Tracadie farmer had a substantially greater production in these two items. Selkirk considered that a supply of hay of one to one-and-one-half tons per head was a requirement to carry cattle through the year.[66] Production among the Highlanders was less than 0.9 tons per head per year; the figure for the Tracadie farmer was approximately 1.2. The Highlander had a tendency to exhaust his hay lands by repeated croppings. This initiated a cycle of diminishing returns. The need for hay meant that pasture lands, a necessity in the summer, became hay lands and in turn these too became exhausted. The disinclination to improve the soil and plow upland meant less production of feed grain, necessary to supplement hay. It also meant that the old hay lands remained unproductive.

Wheat production was fairly high by 1827[67] (Tables I and II), due in part to the promotion of the crop by the newly formed Sydney County Agricultural Society. Before the formation of the society the Dorchester area was an importer of wheat, largely from the northern coast of the country. The high production here (over 24 bushels per farm in 1827 compared to a county figure of less than 20), may have been the result of applications of seaweed for manure, a practice carried from Scotland and still significant today. By 1821 the Dorchester area was producing a small surplus and in 1822 exported in wheat and flour the equivalent of 4,000 bushels to Halifax, Pictou, Arichat and New-foundland. The Arisaig district continued as a strong exporter, sending out the equivalent of 1,200 bushels of wheat a year.[68]

In general the crop was produced without regard to rotation or fertilizer. Moorsom writes of as many as seven successive crops raised on the uplands of Antigonish without the aid of lime or manure.[69] One of the handicaps to agricultural improvement in Inverness had been the landlords' demands for high rent and their refusal in the meantime to maintain or improve the soil which was providing that rent. The Highlander in the New World, now his own landlord, treated the land in the same way.

The production of oats began to increase in the 1820's, following the letters of *Agricola* and the awarding of bounties for oatmeal mills. Oats were recognized as a supplement to, or even substitute for, wheat and the extension of the crop was one of the objects in the program of the Provincial Agricultural Board. The other parts of the program, equally applicable to Antigonish, included the introduction of summer fallow as a preparation for wheat, the increased use of lime, the cultivation of turnips and the promotion of more and better plowing.[70] There was little to criticize in the matter of potato production, except that there was possibly too great a dependence upon the crop. The average annual production per farmer in the county was over 270 bushels. In Dorchester the figure was over 300 bushels (Tables I and II). Here at least was an instance where their background served the Highlanders well.

Potatoes to the contrary, Highlanders in general and Antigonish Highlanders in particular fared poorly at the hands of observers of the day. Moorsom wrote that the Antigonish settlers, "being chiefly Highland Scottish and accustomed to large sheep walks rather than to tillage farms, exhibit . . . very inferior attainments in almost every branch of agriculture."[71] He is wrong about the sheep walks, but his main observation stands. Young observed that inferior crops in his area were due to "blind and wretched husbandry" and deplored the lack of barley, the "very foster child of Nova Scotia."[72] The Rev. Thomas Trotter of the Sydney County Agricultural Society blamed the Highlanders for that organization's slow progress. "We have a very few active people," he wrote, "but the Highlanders are ignorant and Lasy [sic]."[73] Other observers were kinder and saw deeper. To Haliburton, Highlanders were settlers with few wants: "Their ambition is chiefly limited to the requirement [sic] of the mere necessities of life."[74] Selkirk had noted the same characteristics in many of his Highland settlers on Prince Edward Island. As soon as they were able to maintain their families, they would show no further ambition, preferring "the indulgence of their old habits of indolence to the accumulation of property by a continuance of active industry."[75]

It should be remembered that the Highlanders had never been a prosperous group. Many of the immigrants at the turn of the century were largely dependent upon charity. The arrivals who landed at Pictou in 1801 were forced to move eastward because the colony not provide for them, as it had not been able to provide for their predecessors ten years before.[76] Eastern Nova Scotia offered little inducement to settlement except that the voyage from Scotland was short and the fare low. The Scots, made penniless by demands of the voyage, were attracted by the prospect of cheap land, in many cases to be had simply by squatting. They sought little but the means of subsistence. And this they had to find without capital, without skill and without the benefit of instruction. They could draw only on the little knowledge brought with them across the sea. Although surrounded by difficulties, they were able in a few years to provide for their needs. With this, they stopped struggling, much to the dismay of men like Young who tried to stir them to action. But rooted in a certain way of doing things, a way that found outlets in the economic demands of the day, they were not to be aroused by agricultural societies, pamphlets and prizes.

The peak in agricultural activity in the county is generally considered to have been reached in the decade 1881 to 1891. In terms of land occupied and farm population there definitely was a peak. From 1827 to 1881–91 the total number of farms more than tripled and improved acreage per farmer increased from 36.5 to 51.5 (Table I). There was no such peak in production. Wheat declined from 19.8 to 12.9 bushels per farmer. And this was still a time of subsistence farming, before the wheat lands of the Canadian West had been opened up. "Something is wrong" wrote MacDonald, "when a county which contains 16,512 people whose chief dependence is on the production of soil have to pay $70,000 for bread."[77] Oat production was up and was apparently taking the place of wheat and potatoes in the diet. Potato production shows a decrease of almost 60 percent. MacDonald comments upon the potato yield in Antigonish (76 bushels per acre) and compares it to that in Pictou (100 bushels) and Guysborough (83 bushels). He attributes the difference to the "relative skill of the farmers," adding that they had no real inducement to improve their agriculture. The inducement, in the form of the railway, came. It facilitated not agricultural improvement, but movement out of the county. Constant cropping, unaided by rotation or the use of fertilizer, continued as a characteristic of Antigonish farmers. "They depend entirely upon the natural power of the land," wrote MacDonald, "forgetting that thought and skill and labour are required to make the most profit out of the farms and at the same time keep them from losing their fertility."[78]

The livestock industry continued as the source of income for the farmers. But marketing was becoming more and more of a problem. The trade with Newfoundland which had begun as early as 1811 was subject to extreme fluctuations. It frequently happened that cattle were sold at St. John's at prices that failed to cover the cost of transportation. The inducement of this trade was another factor cited by MacDonald for the state of agriculture in the county. Farmers continued to send droves of cattle and sheep to the Halifax markets, but here too the growing expense of transportation was a serious drawback. The difficulties were reflected in a general decrease of stock, especially sheep, on which the margin of profit was smallest (Table I). The smaller number of cattle, together with the increased supply of hay and larger pasturage, probably meant that the animals were better fed, but they were not fed well enough to command prices that would more than defray transportation costs.

*

CONDITIONS AT MID-CENTURY

The most significant agricultural change between 1881-91 and 1941-51 was the sharp decrease in the number of farms (Table I). As in the rest of Nova Scotia, this was the result of large-scale land abandonment, coinciding first (around 1900) with the rapid settlement of Canada's prairie provinces and later (after 1921) with the industrial growth of central Canada. The lure of better opportunities elsewhere, however, was only part of the explanation. Another part was the inability of the Antigonish farmer to adjust his activities to the demands of modern commercial agriculture. It is true that a good deal of the land abandoned, while suitable for a subsistence agriculture, is not suitable, physically, for today's agriculture. It is equally true that on much of the best land, farming is not very different from what it was in 1881.

Farming still revolves around livestock, as it did in the peak and pioneer years and as it did before that in the Highlands of Inverness. However, the number of animals per farm (with the exception of poultry) has changed very little. The numbers of swine and sheep remain very low. The raising of hogs, something the Highlander regarded with aversion, has never been a very sizeable enterprise. In the 1930's the country imported young pigs from Prince Edward Island, and even today not enough hogs are raised for the local market. There is no particular prejudice against sheep. Actually they are well-adapted to conditions in eastern Nova Scotia. They are economical to house and feed and can be finished on good pasture. Too often, however, sheep (which are easy animals to manage) have been left entirely to themselves. The result has been trouble with parasites and dogs, and a poor quality lamb that tended to spoil the market. The farmers, in turn, have shown little interest in improving the situation, preferring instead to cut down on sheep numbers.

Even cattle, the "forte" of the Highlanders, show a slight decrease in numbers. What is more significant is that there has been a shift in the first half of this century from cattle raised chiefly for sale to cattle raised for dairy purposes. Of the 9.3 cattle per farm for the years 1881 and 1891, 3.7 were milk cows. Of the 8.2 in 1941 and 1951, 4.7 were milk cows. The shift began with the virtual disappearance of the Newfoundland market and increased competition from central Canada, made possible by refrigeration and improved transportation. It was facilitated by the efforts of Dr. Hugh MacPherson of Antigonish who introduced Ayrshire cattle, developed a breeding program and distributed young bulls to interested farmers.

Despite the change in emphasis, the livestock industry is beset with problems similar in many ways to those that handicapped previous generations. First, a striking lack of feed crops is produced. Table I indicates that the average farm in 1941 and 1951 produced only 20 tons of hay, 117 bushels of oats, 11 bushels of barley and mixed grain, 79 bushels of potatoes and 52 bushels of other roots—a very small production on which to maintain a livestock industry. The area in cropland is small and the production from it is small. This in turn curbs the outlook and ambition of the producer. D. J. MacDonald stated the problem as one of "small patch plots and small patch mentalities" reinforcing one another to the detriment of agriculture.[79]

Contributing to low production is the condition of the soil. Throughout the county, soils of all kinds have been cropped continuously until almost no lime, phosphate, or potash has been left in them. On the basis of more than 1,200 soil samples collected in the farm-to-farm surveys of the Soil Division, Nova Scotia Agricultural College (1941 to 1944), the following soil picture emerges. Available phosphate, ranked high, medium, or low for each sample, was "low" for 82 percent of the samples. Available potash was "low" for 52 percent, and the pH was "low" (below 5.7) for 78 percent. No surveys have been carried out on organic matter in the soil, but Dr. MacPherson, who for many years has run tests on soil samples for county farmers, declares that this is their most serious soil problem. The full significance of manure is not appreciated. Fields near the farm buildings receive the most manure and those farther away are neglected, a relic perhaps of the infield-outfield method of farming. Manure piles, too, are frequently left out in the open, often under the eaves of the barn where much of the nitrogen is lost.

Another factor in low production has been the general neglect of pasture lands. The first grazing areas in the county were the woods. An extensive system of common pasturage followed with cattle, sheep, horses and hogs ranging the partially-cleared lands and the uncleared hills and uplands. As the hay crop improved, pasture became incidental. Land too poor to grow grain, and meadows too badly "run out" to grow good hay, were given over to pasture. Permanent pasture was (it still is) the last use to which land was put before it reverted to timber. And its deterioration was hastened by the practice of applying the barnyard manure almost exclusively to the arable land. This meant that there was a slow transfer of fertility from pasture areas to cropland. The number of acres of pasture (improved and unimproved) per animal unit in 1941 was 4.5,[80] a high number indicating large areas of unproductive pasture.

One of the most characteristic features of agriculture and one that contributed significantly to low production is part-time farming. Of the 1,164 farms in 1951, only 292 reported sales of farm products of over $1,200. 680 operators reported doing some work off the farm, 443 for more than 50 days. In some areas work off the farm is more than a supplement to farm activity; it is a replacement. An example is the St. Andrew's subdivision, an old established farm district settled almost entirely by Highland Scots. The area has clung to the "old type" of farming, the raising of mixed herds for both beef and cream. The common practice is to keep a few cows for cream and then kill a few steers in the fall. In the post-war years the demand for this beef product was high because of the general shortage of Western beef. At best this was a temporary situation. Most of the farms also regularly sell lambs and wool. This mixture of "livestock and dairying" has the advantage of not demanding a great deal of work from the operator. It frees him to look for a part-time job in road work, construction, or whatever else may be available.

Low production is not confined to part-time farms or to those which ship cream for their main source of income. Even the most prosperous farms, those which ship whole milk to Antigonish or to Sydney, are low producers. They are characterized by a low improved acreage, a small dairy herd, extensive crop operations, a low capital investment and poor pastures. The number of acres in improved land is seldom above 40, and the herds average about ten cows in milk. The farm unit specializing in milk production is usually dependent upon large purchases of feed.

Low production is not peculiar to Antigonish County nor to eastern Nova Scotia. Throughout the whole province agriculture is hindered by its small farms, small herds and extensive utilization—items inherited from a past when farming provided only necessities and it seemed more important that it be associated, where possible, with other activities that were more profitable. The background of the Antigonish settler enabled him to fit readily into this situation. After a few years of clearing land and getting accustomed to his New World environment, he needed to make only a minimum further adjustment. His livelihood continued to center around cattle, and these continued to be underfed because of poor pasture and small feed production. He brought with him an understanding of potato cultivation because it had been his main food. As the significance of the crop for food in his new home decreased, its production fell off. Here he owned his land and could improve it as he chose, but he treated it little differently than had his absentee landlord across the sea. There were no labor conflicts here because of demands of landlords, but a minimum of time was devoted to farm work, in the eyes of the Highlander a menial task to be forshaken whenever other employment was available. And when the opportunity came to migrate to other parts of Canada and the United States, farmers left in large numbers in a stream that has had little let-up since 1891.

Old ideas and practices have persisted to a much greater degree in this section of the province than elsewhere because of its settlement background and because of its relative isolation—factors stressed by MacDonald in his submission to the Jones Commission:

Scientific agriculture in this country is moving eastward and since we are on the fringe we have been the last to be affected by it. Our culture has not been subjected to it as have been the western parts of the province. Many of our farmers know little or nothing about it. Many are not devoting the various kinds of soils found on their farms to the production of the things for which they are most economically suited. The remedy for this . . . is agricultural education.[81]

The remedy remains and there have been some signs of concrete results. The most notable has been the increased use of lime, a prime need of the county's acid soils. With effective promotion by the provincial Department of Agriculture and the Extension Department of St. Francis Xavier University, the total lime used in the county increased from 2,850 tons in 1940 to 7,700 tons in 1950.[82] This accomplishment, by itself, is not a great one. It assumes significance when viewed against the agricultural background of the county. It points up the obstacles that remain. Antigonish at mid-century was in the process of making some definite adjustment to the demands of commercial agriculture. The success of the adjustment will depend upon how resistant the obstacles prove. They have deep roots. They go back to the eighteenth century, to the straths and uplands of Strathglass, Lochaber and the west Highlands and islands of Inverness-shire.

*

FOOTNOTES

1 Figures from Census of Canada. Total population in 1961 was 14,360. Other data is not comparable because of changes in definitions.

2 Richard Brown, *A History of Cape Breton Island* (London, 1869), p. 53.

3 "Statistical Return of the Upper District of the County of Sydney, 1827," *Report, Public Archives of Nova Scotia for the Year 1938* (Halifax, 1939), pp. 23–67. The enumeration is described as one "made with great care and accuracy" by Thomas C. Haliburton in his *An Historical and Statistical Account of Nova Scotia,* Vol. II (Halifax, 1829), p. 276 f.

4 Helen I. Cowan, *British Emigration to British North America, 1783–1827* (University of Toronto Studies in History and Economics, 1928), p. 17.

5 Robert Brown, *Strictures and Remarks on the Earl of Selkirk's Observations on the Present State of the Highlands of Scotland* (Edinburgh, 1806), Appendix.

6 *House of Commons Papers,* Report from the Committee on the Survey of the Coasts and Central Highlands of Scotland . . . Relating to Emigration, Series 80, Vol. IV (1802–1803), p. 38.

7 D. J. Rankin, *A History of the County of Antigonish, Nova Scotia* (Toronto, 1929). The genealogies occupy pages 78–375.

8 C. J. Hunt, "The Mainland of Inverness," pp. 601–661 in the "Higlands of Scotland," parts 9–12 of *The Land of Britain* (London, 1944), p. 610.

9 James Robertson, *A General View of the Agriculture of the County of Inverness* (London, 1808), p. 149. This is one of the county surveys of agriculture carried out under the Board of Agriculture and Internal Improvement for Scotland instituted in 1795. Since Robertson was a minister of the Church of Scotland, some of his ideas tend to be utopian, but his zeal and energy in visiting every significant part of the county whether easily accessible or not, and his care in describing what he saw, have left a valuable record of agricultural conditions of the time.

10 James E. Handley, *Scottish Farming in the Eighteenth Century* (London, 1953), p. 37.

11 *Ibid.,* p. 13.

12 Earl of Selkirk, *Observations on the Present State of the Highlands of Scotland* (Edinburgh, 1806), p. 12.

13 The description is based on Robertson and statistical reports quoted later.

14 Handley, *op. cit.,* p. 93.

15 J. Cameron Lees, *A History of the County of Inverness* (Edinburgh, 1897), p. 265.

16 *Ibid.,* p. 120.

17 *Ibid.,* p. 144.

18 Handley, *op. cit.,* p. 54.

19 Scottish Register House, Forfeited Estates Papers–Papers connected with the promotion of, and improvements in, agriculture and the fisheries, 1745–85. (F. E. Inventory, p. 96, Item 5.) Unpublished.

20 *Ibid.,* p. 153.

21 Scottish Register House, Bught Papers, 1761–1875 (Box 21). Unpublished.

22 *Ibid.,* pp. 18, 24.

23 *The New Statistical Account of Scotland* (here-

after referred to as N.S.A.), Vol. 4 (Edinburgh, 1845), p. 484. The Statistical Accounts, New and "Old," provide the basic material for the descriptions of Strathglass and the other areas that follow. The parish-by-parish reports, which make up these accounts, were drawn from the communications of ministers throughout Scotland and first arranged by Sir John Sinclair. They vary in length and quality but for the most part supply firsthand information for which there is no substitute.

24 The Survey was a careful piece of field work and showed open fields, enclosed fields, plantations, natural woodlands, rough hill land, marshes, roads, buildings and villages. Since it was completed before 1754 it is of limited used for a discussion of agriculture in 1880. The results of the Survey are summarized by Andrew C. O'Dell, "A View of Scotland in the Middle of the 18th Century," *The Scottish Geographical Magazine,* Vol. 69 (1953), pp. 58–63.

25 *The Statistical Account of Scotland* (hereafter referred to as S.A.S.), Vol. 13 (Edinburgh, 1794).

26 *S.A.S.,* Kiltarlity, Vol. 13 (Edinburgh, 1794), p. 510.

27 *S.A.S.,* Parish of Kilmorack, Vol. 2 (Edinburgh, 1798), p. 406.

28 *Ibid.,* p. 405.

29 *N.S.A.,* Vol. 14 (Edinburgh, 1845), p. 502.

30 *N.S.A.,* Parish of Kilmonivaig, Vol. 14 (Edinburgh, 1845), p. 503.

31 Thomas Pennant, *A Tour in Scotland and Voyage to the Hebrides,* Vol. 1 (Edinburgh, 1775), p. 204.

32 *Ibid.,* p. 208.

33 *S.A.S.,* Vol. 17 (Edinburgh, 1796), p. 544.

34 One of the great "finds" of the author's own tour of the Highlands were the remains in Glenspean of the village of Achnacoimhachan, abandoned by families who settled in Antigonish.

35 *N.S.A.,* Vol. 14 (Edinburgh, 1845), p. 505.

36 The districts lie in two parishes. Moidart, Arisaig, and South Morar are in Archamurchan, whose parish church is in neighbouring Argyllshire. North Morar and Knoydart are parts of the parish of Glenelg. (Fig. 3.).

37 *N.S.A.,* Vol. 14 (Edinburgh, 1845), p. 138.

38 *Ibid.,* p. 656.

39 Society for the Propagation of Christian Knowledge (hereafter referred to as S.P.C.K.), "The Present State of the Highlands and Islands in Scotland," in *An Account of the Society... for 1774* (Edinburgh, 1775).

40 *Ibid.,* p. 197.

41 *S.A.S.,* Vol. 20 (Edinburgh, 1798), pp. 290–295.

42 *Ibid.,* p. 121.

43 James MacDonald, *General View of the Agriculture of the Hebrides* (Edinburgh, 1811), p. 791.

44 This is MacDonald's contention. Another view is expressed in the *N.S.A.,* Vol. 14 (Edinburgh, 1845), p. 199. Here the mountains are described as "yielding to no other place of its extent in the Highlands of Scotland for pasture." The description is worth little, in the light of MacDonald's own careful investigations.

45 *N.S.A.,* Vol. 14 (Edinburgh, 1845), p. 213.

46 J. MacDonald, *op. cit.,* p. 737.

47 J. A. S. Watson, "The Rise and Development of the Sheep Industry in the Highlands and North of Scotland," *Transactions of the Highland and Agricultural Society of Scotland, Fifth Series,* Vol. XLIV (Edinburgh, 1932).

48 *Ibid.,* The quotation is from a poem (translated from the Gaelic) by Duncan Ban McIntyre, written around 1800, entitled "The Song of the Foxes." The fifth line declares the theme, "My blessing be upon the foxes, because that they hunt the sheep."

49 House of Commons Papers, *op. cit.*

50 *S.A.S.,* Vol. 13 (Edinburgh, 1793), p. 432.

51 *S.A.S.,* Vol. 20 (Edinburgh, 1798), p. 432.

52 *S.A.S.,* Vol. 17 (Edinburgh, 1796), p. 281.

53 *S.A.S.,* Vol. 16 (Edinburgh, 1795), p. 269.

54 *S.P.C.K.,* "Report of the Secretary on a visitation of the Highlands," *Proceedings of the Society 1791* (Edinburgh, 1792), Appendix.

55 Margaret I. Adam, "The Causes of the Highland Migrations of 1783–1803," *Scottish Historical Review,* Vol. 17 (1920), p. 85.

56 See *Report of the Commission of Enquiry into Crofting Conditions* (Edinburgh, 1954), Chapter II.

57 J. S. Martell, *Immigration to and Emigration from Nova Scotia, 1815–1838* (Halifax, 1942).

58 Cowan, *op. cit.,* p. 38.

59 *House of Commons Papers,* "Report by Lt. Col. Cockburn on Emigration . . . with statistical information relative to Nova Scotia," Vol. 21 (1828), pp. 109, 148. The map accompanying the report, part of which is reproduced as Fig. 4, is more diagrammatic than cartographic, but does indicate the relative locations of the settled and unsettled land.

60 The "intervals" still stand out as a distinct feature on aerial photographs and topographic maps of the present day.

61 Selkirk, *op. cit.,* pp. 185–186.

62 J. W. MacDonald, "A Brief Sketch of the History of the County" (1876) in Rankin, *op. cit.,* pp. 1–46.

63 John Young, *The Letters of Agricola* (Halifax, 1922; first printed 1822). Writing under

the pen name of "Agricola", John Young was Nova Scotia's first agricultural missionary seeking to stir the province from the "lamentable state of its agriculture" by instructing and exhorting through the columns of the Halifax newspaper, *The Acadian Recorder.*

64 *Ibid.,* p. 168.

65 *Ibid.,* pp. 293, 318.

66 Selkirk, *op. cit.,* p. 227.

67 This was a poor year for wheat. According to Haliburton, returns in some districts including nearby Pictou, were as low as one third of the average. In addition, data were lightened because of fear that they would be used for taxation purposes.

68 From correspondence quoted in J. S. Martell, "The Achievements of Agricola and the Agricultural Societies, 1818–1825 (Halifax, 1940).

69 W. Moorsom, *Letters from Nova Scotia* (London, 1830), p. 181.

70 Young , *op. cit.,* pp. 296–297.

71 *Ibid.,* p. 182

72 *Ibid.,* p. 42.

73 Martell, *The Achievements of Agricola,* p. 96.

74 *Ibid.,* p. 279.

75 *Ibid.,* p. 218.

76 Cowan, *op. cit.,* p. 257.

77 J. W. MacDonald in Rankin, *op. cit.,* p. 44.

78 *Ibid.,* p. 45.

79 *Report of the Royal Commission, Provincial Economic Enquiry,* J. H. Jones, Chairman (Halifax, 1934), p. 163.

80 Census of Canada, 1941. Figures for unimproved pasture not available for 1951.

81 Report of the Royal Commission, *op. cit.,* p. 164.

82 In 1950, a considerable quantity of marl was mined from local pits in the county. After 1950, the quantity of lime used fluctuated a good deal. In 1960, the figure was only 3,000 tons; in 1967, approximately 5,000 tons were used.

5

Western Canada in 1886[*]

JOHN H. WARKENTIN

[*] From Historical and Scientific Society of Manitoba, Papers, Series III, No. 20. (1963–64), pp. 85–116. Reprinted by permission.

The latter part of the nineteenth century is an important period in the development of the Canadian West, and I believe that in order to gain a fuller understanding of the present problems of the prairies one should have a knowledge of the geography of that period. Before 1870 the geography of the fur trade dominated in the West, but it is in the years after 1870 that many of the present basic geographical features of the prairies have their roots. I do not propose to reconstruct the geography of the prairies over a long time span, but only for the year 1886. I am adopting this procedure in order to be able to concentrate on the relationships between the significant forces at work in the West and selected geographical patterns. But why select 1886 as the year in which to reconstruct the geography of Western Canada?[1] In the first place, there had been a decade and a half of immigration and agricultural development since the transfer of Rupert's Land to Canada and the end of the domination of the fur trade. Thus we can learn something of the problems encountered by settlers in occupying the plains. Yet, the cross section[2] is not taken so late that we fail to catch the pioneer stage in the development of commercial agriculture in the West. Furthermore, the Canadian Pacific Railway's transcontinental line was functioning efficiently by 1886. Besides the C.P.R. main line, a few other lines were in operation in 1886.

The railway net was barely begun, so that some interesting tensions are revealed, pointing up the great importance of transportation as a factor in shaping the geography of an area. Finally, data is available in 1886 for a geographical analysis. A fairly good census was taken in 1886, and enough newspapers were being published by that time to make information on settlement available.

On July 1, 1886 the first Canadian Pacific Railway transcontinental train passed through Winnipeg, marking the inauguration in Canada of fast, efficient transportation from the Atlantic to the Pacific Oceans. Between Lake of the Woods and the Rocky Mountains this train did not cross an empty land. By 1886 there were approximately 163,000 people in the province of Manitoba and the provisional districts of Assiniboia, Saskatchewan and Alberta in the North-West Territories (Figure 1).[3] (The great flood of immigrants did not come until after 1900.) Ontario had a population of 2,020,000 in 1886, and British Columbia 74,000. Most of the people in Ontario were in southern Ontario, over a thousand miles from the prairies, and those of British Columbia were concentrated along the Fraser River and on Vancouver Island, roughly four hundred and fifty miles from the plains. A great, sparsely settled land, inhabited by natives and a few traders, extended in an arc around the northern limits of the plains, stretching to Hudson Bay and the Arctic Ocean. But south of the 49th parallel, in the United States, occupation of the plains had been well advanced. Grain farmers had reaped some great crops

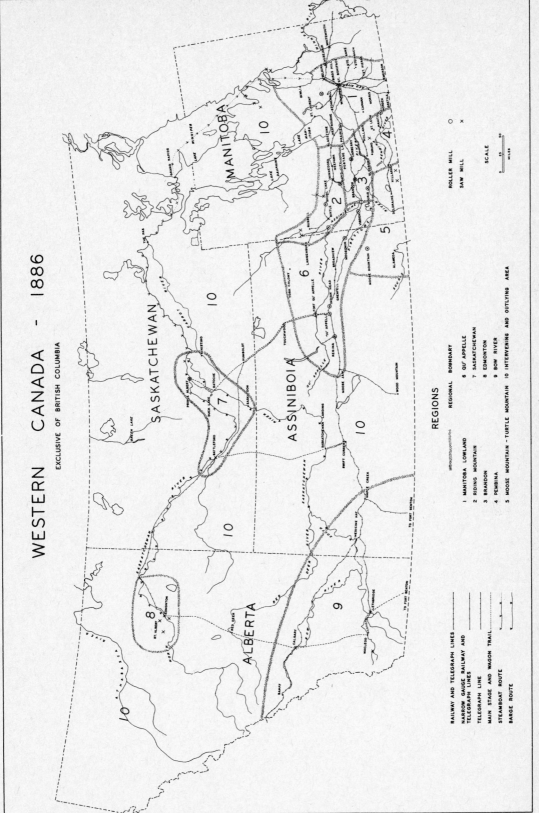

WESTERN CANADA - 1886

EXCLUSIVE OF BRITISH COLUMBIA

REGIONS

RAILWAY AND TELEGRAPH LINES

NARROW GAUGE RAILWAY AND
TELEGRAPH LINES

TELEGRAPH LINE

MAIN STAGE AND WAGON TRAIL

STEAMBOAT ROUTE

BARGE ROUTE

REGIONAL   BOUNDARY

1 MANITOBA LOWLAND   6 QU' APPELLE
2 RIDING MOUNTAIN   7 SASKATCHEWAN
3 BRANDON   8 EDMONTON
4 PEMBINA   9 BOW RIVER
5 MOOSE MOUNTAIN - TURTLE MOUNTAIN   10 INTERVENING AND OUTLYING AREA

ROLLER MILL   ○
SAW MILL   ×

SCALE

0   25   50
|___|___|
MILES

FIG. 1.

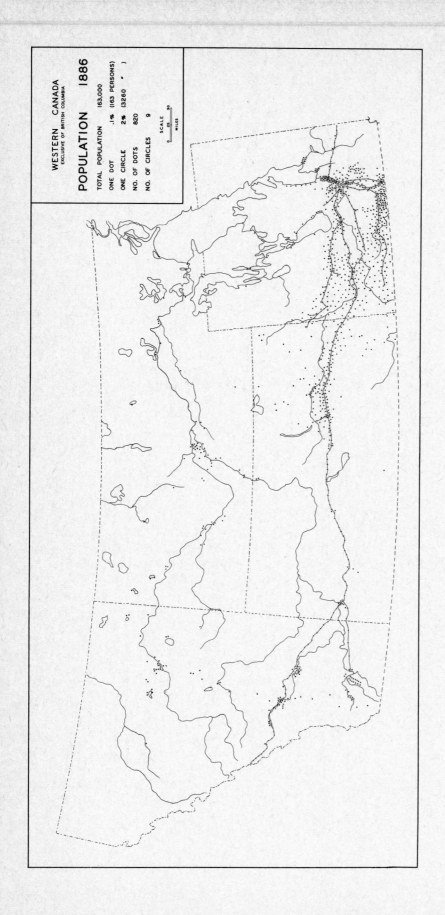

WESTERN CANADA
EXCLUSIVE OF BRITISH COLUMBIA

POPULATION 1886

TOTAL POPULATION	163,000
ONE DOT	.1% (163 PERSONS)
ONE CIRCLE	2% (3260 ")
NO. OF DOTS	820
NO. OF CIRCLES	9

SCALE
0 25 50
MILES

FIG. 2. Population statistics are from the Census of Manitoba for 1886, the Census of the North-West Territories for 1885 (with the population figures adjusted to 1886) and the Annual Report of the Department of Indian Affairs for 1886. The distribution of the population is based on contemporary maps, and the locations of post offices, school districts and the Indian Reserves as given in Canadian government reports for 1886.

in the Red River Valley of Minnesota and Dakota Territory, and were spreading west towards the Missouri River. The Northern Pacific Railway had reached Bismarck in 1873, Miles City in Montana Territory in 1881 and Portland two years later. Little land was broken by farmers beyond Bismarck, but ranchers had been moving into the Dakota and Montana Territories in the '70's and the livestock industry was well established in the '80's. Settled areas, however, were far apart in 1886, and the land along the 49th parallel was virtually unoccupied, except in the area extending from the Red to the Souris Rivers.

A study of the geography of Western Canada in 1886 not only provides us with the opportunity of seeing the faint outlines of the West we know today, but also sheds some light on the process of settlement in the area at a critical period. In 1886 the agricultural potentialities and limitations of the physical environment were not yet understood, so that the settlers could only proceed by trial and error, and gradually develop a suitable agricultural technology.[4] Changes in farm implements at this time did not have nearly the importance they were to have in the next century, when steam power was more widely used and the gasoline engine introduced. But another group of factors had an important effect on the development of the West in the 1880's. Improved transportation facilities were touching off great changes in some districts in the West, whereas their absence was holding back other districts where the land was of equal quality. The ideas of individual homesteaders regarding farm operations, the experiences that the immigrants in group

settlements could apply to a new land, and the ambitions of investors all played a part in forming Western Canada.

Predominantly, then, it is the interplay of the nature of the land with the form and extent of transport available, the homestead and immigration policy of the Canadian Government, the agricultural technology of the time, and the aspirations, ideas and abilities of the farmers that created the geography of Western Canada in 1886.

For the purpose of this study I have divided Western Canada into nine occupied regions and a nearly empty intervening and outlying area within which these more developed regions are found. (Figure 1 shows these regions). In 1886 there was no continuous settlement through the West, so that some of the regions were simply isolated focal districts of occupation within a sparsely settled matrix (Figure 2). Further differentiating characteristics used in defining the regions were the character of the settlement pattern and the nature of the prevailing land use. I do not intend to analyze the advance of the farming frontier across the West, but most of the reasons for the varying pace of exploitation will become evident from the regional discussion. Almost certainly, the inhabitants would have recognized other regions both smaller and larger than the ones I have selected, depending on the definitions they were using. The division used here, however, distinguishes satisfactorily the major geographical variations in the area between Lake of the Woods and the Rocky Mountains.[5]

*

MANITOBA LOWLAND

The Manitoba Lowland (See Figure 1 for boundaries and the location of neighboring regions) is a flat lacustrine basin ranging from 713 to 1200 feet above sea level, bounded on the east by a higher wave-

worked till plain, and on the west by the alluvial slope to the Manitoba Plateau. It is paradoxical that this monotonously flat prairie, with trees only along the rivers and in the area north of the Assiniboine River should, in 1886, have been the most complex geographical region in Western Canada. Yet the paradox is not difficult to explain. Flat clay plains with extensive marshes can ward off farmers just as effectively as very rough terrain. Settlers faced with the wet plain clung to the natural levees bordering the Red and the Assiniboine rivers or settled on the edges of the region where the land was higher and better drained and the waterlogged clays had given way to coarser-textured loams. In future years, millions of dollars were to be spent in draining this rich lowland, but in 1886 the magnitude of the task had only been revealed by a few futile attempts at drainage. Consequently, continuous agricultural settlement was impossible in the lowland. The development of settlement over three quarters of a century added further complex human contours to this region. Situated between Lake Winnipeg and the United States boundary, this region was the threshold to the West, almost a bridgehead beyond the Canadian Shield from which an agricultural start could be made on a vast unknown land. Since the time when Lord Selkirk's agricultural colony was established on the Red River in 1812, all settlers from Eastern Canada or Europe passed through here, whether they arrived via Hudson Bay, Lake Superior or St. Paul, and, naturally, the earliest immigrants made this area their home. Only in the 1870's did settlement increasingly begin to fan out from this marshalling ground of the West.

In 1886 the Lowland held approximately 63,000 people, 39% of the total population of the West, and contained about 24% of the cultivated land.[6] Settlements were densest along the Red and the Assiniboine near Winnipeg, where the descendants of the Selkirk colonists on their river lots formed the oldest agricultural settlement in the West. Scotsmen, Englishmen and Scots half-breeds predominated north of Winnipeg, but to the south the French half-breeds, called *métis*, were in the majority. A notoriously careless mixed farming characterized these long-settled river lots, a far cry from the commercial grain farming prevailing even as close as Portage la Prairie.[7] Beyond the river lots the prairie was empty, partly because of the marshes, partly because the land was in the hands of speculators. Winnipeg businessmen were conscious of the bad impression visitors gained of Manitoba when they saw these empty lands surrounding the capital city of 20,238 people, and in 1886 were anxiously looking for solutions to the problem.[8]

Away from the confluence of the Red and the Assiniboine the settlements were much more recent, most of the farmers having arrived since the creation of Manitoba in 1870. Generally, these settlers homesteaded 160-acre lots, laid out according to the regular rectangular survey which was used through most of the West.[9] As yet, the settlements established in different parts of the region had not coalesced, remaining separated by scattered marshes.

Ontario people of English, Scottish and Irish ethnic origin established themselves on the eastern fringes of the region, near woods and meadowland at Emerson and Birds Hill and in similar country north of Winnipeg at Stonewall. Drainage works had been undertaken in these districts during the Manitoba land boom of 1881-82. After the boom broke, in the Birds Hill district at least, there was such a burden of public and private debt that further progress was difficult.[10] By comparison, the Ontario settlers who had leap-frogged the marshes and settled on the western margin of the region at Portage la Prairie, Carman and Morden had extremely bright prospects. These western slopes consisted of well drained, coarse-textured high quality soils, and by 1886 it had been proven that they were excellent for growing grain. Even in the drought year of 1886 these districts produced adequate crops. Already these farmers were experimenting with new varieties of wheat and with fruit-growing; horses were replacing slow-moving oxen and frame buildings log structures, and land was selling for high prices. The progress is best revealed in the fact that on the Portage Plains, north of Portage la Prairie, the average farmer was already cultivating 85 acres in 1886. Such results attracted to the West people who often ignored the fact that conditions elsewhere in this extensive country might be quite different.

Non-British ethnic groups had also made their homes in the lowland. At Ste. Anne and St. Pierre, French Canadians from Quebec and New England lived on river lot settlements along small tributaries of the Red, depending upon mixed farming for their livelihood. In 1874 the first large group-migration from Europe since Lord Selkirk's colonization, brought Mennonite farmers into the bush and meadow country near Steinbach, and a year later to the well-drained prairie west of Gretna. Both Mennonite settlements consisted originally of agglomerated farm villages, but by 1886 these villages were beginning to break up. This was particularly so at Gretna where the Mennonite farmers had made a success of growing grain, and felt that more land could be acquired and greater flexibility of operations achieved on the dispersed homesteads. In 1886 this was the most densely settled area in the West outside the Winnipeg district.

Since 1875 a group of Icelandic settlers had been living in the northern part of the region near Gimli, completely separated from the other settled areas, in a district where farming was virtually impossible. By 1886 many of the Icelanders had left for better lands in Manitoba and the United States. Those who remained made their living partly from fishing but mainly as lumbermen.[11] On Lake Manitoba at St. Laurent there was a *métis* fishing and trapping community dating from the 1850's.

Gimli and St. Laurent could be reached only by long trails through bush country, though in summer the former could also be visited by steam boat, but nearly all the other settlements in the Lowland were connected to Winnipeg by rail. Local roads were very poor. Road allowances were generally ignored and trunk routes followed the higher ridges, except in the Portage Plains where roads were already built along section lines. Because of the poor roads, grain was often not hauled to the trading centres until freeze-up.

Trading centres were always quickly established once farmers moved into a new area, and all parts of the Lowland were well served. Winnipeg on the Red River was a centre for the entire West as well as for the surrounding area. All the trading towns offered essentially the same services. Each had a post office, a number of stores, a lumber yard, hotel, blacksmith shop, grain buyer, a grist mill, and perhaps a roller mill.

In addition to Winnipeg there were two other important towns located on the Red River. Selkirk (population 705) had hoped to become the hub of railway operations in the west, but when the C.P.R. crossed the Red at Winnipeg, Selkirk had to be content with remaining the centre of steam boat, lumbering and fishing operations on Lake Winnipeg. Seven steam boats operated out of Selkirk, including three on the run to Grand Rapids connecting with the Saskatchewan Rivers service.[12] The saw mills on Lake Winnipeg (Figure 1) shipped their products to market via Selkirk, and the two largest fishing firms in the West were based in the latter town. Emerson (population 796) had thrived as the supply base of southwestern Manitoba until 1883, when the Pembina Branch of the C.P.R. diverted the trade of that area to Winnipeg. In 1886 Emerson was a dull place with empty warehouses and stores. Many houses were vacant, and people were leaving to establish businesses in the new towns along the Pembina Branch.[13] Morris, in the midst of the poorly drained area, had been built up in the Manitoba boom of 1881–82 even though there was no sustaining hinterland around it, but by 1886 it had declined so far that even its grist mill was moved west.[14] Portage la Prairie (population 2,028) had suffered severely from over-expansion and dispersion of buildings in the boom, but it had a sufficiently productive hinterland so that it had weathered these conditions and was recovering in 1886. It was reported that "the dull times are benefiting the town by forcing the centralization of business and giving the business street a more compact appearance."[15] The Manitoba and Northwestern Railway (M. & N.W.R.) line built from Portage la

Prairie to the Riding Mountain region during the 1880's added to the town's importance.

Railways were a matter of life and death to all these trading centres. Morden came into existence in 1883 when the Pembina Branch reached the Escarpment, and it grew quickly at the expense of Nelson, five miles to the northwest, which had been the leading centre in southwestern Manitoba. In 1886 Morden had about 600 people, Nelson only 83. However, Nelson was not a ghost town, for instead of abandoning their buildings the departing townsmen had dragged them to Morden. Small centres such as Steinbach, Ste. Anne and Gimli survived away from the railways as centres of various ethnic groups.

In this region the first wave of development was completed, and many farmers were sadly bound here with the investments they had made on poorly drained land. Further settlement here would require the investment of thousands of dollars in drainage works, so most immigrants were continuing west, to the chagrin of local municipal officials.[16] But in this region there was already a sense of history, for the distinctive ethnic groups— Scots, French Canadians, *métis*, English, Mennonites and Icelanders—were proud of their established settlements. And this region was already, in 1886, contributing people to the regions farther west where more easily developed lands were open for homesteading.

*

RIDING MOUNTAIN REGION

In 1886 the Riding Mountain region was virtually the northern fringe of settlement in Manitoba; not because there was no good land farther north, but because it was at the limit of adequate transportation facilities. The region was almost entirely located above the Manitoba Escarpment on the southern and southeasterly slopes of Riding Mountain. Most of the area was an undulating till plain, covered by many shallow lakes, sloughs, meadows and scattered clumps of aspen. In 1886 this region was often referred to as the Manitoba Highland because of the prominence of the moraine-covered Riding Mountain which rose to 2,200 feet above sea level towards the north. Streams flowing from Riding Mountain across the region have eroded valleys over 100 feet deep in the plain, most of which lies at an elevation of 1,400 to 1,900 feet. The old cart trail from Winnipeg to Edmonton wound through this area, and by the 1850's the country was well known at Red River for its quiet beauty. It was part of the famous "Fertile Belt" that both Captain John Palliser and H. Y. Hind recommended as suitable for settlement.

Settlers began to move into this pleasant park country in the 1870's, well in advance of the M. & N.W.R. which was not completed through this region until 1886. About 12,000 people were living here that year; most had come from Ontario but there were also many from Great Britain. However, the M. & N.W.R. was beginning to change the composition of the population by placing settlers from Hungary, Scandinavia, Iceland and Germany in the rougher lands north of the railway close to Riding Mountain[17] and on prairie land at the end of the line at Langenburg, Assiniboia. Despite the fact that the park landscape had drawn many of the settlers here, some farmers became impatient waiting for a railway, and in 1886 there were already many vacant homesteads in the area, the farmers having taken up new holdings near the C.P.R. main line.[18] Fortunately the approach of the railway had halted this exodus, but as the editor of a local newpaper said, "in the meantime the number of vacant farms is a sad evil, injuring the trade, making it difficult to operate schools, discouraging farmers."[19] Roads were starting to follow the road allowances between farms, though on the flat interfluves between Minnedosa and Birtle, where there were many sloughs, the cart trail to Edmonton was still in use, crossing section lines and farms indiscriminately.[20]

This region was the great mixed farming area of Manitoba in 1886, with a substantially higher number of cattle per 1000 acres of improved land than the southern part of the province. A few enterprising persons with capital had even brought in large herds of purebred cattle, and sheep ranching was being introduced. But grain farming was still important; the region contained about 9% of the cultivated land in the West. Wheat was the most widely grown of the grains, but oats and barley did have greater importance than elsewhere in the province. Acreages cultivated on each farm were relatively small, and as a result, there were still comparatively many oxen in the region. Oxen even outnumbered horses in the newly formed Hungarian and Scandinavian colonies. Log buildings were still very common, though those farmers close to the railway had been established long enough to replace log with frame structures.

The trading centres of the Riding Mountain region were like all the others in the West, except that there were saw mills in some places (Figure 1), sawing logs obtained from the highland to the north. Minnedosa (population 549) was the largest centre in the region, and the great concern of its citizens in 1886 was to secure a road across Riding Mountain to the fertile Dauphin country in the hope that they could then control the future trade of that region.[21] All the centres of the region were strung along the M. & N.W.R. except Rapid City, 23 miles

southwest of Minnedosa. Rapid City, founded in 1878 on a projected route of the C.P.R., had at one time been the largest village in this region. But both the C.P.R. and the M. & N.W.R. had bypassed it and brought Brandon and Minnedosa respectively into being; as a result, Rapid City lagged far behind. By the spring of 1886, businessmen had begun to desert the village, despairing of ever getting a railway,[22] but late that year a spur line did reach it from Minnedosa. This was the first branch line in the West that was constructed to reduce the length of haul for farmers living between main railway lines. In their descriptions of the Riding Mountain region, travellers invariably dwelt on the opportunities for hunting, but in 1886, settlers were feeling the need of other forms of recreation besides shooting, and the M. & N.W.R. was making plans to create a recreation centre at its settlement of Shoal Lake. But, though newspapers went so far as to call the settlement the "Saratoga of the North," the project came to nothing, and Shoal Lake was to remain a farm centre.

There was a peaceful quality about this region: the feeling of a people well satisfied with their choice of a home, even though everyone realized that much work remained to be done and that progress could never be as quick as in the grasslands south of Brandon. But the feeling of haste had receded; mixed farming made an adequate living possible and shooting provided relaxation. This region, with its ravines and the gentle mountain, was very appealing, and there are many sympathetic descriptions of the country in travellers' accounts.

*

BRANDON REGION

Most of the Brandon region is a well-drained plain rising in a gentle gradient from 1000 feet in the east to 1400 feet in the west, containing soils suited for grain growing and with enough trees to give variety to the landscape. Further, there are some distinctive

landforms in the region which enabled settlers to identify themselves with a locality far more readily than the settlers lost in the indeterminate Manitoba Lowland. The Assinboine River flows through the region in a trench that is up to 200 feet deep and a mile wide. There are some extensive duned areas in the eastern part of the region and there is an end moraine (fondly known as the Blue Hills of Brandon) to the south of Brandon. The history of agricultural settlement here was brief, but it was an area in which farming was spectacularly successful. Frost damage to crops had caused some concern to farmers, but not until the drought of 1886 did there appear to be a serious obstacle to farming in the region.

Fur traders had been active in this area from the 1790's to the 1830's (partly to prevent the furs from going to the United States), but after 1830 the trade swung more and more to the northwest so that this area was practically ignored for about forty years until 1874, when the C.P.R. announced that it would build the transcontinental line south of Lake Manitoba. In the late 1870's, steamboats brought farmers up the Assiniboine, and then, when the railway was constructed through the region in 1881, settlers entered in force. This region was quickly overrun by farmers from Ontario, and also many from Great Britain, who saw the advantages of the light-textured soil for easy breaking of the sod, and appreciated the convenience of having the railway right at hand for delivering grain. In 1886 there were about 11,500 people here, and the region contained approximately 17% of the cultivated land in the West. Many of the farmers had come in with some capital as well as experience and rapidly turned this region into a great wheat growing area, comparable to the Portage Plains and the Mennonite area near Gretna. Amazing progress was made. In no other region was there such a high acreage of cultivated land per farmer. In the municipality, over 95% of the land occupied was under cultivation, and in another, the average land cultivated was 125 acres per farmer. In 1886 almost a million bushels of grain were shipped from Brandon alone.[23] Cattle were of little significance and oxen had been largely replaced by horses.

Farming on such a large scale meant that the carrying out of farming operations began to be a problem. Even with the use of horses,

it was impossible to prepare large acreages carefully in spring for seeding, and therefore fall ploughing was adopted. Sometimes it was found that fallowing had "to take the place of fall ploughing, which is generally so largely interfered with by wet weather and threshing operations."[24] The value of summerfallow to conserve moisture was also becoming apparent in 1886, when only 8.75 inches of precipitation fell between April and September[25] (21% less than the average for those months) in Brandon. This is well revealed in the *Manitoba Crop Bulletin*: "This season will have the means of teaching Manitoba farmers a valuable lesson. By the judicious management of lands under cultivation, through summerfallowing, there is no reason to dread even a year of drought. . . ."[26] Others were making similar observations,[27] but an even fuller appreciation of the value of fallowing for conserving moisture was developing in the drought-stricken Qu'Appelle Region, and will be described later.

The advances in agriculture were apparent in the landscape. Roads were good, barbed wire fences were common, farmers were planting shelter belts, and journalists were commenting on the exceptionally fine farm buildings in the region,[28] though there is little likelihood that the latter were very numerous. But, these advances had not been achieved without some casualties, because there were reported to be extensive mortgages in the region, as farmers recklessly embarked on great farm improvements.[29]

Brandon (population 2348) was the second largest town after Winnipeg in the West. After its founding in 1881 on the C.P.R. main line, it had grown rapidly as the supply point for the surrounding area, and in 1886 it was actively working to retain its dominance against all possible rivals. Brandon grimly watched the extension of two lines from Winnipeg into Southern Manitoba in the summer of 1886, being well aware, as the *Birtle Observer* warned, that her trade was "endangered by the building of railroads to the south. Two lines are creeping up into the fine country tributary to the country town."[30] Brandon interests argued that "What we desire to see in this country is a network of roads that will leave no farmer more than twenty miles distant from an outlet; but at the same time we are for easily supported reasons desirous of seeing these same roads centering where general interests desire their convergence."[31] Naturally, the Brandon newspapers recommended and pleaded that the C.P.R. build a branch southwestward from Brandon into the Souris country, but nothing was resolved in 1886, though the approaching lines from Winnipeg were extended far enough (Figure 1) to cut seriously into Brandon's trade and to ensure that Winnipeg wholesalers would control south-western Manitoba. Many small community centres (often consisting merely of a school or church and post office) served the farmers in the region, and most of these not on the railway line were connected to Brandon by mail stages.

This region specialized in wheat production; it had been hurt by frosts in 1885 and again by drought in 1886, but not enough to cause any basic change in land use. Farmers here did not have the extra work of clearing trees as in some areas to the north, the drainage difficulties of the lowland farmers, nor the problem of severe aridity that was plaguing the Qu'Appelle region to the west.

*

PEMBINA REGION

The Brandon region comprised the gradual rise from the Manitoba Lowland to the Manitoba Plateau. The Riding Mountain region part of the southern slope is separated from the Lowland by a relatively abrupt escarpment formed of Cretaceous shales. There is a sharp rise of from 400 to 500 feet over a distance of a few miles to a plateau, at approximately 1500 feet. The surface of the plateau, in 1886, consisted of undulating tree-covered slopes, meadows for grazing and many potentially arable stretches of grassland. The plateau also has its more scenic features. An impressive valley, up to three miles wide and 350 feet deep that is occupied by the Pembina River and a number of long narrow lakes, crosses the region from northwest to southeast. The eastern and northern margins of the plateau are crowned by rough forested hilly country, partly morained and rising to over 1700 feet, called the Pembina Mountains and Tiger Hills respectively. A plain, sloping from the Tiger Hills to the Assiniboine River, is included in this region because the deep valley of the river and a large tract of sand dunes separated it from the Brandon region.

Settlers began to move to this plateau in the late '70's, when heavy rains made the high plains greatly preferable to the flooded lands of the Lowland region. Many farmers preceded the railways, since the Pembina Branch only reached Manitou in 1883 and was not extended through the region until 1885, and the Manitoba and Southwestern Railway (Glenboro Branch) was only built to Holland in 1885 and reached Glenboro the next year. Ontario people predominated in this region of 11,000 people, particularly in the southern rather open plains, which had been reached easily from Emerson by what was called the Boundary Commission Trail in the '70's. In the Tiger Hills to the north there was a greater variety of settlers. French Canadians from Quebec and New England had settled near St. Léon. In the western part of the hills at Grund, some Icelanders, who were dissatisfied with the Gimli area, had started a settlement in 1880, which was progressing more quickly in 1886 than the settlement on Lake Winnipeg. British people had also selected homes in this region, and one journalist commented that "Wherever in the Pembina or Tiger Hills you come upon a picturesque spot, you find that an Englishman had caught on, if obtainable."[32]

Mixed farming was characteristic of the entire region, and in 1886 it held 10% of the cultivated land in the west. Along the railway line, grain farming was nearly as far advanced as in the Brandon region; at Pilot Mound the farms averaged 75 acres under cultivation. Some high quality cattle herds belonged to a few of the farmers of Ontario origin, and this area resembled the Riding Mountain region with regard to the livestock enterprise. In the rougher country north of the Pembina River, among the French, Icelanders and some German settlers, agriculture was not as far advanced, less grain was grown and the stock was of low quality.[33] As yet, all parts of the Pembina region had a raw appearance, and one journalist was quite critical of the farmsteads near the Pembina Branch:

I expressly exclude the average farm house from everything I may say as to the beauty of the country. With a few noteworthy exceptions they are veritable Bleak Houses in appearance. Here and there a house was met with a coat of paint and some trees planted before the door, and if the farmer only knew how much more comfortable and home like it made them look, there would be very few bare farm houses left to mar the landscape.[34]

The dry weather of 1886 made the grasslands everywhere in the west extremely susceptible to fire and from this region in particular there are some descriptions of the disastrous consequences of the prairie fires. Hay stacks were consumed, many farmers lost their cattle, stables and houses, and even trees on the hill tops were burned. It was reported that the prairie fires of 1886 caused more damage than the frosts of previous years.[35] The feeling of utter frustration the fires produced is revealed by a letter published in the *Brandon Times,* where it was suggested that anyone caught firing the prairie in fall "would meet that summary justice which would save all legal disputes in the matter."[36] Prairie fires remained a problem in Western Canada until settlement

was sufficiently dense to make it possible to control the fires.

In this region, trading points had been established before the railway lines were built, but as new townsites were surveyed on the railways, the buildings in the existing centres were moved to them. Only in the area between the two railway lines did the first centres like St. Léon and Grund remain intact, but they had little hope of growing.[37] As the townsites were laid out, occasional businessmen from older trading centres, usually located in the Lowland, came out to appraise the new districts in the region and then settled in the places where they thought it would be most advantageous to found new businesses.[38] This approach was most often followed on the sites along the Pembina Branch because it was built through country already partly settled, so that there was a farm community waiting to be served. A credit reporting agency stated that, in 1886, the trading centres on the Pembina Branch expanded more rapidly than anywhere else in the West.[39] But, by 1886, there were more than enough prospective tradesmen in the region, so that one local correspondent felt it wise to "inform outsiders that there is not room for more businessmen than we have at present except perhaps in a few callings that are not represented." [40] But it was still difficult at times to bring grain buyers to a station, and there were frequent complaints in the weekly press that no buyers had arrived at particular points. They were essential to attract trade. One village even sent delegates to Winnipeg to fetch buyers to the community.[41] At this time, trading patterns were just being established, and sometimes there were great shifts in trade when buyers arrived at a station. In the winter of 1885–86, the Icelandic farmers transferred their grain trade from Brandon (a fifty mile haul), to a station on the Pembina Branch (a thirty-mile haul), and to Holland (a twenty-mile haul), as buyers finally appeared at the latter two places.[42]

*

Most of the Moose Mountain-Turtle Mountain region, despite its name, is Great Plains country. This area is about 1400–1700 feet above sea level and has the characteristic rolling surface of the plains. It is covered nearly everywhere with buffalo grass except for the bushes around depressions. If it had not been for two forested moraine-covered uplands, Moose Mountain (2730 feet) and Turtle Mountain (2525 feet), that are really oases within the plains, and a major stream, the Souris, with fertile bottom lands and a belt of trees along it, this region would have attracted few settlers at this time. Some settlers, however, moved here, because they thought that on their claims they would escape the frosts that had damaged so many crops in the West in the '80's.

There were about 7,000 people in this region in 1886, not scattered over the countryside as in the older settled regions of Manitoba, but gathered in carefully selected sites on the Souris River or close to the forested and ravine-scored slopes of the two "Mountains." Before settlement, this area had often been visited by Canadian fur traders on their hurried visits to the Mandan Indians on the Missouri, but it had not been on any important route until the Boundary Commission marked a trail close to the 49th parallel in 1873. A few squatters, usually coming in by this trail, had taken up favoured spots in the region before 1880,[43] but widespread agricultural settlements did not really begin until the railway reached Brandon in 1881. Settlers deliberately left the lands near the railway to hunt out favourable sites. They followed the Souris River to the flanks of Turtle Mountain, and also proceeded from Moosomin to Moose Mountain and the country about Alameda, where there were coal deposits on the Souris. In the Manitoban part of the region, most of the settlers hailed from Ontario, with a few from Britain as well, and by 1886, this district was part of a continuous (though greatly thinning) zone of settlement extending from the Brandon and Pembina regions. Saw mills on Turtle Mountain supplied these farmers with lumber. Moose Mountain was the centre of a British colony where the settlers hoped to re-create English country life on the park-like slopes of the highland. This colony was unique in the West because it was the only large group settlement whose location had been deliberately selected on the basis of the beauty of the landscape, as well as for the agricultural potentialities of the land itself. The colony and the farmers at Alameda were still separated from both the C.P.R. to the north and the Pembina Branch to the east by relatively empty plains.[44] This, then, is the region where the westward advance of settlement had stopped in 1886.[45] But the farmers were still tied closely to the trees and water of the higher lands or the rivers, and not many had really ventured on the plains.

Effective agricultural settlement dated back only to 1881, yet the area already contained about 6% of the land cultivated in the West. The census figures indicate that this was a wheat growing region, though little grain was marketed, because, until the Pembina Branch reached Deloraine in October, 1866, grain had to be carried up to one hundred miles to market, and half the proceeds or more were used to pay for the haulage. Farmers intended to turn this into a grain growing region, and cattle were scarce, though there were surprisingly many oxen in use, partly because they could endure long distance trekking to market better than horses.

For the eastern part of the region, the year 1866 was rather exciting, because the railway finally penetrated into the region, reorienting the trade from Virden and Brandon to new towns on the Pembina Branch. Profiteering lumber and implement dealers flocked to the new places,[46] their arrival resented by residents who knew that these businessmen were generally only transients. This feeling is expressed in the following quotation concerning Killarney, one of the new villages: "Those who come here should do so with the intention of staying and growing up with the place, and not of coming here expecting to reap a harvest and then move on."[47] Killarney even received trade from North Dakota, and some immigrants heading for North Dakota travelled via the Pembina Branch and Killarney because it was the easiest route to their American homesteads.[48] At Moose Mountain, a townsite was being developed to serve the British colony, and the only roller mill in the West, away from a railway, already expressed the ambitions of these colonists. Mail stages connected the settlement to Moosomin, forty miles away.

The eastern part of the Moose Mountain-Turtle Mountain region resembled the Brandon region in that it lacked cattle, but as yet it had not become an important grain producing district. The western part of this region was unique in that it was the only settled farming area in the territories located well south of the C.P.R. main line. Unlike the farming districts on the Saskatchewan river, which were also well away from the railway, it was growing without the help of direct government expenditures. The fact remains that the sustained development of the region was going to be dependent upon a railway and in 1886 there was talk of building a line from Brandon to the Souris coal fields.

*

QU'APPELLE REGION

The Qu'Appelle region is a plain, varying between 1500 and 1800 feet in elevation, extending from Virden in Manitoba to Moose Jaw in Assiniboia. Around Regina, is a flat lacustrine basin, that looked especially barren in 1886 because of the lack of trees. East of Qu'Appelle the land is a gently rolling till plain, with the trees along the creeks and in the numerous depressions setting off the many meadows which could easily be ploughed. There are no higher lands in this region to attract settlers as in the Moose Mountain-Turtle Mountain region, but the wide valley of the Qu'Appelle River, similar to the Pembina Trench, with its small lakes, partially compensated for this. The C.P.R., which passed through this region in 1882, tipped the balance in favour of this region, even over the once much-publicized lands along the Saskatchewan River. A large part of this region was within "Palliser's Triangle" and the main problem of the settlers was the uncertainty of rainfall. Obtaining water for domestic purposes and livestock was also of concern, and in the Regina and Moose Jaw areas government-owned well boring machines were being used in 1886 to try and find water.[49]

Settlers had bypassed the Qu'Appelle region for the more wooded Saskatchewan country in the 1870's, anticipating that the first transcontinental railway would be built through that area. As the C.P.R. pushed past Brandon in 1881, the same wave of Ontario and British settlers, that had occupied the regions to the east, moved in here, till it was stopped by the semi-arid lands of the Missouri Coteau west of Moose Jaw. In 1886 settlement extended south of the C.P.R. for 15 to 20 miles, and north for about 30 miles, right across the Qu'Appelle valley; some group farm settlements had even penetrated 50 miles into the park country beyond (Figure 2). The Brandon region had received Ontario and British settlers almost exclusively, but here these groups comprised only half the population of about 23,500 people. Immigration agencies and societies found this a most suitable area for promoting settlement in the West, since it was an extension of the central Manitoba settlements and was served by the railway. Groups of Jews, Germans, Hungarians, Icelanders and colonies of poor folk from Great Britain were placed in this region—an indication of the diverse ethnic groups that would populate these plains in later years.

A considerable variety of farming enterprises was to be found in this region, but the individual homesteader was still the most significant human element in the development of this land. Each homesteader had psychological as well as climatic hazards to face. Some settlers complained about the scattered settlement resulting from the regulation that only even-numbered sections could be homesteaded. This made it difficult to create true communities,[50] and even the Assiniboia Agricultural Society deplored the day to day isolation, and admitted that "The loneliness preys on the minds and nerves of the women."[51] An attempt to solve at least part of this problem of isolation was made in the winter of 1886 at Qu'Appelle, where a market was organized on the first Saturday of every month bringing the farmers of the district together to exchange and sell stock.[52]

The colonies made up of people who had little or no experience in farming and no capital fared worst of all. Not only did these settlers face a new environment but they also had to learn how to farm. A Dominion Immigration Agent reported in 1886 that most of the colonies found farming a very severe struggle.[53]

There were also settlers of some means in this region. Along the Pipestone River near Grenfell, just south of the C.P.R. line, there was a district, occupied by Englishmen with capital, where the well-equipped farmsteads contrasted sharply with the average pioneer homestead of the West. But, by 1886, some of the Englishmen had already regretted their decision to settle on the prairie and had departed with a bitter feeling against the country. A few large "bonanza" farms, similar in conception to those of the Red River Valley of the United States, were operated in this region in the 1880's. Yet not nearly as many investors were operating company farms here as were involved in the cattle ranches of the Bow River region, probably because wheat growing was still too precarious. The Bell Farm at Indian Head, owned by a Winnipeg-controlled syndicate, was the largest company farm in the West, extending over 57,000 acres (6,000 were under cultivation in 1886). It employed 300 men with 150 teams in the summer season, and paid out $10,000 a month in wages.[54] Homesteaders resented the

few company farms that were in existence because they brought few permanent residents into an already sparsely settled land.[55]

All these settlers had moved into this region with the intention of growing grain, and about one quarter of the cultivated land in the West was found in this region. Farmers were specialized. In some districts there were fewer cattle than in any other part of the West, and horses already outnumbered oxen in the western part of the region, though in the east, where there were more settlements well away from the railway, oxen were still of great importance. The drought of 1886 caused a crop failure in this region and pointed up the hazards of growing grain in areas where there was still an inadequate knowledge of the environment. Stock raisers at Regina even resorted to driving cattle to Saskatoon for the winter after hay and water had given out in the drought.[56] Little wonder that settlers were apprehensive that another crop failure would ruin the country's reputation.[57] Outside newspapers were already suggesting that more immigrants should not be sent into the region until an appropriate method of farming was devised.[58]

The habit of neglecting even the most self-evident farming requirements, stemming from the first years of settlement when some farmers had only thrown the grain on the ground and obtained a crop, had aggravated the basic problem of uncertain rainfall. But astute farmers everywhere were aware that not only would tillage operations have to be carried out more carefully, but that some changes in techniques would have to be made. There was already a strong indication as to what the solution would ultimately be. At Indian Head, Mr. Angus Mackay was experimenting with a system of summerfallowing, fall ploughing and harrowing, early seeding and heavy rolling, and he found that land treated in this way produced far better yields in 1886 than land ploughed and seeded in spring, even though the rainfall was the same.[59] Correspondents in a number of papers suggested similar agricultural recommendations. It is interesting that in Manitoba mixed farming was strongly recommended as the best means of improving agriculture, whereas in this area of wheat specialization, careful tillage that would ensure a good seed bed for grain was advocated as the key to successful farming. Unless summerfallowing was adopted there simply was not time to accomplish this over large acreages in fall and spring alone.[60]

The trading centres spaced at regular intervals along the C.P.R. had a special importance in 1886 as supply bases for the settlements to the north and south of the line. Virden and Moosomin, however, were beginning to be affected by competition, as Birtle on the M. & N.W.R. started to cut into their hinterlands in 1886. Most of these places had only from 100 to 200 people,[61] yet great quantities of supplies were distributed from each. Broadview served the York settlement, and Qu'Appelle was the main supply centre for the 5,000 people in the Prince Albert area. Regular stage and freight services were maintained between the latter two points.

Regina, with a population of 1,000[62] and the capital of the Northwest Territories, deserves special mention. The bitterness felt by most other centres in the Territories, over the selection in 1882 of Regina as the capital, had somewhat abated by 1886. Many people, though, were still genuinely dismayed about the site; one correspondent suggested that the capital be moved to Long Lake but that some building should be left behind "as mementoes of the failure of founding the capital of the Northwest on a treeless and waterless plain."[63] Once established, however, the capital city was intent on commercial advancement. Regina citizens were envious of Qu'Appelle's northern trade and unsuccessfully attempted to wrest the northern mail route from it over Qu'Appelle's strong protest.[64] Nothing daunted, the Regina Board of Trade later in the year endeavoured to gain a share of Moose Jaw's trade with the Saskatoon and Wood Mountain settlements, by marking and improving the trails from Regina to those places.[65] Moose Jaw countered by holding a public meeting to decide what improvements could be made to the trails leading towards it. But there were indications that trails alone would not suffice to control trade with outlying points for many more years. In June, 1886, the Regina and Long Lake Railway was opened for 22 miles north of Regina,[67] and a boat was later brought from Selkirk, Manitoba,[68] to operate on the lake and bring steam transportation another 40 miles northward.

There is no denying the fact that the Qu'Appelle region was settled at this time mainly because of the railway, and that settlers had moved in before anyone really knew whether arable agriculture was possible. Half a decade of settlement in the region was revealing important farming problems, and eyes were turning again to the "Fertile Belt" along the North Saskatchewan River as a more suitable place for settlement.[69] But settlers were in the Qu'Appelle region to stay —and they were in the process of learning how to live in this environment. This was the only region where "Palliser's Triangle" was really being penetrated by homesteaders in 1886, but Palliser's view that the area was virtually a waste land was only slowly being revised.

*

SASKATCHEWAN REGION

The Saskatchewan region is part of the northern park country of woods and meadows that was so widely praised for settlement by all who saw it. It is a rolling land occasionally rising to hummocky end moraine, which gains its separate identity within the West from the North and South Saskatchewan Rivers whose waters meet in the area. Fur traders used the North Saskatchewan for many decades to travel westward; when a mission settlement was planned for this land in the 1860's and when the *métis*, many from Manitoba, began to rendezvous and then settle here, it was only natural that they would live on, or close to, the great rivers. Prince Albert—the mission settlement—and the *métis* settlements near Duck Lake and at Batoche would probably have remained relatively unnoticed for many years if the first route of the C.P.R. had not been projected through this area in the 1870's, and the telegraph line actually built at that time. The headquarters of the telegraph contractors, called Telegraph Flats (later Battleford), became a new centre of settlement in 1874 (it became the territorial capital three years later), and Manitoba and Ontario settlers anticipating the railway, moved into the region. After the decision was made in 1881 to build the C.P.R. along a southern route, the region stagnated and even the capital was transferred to Regina. Only one new settlement, Saskatoon, was founded in the 1880's, in contrast to the many which were growing along the railway line to the south. In 1886 there were 7,000 people living in the region, including many Indians, *métis* and English and Scots half-breeds.

Potentially, this was a splendid mixed farming country, but in 1886 it contained only about 3% of the cultivated land in the West. Agriculture had received a severe setback in the rebellion of 1885. Much stock had been destroyed and farmers had not even raised enough grain for seed, with the result that the government had to supply it on loan for the 1886 seeding. During the year following the rebellion, foodstuffs were brought in by barge from Edmonton, and grain hauled by cart from points on the C.P.R.[70] The *métis* in the mesopotamia of the North and South Saskatchewan Rivers were particularly poor,[71] and the government was only able to prevent widespread suffering by donating provisions and furnishing remunerative employment in freighting.[72] Though the region was not receiving immigrants in 1886, no one had any doubts about the suitability of the land for agriculture. The

farmers were very proud of the results of their efforts, and two agricultural societies held exhibitions in 1886.[73] Since the farmers did not have an outside market for their produce, the purchase of supplies by the government for the Indians and the North West Mounted Police was extremely important in the economy. Advertisements requesting tenders for supplies, such as grain, hay, wood and ice, frequently appeared in the weeklies, and even when commodities were brought in from the outside, money could still be earned by freighting.

The region was connected with the outside world in a variety of ways. There were four steamers operating on Lake Winnipeg between Selkirk and Grand Rapids, and at Grand Rapids they connected with three steamers (two at the end of the season) that ran on the North Saskatchewan as far as Edmonton. The boats did not operate on fixed schedules, but the time required to go in 1886 from Selkirk to Grand Rapids was roughly one and a half to three days, and from there to Edmonton fifteen to seventeen days.[74] The Hudson's Bay Co. used these steamers for goods and employees. Goods were also conveyed down the two great rivers. Coal, timber and grain were carried from Edmonton to Battleford, and goods were barged from Medicine Hat to Prince Albert, but this latter route was too slow to make the venture successful.[75] The overland stage and wagon route to the C.P.R. railway remained the fastest connection for passengers and the most reliable for freight, so most people used it while the region was waiting for railway service. Prince Albert received most of its goods via Qu'Appelle, Battleford via Swift Current (Figure 1), along routes that were well marked and had stopping places. Occasionally freight for Battleford was also shipped via Regina or Moose Jaw. The 194-mile stage coach trip from Battleford to Swift Current was scheduled for 96 hours. Freight was usually carried in Red River carts for two cents a pound; in the 1886 freighting season, four million pounds of freight were hauled to Swift Current from Battleford.[76]

Prince Albert (population 600) was the trading and administrative centre of the region.[77] The main street paralleled the North Saskatchewan River, and its occasional substantial buildings of brick and stone made the town stand out in strong contrast to the hastily built trading centres to the south.[78] Battleford had not achieved Prince Albert's solidity as yet, but improvements were under way; new buildings were being constructed as the site of the town was shifted to higher ground from an area that was prone to flooding. This move was hastened after most of the old town was destroyed during the rebellion of 1885.[79] Kinosota on the Carrot River and Saskatoon on the South Saskatchewan were only small farming communities as yet.

The settlements in this region were not growing in population through immigration, but neither were many families leaving. Everyone was positive that the area would receive railway service before many more years either from an extension of the M. & N.W.R., or a branch line from the C.P.R. In the meantime the inhabitants liked to point out that life here was much more pleasant than in the southern prairies, and in Prince Albert there was even humourous speculation as to whether the town would accept connections by rail from a place like Regina.[80]

*

EDMONTON REGION

There really was little difference between the topography of the Edmonton and the Saskatchewan regions in 1886, and they need to be distinguished only because there was no continuous settlement between them. Forts located in this region had served as the co-ordinating centres for northwestern fur trading operations for a hundred years, and in 1886 Edmonton still continued this function. Settlement followed the pattern of the Saskatchewan region. Many *métis* had settled on the shores of lakes or on the tributaries of the Saskatchewan River, and in the '70's other settlers entered from Manitoba and Eastern Canada following the projected route of the C.P.R. Many remained, even when the railway was not built, when they found that this region had a wide variety of resources. Of the 4,000 people in the region, over 25% were of Indian origin.

This was another mixed farming area, in which coarse grains were more important than wheat, though less land was cultivated in the entire region than in many single municipalities in Manitoba. The editor of the *Edmonton Gazette* extolled the advantages of the region for mixed farming, and suggested that farmers in this park land could play a "waiting game" until a viable agricultural economy developed, whereas the farmers along the C.P.R. line would not be able to weather an economic storm.[81] In any case, farming here was restricted by a lack of market and low prices so that in 1886 less land was in crop than in 1885.[82] Lumbering was important west of Edmonton, and coal was mined on the banks of the North Saskatchewan, with 1200 tons produced in 1886.[83] Besides this, the operations of the Hudson's Bay Company were still important to the economy of the region, and a prospector could average $5.00 in gold dust a day, panning in the North Saskatchewan River.[84]

As in the Saskatchewan region, the steam boats were in competition with the railway and stage route, and in 1886 were even offering a lower rate for freight.[85] Local residents felt that the river connections with Battleford and Prince Albert were inadequate, and hoped that a local steamboat service on the upper North Saskatchewan would be started.[86] But, since 1883 when the stage connection with the C.P.R. at Calgary had been established, the river's importance in carrying passengers had decreased. The stage was well patronized, and with stopping places every twenty miles the journey could be made in reasonable comfort. North from Edmonton there was an overland route to the Peace River, and it was suggested that a proper trail should be built in order to open a new market for Edmonton farmers.[87]

In this region there was still a sense of continuity with the fur trade days; as yet its character had not been greatly changed by agricultural immigrants. There was great confidence in the future possibilities of this region, and the editor of the *Gazette* stressed that Canadians should recognize that there were regional variations within the West. He maintained that such differences were especially evident in a year such as 1886 when Edmonton had a good crop whereas there was a general crop failure in the south.[88] A pointed reference to other centres in the West, made four years earlier, reveals the prevailing spirit: "The people here rest their hopes on the country and on themselves, not on the railway and the Government."[89]

*

BOW RIVER REGION

The Bow River region extends from the Cypress Hills to the Rocky Mountains, rising from 2,500 feet near Maple Creek to 4000 feet at Calgary and then to over 10,000 feet in the mountains. Precipitation averages as low as twelve inches annually in the east, but increases to eighteen inches in the foothills, so that short grasses cover the area, except in the forested Cypress Hills and in the mountains. Winters, as elsewhere in the West, are cold, but the chinook winds occasionally bring warmer weather, melting the snow and making winter grazing possible. The chinook, together with the many valleys and ravines in the foothills that provide shelter for cattle, makes this a fine ranching country.

Unfriendly Indians kept fur traders away from this area, except for an occasional foray, until the 1870's. By that time steamboats were navigating the Missouri to Fort Benton in Montana so American traders crossed into Canada in one direction, while settlers from Edmonton passed through the region to obtain supplies from Fort Benton in the other. In 1872, an Edmonton missionary drove cattle from Montana to his mission. Two years later the North West Mounted Police ousted the "whiskey traders" and brought order to the region. In the same year cattlemen from the United States drove their herds into the district about Macleod.

Their example was shortly followed by British and Canadian investors who established ranches in the foothills and stocked them with American cattle. By 1886, about 12,000 people lived in the region, over half of whom were Indians living in two large reserves. Most of the newcomers were from Great Britain and Canada, though in some districts there were many Americans.

The total area cultivated was little more than in the Edmonton region; but on the other hand the ranching industry was off to a good start. Ranchers leased land from the government for two cents an acre (though the even-numbered sections remained open to homesteading), and were required to stock the range within a certain time. In 1886, 101 leases covered an area of 3,793,792 acres.[90] In the early '80's it was still thought that the only land suited to ranching lay near Macleod, but by 1886 the Calgary, Medicine Hat and Maple Creek districts were being stocked.[91] Most of the animals were still driven in from Montana, but with the completion of the C.P.R. in 1886, many cattle were obtained from British Columbia,[92] and carloads of carefully selected stock, including pedigreed bulls, were brought from Ontario.[93] There were few sheep in the region before 1886, but that year a large number were driven in from Montana to the range north of Calgary, high quality rams were imported from Ontario,[94] and a wool depot was established at Calgary.[95] There were 104,000 cattle and 25,000 sheep in the region in 1886; 34,000 cattle were imported in 1886, 26,000 from the United States, the rest from Ontario, British Columbia and Manitoba.[96] The industry was just reaching its first turning point in 1886, because until then government purchases of beef for the Indians had supplied a sufficient market, but the ranchers were beginning to realize that the industry's current rate of expansion would force them to find an outside market. The severe winter of 1886–87 was a devastating one for the cattle industry of Montana and Dakota Territories, but though cattle died in the blizzards of 1887 in Alberta, the Canadian ranches were not hit quite so hard as those in the United States because the ranges were not overstocked and the grass was heavier so that the cattle entered winter in a better condition. In fact, some American ranchers drove their herds into Alberta during the arid summer of 1886 seeking better grass.

Mining was very important in the economy of the region. The mines at Medicine Hat were opened in 1883, and after being closed for a time, were producing 100 tons a day in 1886.[97] Colliers at Lethbridge were producing double this amount of coal, and sales were made as far east as Winnipeg.[98] Coal was mined in small quantities at Calgary, and an important anthracite mine was being developed near Banff in 1886. Oil seepages were only being noted as yet in the region, but natural gas was being used as a fuel at a railway station near Medicine Hat,[100] and there was talk of using it in the larger centres.[101] The spectacular mountains also had their uses. Besides supplying lumber for the ranching country, they also provided opportunities for health and recreation seekers, and by Order-In-Council November 25, 1885, the government created the first National Park in Canada at Banff.[102]

There was more variety among the trading centres than in any other region in the West. Calgary was the dominant centre, with about 1700 people; because of its loca-

tion close to the Rockies it often was called the "Canadian Denver."[103] It was already the supply centre for the Edmonton region and was increasing in importance as a distributing point for all Alberta.[104] Macleod was frequently described by visitors as an American frontier ranching town. Lethbridge, a ranching and a mining centre, had the appearance of a company town with company-owned houses in the midst of the mining buildings and coal loading facilities.[105] Medicine Hat was an important railway divisional point and, together with Maple Creek and Lethbridge, served as a shipping point in 1886 for some ranchers from northern Montana, who were dissatisfied with the service provided by the Northern Pacific Railway. Cattle and sheep were driven to these points for shipment to Chicago.[106]

Lack of transportation facilities was no problem in this cattle country. It was even reported that ranchers at Macleod were strongly opposed to having rails brought any closer, because they thought that this would cut up the range and locomotive sparks burn the grass. But the reporter cynically added that "I have heard it said that they fear their monopolies will be destroyed."[107] Farmers were taking up homesteads peaceably along the C.P.R. line, but at Macleod, relations between farmers and ranchers were not so agreeable. Ranchers complained that farmers selected homesteads on the bottom lands along the streams which were needed for watering stock, and it was reported that "There is little or no animosity now, but there is a feeling that may lead to it."[108] The government was trying to devise a scheme that would protect the ranchers' interests,[109] and there was even a suggestion that farmer and rancher could work together, with the farmer supplying the feed for the final feeding of the animals.[110] A few of the ranchers were seeding grain in the bottoms already.[111] The idea of irrigation for this dry land was being prophetically suggested by one government official,[112] and one Alberta rancher was already attempting to irrigate 190 acres.[113] Mormons from Utah began to migrate into this region in 1887, and it was they who later developed the first comprehensive irrigation system in Alberta.

The Bow River region had a distinctive way of life in 1886. Here there seemed to be a love for the spacious country as a whole, in contrast to the tie with the particular individual homestead that characterized the Manitoba and Assiniboia farming countryside. Nor did the region in 1886 feel the economic stress that affected many of the farming districts to the east; this seemed to be a land of great and varied resources, and already by 1886 a man from the United States was transferring the phrase "God's Country" to this region.[114]

*

INTERVENING AND OUTLYING AREAS

Many of the regions that have already been described were only thinly settled, but the intervening and outlying areas were virtually empty, except for the Indians on Reserves and a few settlers in selected localities. Yet so great was the size of this "left over" area that there were about 12,000 people within it—mostly Indians. In eastern Manitoba, the Canadian Shield prevented agricultural settlement; in northern Manitoba, Saskatchewan and Alberta, the lakes, muskeg, poor drainage and short growing season kept out farmers, and in southern Assiniboia, aridity was effectively halting arable agriculture. The plain, between the C.P.R. and the North Saskatchewan River was not physically formidable, but so far there was not sufficient population pressure in the West to send many settlers into the region. And always, of course, there was the deterrent of poor transport facilities.

In many places, however, pioneers were investigating the resources of this empty land and even beginning to occupy it. At Whitemouth, fifty miles east of Winnipeg, saw milling had been started, and just to the north, settlers were occupying the belt of clay along the Winnipeg River.[115] Farmers were looking at the Dauphin country across Riding Mountain from Minnedosa, and homesteads there were being taken up in 1886.[116] Oil seepages had been noticed and drilling for oil had commenced.[117] If the area had been on a major route it would undoubtedly have been settled earlier. At the other end of the region, at Red Deer in Alberta, a mixed farming district had been growing on the trail from Calgary to Edmonton since 1882.[118] But between these embryonic settlements there were few settlers, only some stopping places, such as Touchwood and Humboldt, on the main north-south trails.

The real problem in 1886 was the semi-arid district extending from Moose Jaw to Maple Creek and south to the United States boundary. The newly established farmers at Moose Jaw, for instance, suffered severely from the drought of 1886. "A majority of the buildings (around Moose Jaw) are deserted and the scene presented to the eye is not a cheerful one, particularly when one remembers the toil and care it took to build these places only to be deserted in the end."[119] At Swift Current, the shipping point for Battleford, there was no farm settlement visible, though two or three homesteads had been taken up in 1886,[120] and the *Regina Leader* reminded its readers that "Its entire vitality is received from Battleford".[121] In 1886, the equivalent of 2,725 Red River cart loads were hauled north, and the freighting season extended from April 15 to November 11.[122] To the south of Swift Current, the land was nearly empty, except on the Wood Mountain plateau where an American rancher leased land in 1886 and drove in 5000 to 6000 cattle to start a ranch, close to a settlement of *métis* and a Mounted Police post.[123]

In 1886, in the outlying area in the north, the life associated with the fur trade continued to survive, but it will not be described here. The hardships that went with trapping and making long wearisome trips through the many inter-connecting waterways were of another kind than those involved in starting a homestead in an unfamiliar climate where the settler could only wait and hope that farming would eventually bring returns.

At this time there was no talk of the pioneer fringe, though there was much said of pioneering. Farmers as yet had barely touched the lands to which scholars later would apply the term pioneer fringe. However, in the 1880's, one could readily see the change in relative desirability of lands within the West, as southern districts began to be served with railways, making commercial grain and livestock farming possible, and other areas were left to stagnate. The park country that runs from Edmonton through Prince Albert into Manitoba was successfully settled in the next generation, and during that time the district on the outer margin of the park lands gradually assumed the character of a persistent pioneer fringe with an immature economy relative to agriculture in other parts of the West.[124]

*

WINNIPEG AND THE WEST

Winnipeg, in 1886, contained nine times as many people as the next largest urban centre, and had more inhabitants than all of Saskatchewan. Its growth is easily explained; the C.P.R. had made it the communications heart of Western Canada, and it grew into the distributing, collecting and administrative centre of the agricultural lands that were being settled. In December, 1886, construction was commenced on a railway from Winnipeg to Hudson Bay, though the Bay was not reached for another four decades and then by another route. It was anticipated that this railway would ensure Winnipeg's commercial supremacy in the West.[125] In terms of time the railways had brought Banff almost as close to Winnipeg as places in southeastern Manitoba. Of the main settlements in the West only those along the North Saskatchewan could not be reached quickly.

Improvements in transportation caused many changes in the flow of goods in 1886. British Columbia lumber and fruit began to arrive on the prairies, Manitoba flour drove American flour from the British Columbia market,[126] Manitoba beer was shipped to British Columbia for the first time,[127] and it was anticipated that the Pacific Slope would become a market for Alberta beef. It was even suggested that Victoria and Winnipeg might become rivals for the wholesale trade of the West,[128] though of more immediate concern to Winnipeg were the attempts of Brandon, Regina and Calgary to become wholesale centres. Wholesale trading began in each of these cities, but none of them was an immediate threat to Winnipeg. Winnipeg already had 88 wholesale houses in 1886, and over fifteen million dollars worth of wholesale business was done in that year, making up more than 60% of the city's total business turnover.[129]

There were few large industries in Winnipeg. Except for a substantial iron works, the factories were mostly devoted to producing flour and lumber. Pork was packed on a small scale and there was considerable enthusiasm for erecting a stock yard in order to emulate Chicago as a meat packing centre. Nothing concrete was accomplished in 1886, though meetings were held that brought employers and employees together to discuss ways of promoting industry in Winnipeg.[130] But, in 1886, Winnipeg's distributing function still overshadowed all others. As yet the city was small enough to be extremely conscious of its role as a service centre for the farmers of the West. News of the activities of agricultural associations was carried in full in the daily papers, and such questions as suitable locations for experimental farms, or the best varieties of grain for the West, were keenly debated in the press.

Winnipeg was suffering from growing

Occupance

pains. In the boom of 1881–82 many shoddy structures were built; one newspaper suggested that great ingenuity had been shown in making buildings of as temporary a character as possible.[131] Construction methods had improved, however, and in 1886 the business streets were lined with two to four-storey brick structures, with overhanging stamped metal cornices ostentatiously framing the the rectangular fronts. One discerning local critic suggested that the only problem was the "snag-toothed" appearance that resulted from the uneven heights of adjacent buildings.[132] A financial and a wholesale district had already evolved, and there were areas of better quality housing. Streets were being paved in Winnipeg, and there was a gas works (using petroleum from Ontario for the raw material) and a small electric light plant. Water was obtained from the Assiniboine River, but distributing it was a problem. The water mains served only a limited part of the city, and people in many streets were still buying water by the barrel. The sewage system too was inadequate, and cess-pools were still quite common, though water closets had already been introduced to Winnipeg.

There was little concern for town planning or for preserving historic districts within the city. In 1882, for instance, old Fort Garry had been torn down to make way for an extension of Main Street. There were many complaints that the park system in Winnipeg was inadequate, though hope (forlorn, as it turned out to be) was held that the land near the junction of the Red and the Assiniboine Rivers would be turned into a recreation area.[133] Since little space was provided in the city for their summer recreational needs, people were taking the trains out to Selkirk, Hawk Lake and Kenora.

*

CONCLUSION

In 1872 it was still quite appropriate for an author to title his book on the West "The Great Lone Land".[134] Consequently it is surprising to see the extent of economic development that had taken place in Western Canada by 1886. Transportation facilities, of course, had guided the flow of settlers, so that areas having similar natural environments did not necessarily have corresponding levels of development. Only more railroads and continued immigration could (and did) change that. Mixed farming in Manitoba, Saskatchewan and northern Alberta, grain growing in Assiniboia, ranching in southern Alberta, fishing in the Manitoba lakes, lumbering in many scattered wooded areas, utilization of fossil fuels in Alberta and the development of recreational facilities in various areas had already begun, even if only sporadically. Agricultural techniques were being devised to cope with the farming problems presented by the low rainfall, and there was talk of starting irrigation projects.

Industries at this time were small and, like the roller and saw mills, were, in the main, related to local resources and local requirements. As yet, few processed goods, except flour, were exported from the West, though there was much said of establishing meat packing plants to process meat for export. In 1886, the first cattle from Western Canada were shipped to Great Britain and there was much interest in this experiment to determine the commercial feasibility of shipping livestock across the Atlantic.[135]

There were indications in 1886 that the migration of many different ethnic groups might create a problem of integration in the future. The Mennonites and Icelanders had apparently been inserted with little difficulty into the midst of the Ontario Canadian majority, yet already a few differences between the Mennonites and their neighbors had arisen. But, most groups were still so isolated from each other that close contact, leading to possible difficulties, was only limited. It is therefore of interest to note that the only apparent problem, though how real it was is difficult to assess, was that of integrating the Englishman into Western Canadian life. This was first really faced in Assiniboia. Here the newspapers entered gaily into discussing the qualities of the English. It was politely suggested that "a man without a definite purpose to accomplish on landing in Canada had better remain on the other side of the Atlantic,"[136] but on the other hand it was also realized that Canadians often mistreated the immigrants, who were "frequently fleeced of their money by interested parties who often induced them to purchase unnecessary things which could be well done without for the first two or three years."[137] In general, despite some unfortunate exceptions, the Englishman was considered "a worker".[138] The newspaper discussions of the experiences of the English often appear somewhat patronizing, because many Ontario settlers (not to mention people from every other group as well) also found life difficult in the West. There appears to have been remarkably little concern about the Indians and *métis,* even though the rebellion had only occurred in the previous year. Some people, of course, feared that there would be continued Indian troubles, but most settlers seem to have been so busy with their own affairs that they gave the Indians little serious thought. Ill feeling against the *métis* is still reported at Prince Albert,[139] but even in Batoche the *métis* who had taken part in the rebellion were returning to their homes in late 1886.[140]

In my discussion of the regions of Western Canada, no attempt has been made to identify regional attitudes and to determine whether people had a real sense of place. Various regional viewpoints can, however, be found in the newspapers, though by 1886 there had been insufficient time for regional characteristics to evolve and attain a deep meaning. It appears to me that the people in the West did not feel any need to make a deliberate distinction between themselves and the inhabitants of either Eastern Canada or British Columbia, because in those days

of new settlement and slow communications they already felt very definitely that they were in another and a very distinctive world. It is a very revealing comment on the attitude of the people to themselves, however, that an able author and editor while campaigning in an election had to explain why he would "condescend" to live in the West.[141] Apparently it was felt that the raw West was quite good enough for farmers and tradesmen, but other men sometimes were distrusted until they had proven themselves as genuinely tied to the West as a farmer on a homestead.

During the 1880's, the progress of settlement and the development of the settlement pattern in the interior plains of Canada and the United States seemed to be proceeding along parallel but independent lines within each country. But, despite the appearance of separateness there was considerable interaction. It was most effective, however, at a higher, less apparent level than the occasional direct contact between individual Canadian and American settlers.[142] When government officials were formulating immigration regulations, when railroad executives were devising promotion schemes to attract settlers, when machinery manufacturers were designing implements or when editors of farm magazines were looking for ideas, they were eager to modify their own procedures or adopt new concepts from others so as not to be left behind. Any new techniques or procedures that might be adopted from the other country would then be transmitted and diffused through the administrative structure and communications system of each country. Thus, the same general pattern of development and level of technology prevailed on both sides of the 49th parallel, not as the result of the direct movement of ideas across the border, as is sometimes believed, but by the movement of these ideas through a few key channels, many of which were in the Eastern United States and Canada, and then from higher to lower levels within each country, via the existing structure of government agencies and newspapers.[143]

There was an occasional conscious effort

to establish a difference between the American West and the Canadian West. It was recognized, for instance, that the southern part of the Bow River region was similar to Montana; American currency still circulated freely and the *Macleod Gazette* regularly carried Montana news.[144] But from the frequent references to the havoc caused by tornadoes in the United States (to cite only the favorite example), one must conclude that the editors wanted to assure themselves and their readers that they had made a good choice after all in settling in Canada. The Regina newspaper comforted its readers by telling them that there was a characteristic respectability in the communities of Western Canada that stood out in strong contrast to the rowdy behaviour generally found in American settlements. Western Canada's greater propriety was attributed to prohibition and a good and fearless press.[145] But settlers in 1886 must have begun to doubt such extreme contrasts because there were two stage robberies that summer, one each on the Prince Albert and Edmonton stage coach runs, and the Edmonton editor was complaining that a "criminal element" had accompanied the railroad.[146]

Some major regional differences within the West were clearly recognized by the inhabitants. Their distinctions were not so much related to the famous three prairie levels, first recognized by Dr. James Hector in 1857, and ever since a favoured device of geographers for describing the West. Northern Alberta and Saskatchewan were quite emphatic about their distinctiveness vis-à-vis the communities along the C.P.R. The northern farmers were confident that mixed farming would provide an assured livelihood for many future immigrants. In the plains districts to the south, a stable agricultural economy was still not established, and there was an undertone of anxiety in this area though there was an indication that a solution to the low precipitation was in the process of being found. The Bow River ranching country was proud of its unique character and the Macleod editor was affronted when the Regina people founded a Stock Association in 1886, in what was after all supposed to be a wheat growing region.[147] In comparison with these younger settlements of the Far West, Manitoba in 1886, with its railroads and proven agriculture, its comparatively dense settlement and established communities, already appeared staid.

*

1 Western Canada (or the West) as defined in this paper comprises the area organized in 1886 into the province of Manitoba and the provisional districts of Assiniboia, Saskatchewan and Alberta in the North-West Territories. It does not include British Columbia.

2 I am deliberately not making any incursions into the realms of geographical change through time. I regard this study of geographical change as very important, however, and this study is a side excursion from a broader and larger study of the province of Manitoba in which I am investigating how the present geographical pattern of Manitoba evolved through time.

3 This is not a precise figure, because a census was taken in Manitoba in 1886 (population 108, 640) and in the North-West Territories in 1885 (population 48,362). To obtain the 1886 population for the Territories, I have followed the estimate of population increase made by the Secretary of the Department of Agriculture in 1886 and adjusted the 1885 population figures as given in the census. See Canada "Report of the Selected Standing Committee on Agriculture and Colonization," Appendix 4, *Journals of the House of Commons* (1887), p. 27. Further information on the Indian population for 1886 was obtained from Canada, "Annual Report of the Department of Indian Affairs for 1886," *Sessional Papers* (1887), pp. 252–257.

4 Special mention must be made of the effect that climate had on agriculture in the Territories in the early 1880's. In 1881 and 1882, when settlers first really started to move into Assiniboia, the precipitation and temperature conditions appeared favourable for wheat growing, and what little seed had been sown produced good yields. In 1883, 1884 and 1885 there was barely enough precipitation to produce crops and there were also disastrous fall frosts in many areas, especially in 1885. But the worst blow of all came in 1886: the first drought to affect the Territories after the settlers had started to occupy the land along the C.P.R. line. Winnipeg had 14.8" precipitation in 1886, Qu'Appelle 10.1", Swift Current 10.6", Medicine Hat 6.7", Calgary 11.3", Edmonton 9.2". Long term average precipitation figures are: Winnipeg 19.72", Regina 15.09", Swift Current 14.89", Medicine Hat 13.55", Calgary 17.47", Edmonton 17.6". (*Canada Year Book 1963-64*) In these years farmers were enduring hardships because of their lack of knowledge of the climate. Some farmers were gradually learning how to carry out field operations that would ensure at least some return of crop under these marginal conditions. But others felt it was useless to remain, and by 1886 some of these had already moved elsewhere.

5 The Indian Reserves are not discussed, since they are a special problem in themselves. The Indian population is, however, shown in Figure 2. There were approximately 24,600 Indians in the West.

6 All the agricultural statistics are based on the Census of Manitoba for 1886 and the Census of the North-West Territories for 1885. To obtain the cultivated acreage for the Territories in 1886, the Acres Broken, Fall, 1884 and Spring of 1885, have been added to the Total Cultivated in 1885. I have assumed that approximately the same acreage of land was broken in the fall of 1885 and spring of 1886 as in the previous twelve months.

7 *The Nor'-West Farmer and Manitoba Miller* (March, 1888), p. 71.

8 *Manitoba Daily Free Press* (October 9, 1886).

9 J. Warkentin, "Manitoba Settlement Patterns," Historical and Scientific Society of Manitoba, *Papers*, Series III, No. 16 (1961), pp. 62–77.

10 *The Nor'-West Farmer and Manitoba Miller* (October, 1886), p. 624.

11 Canada, "Report of the Minister of Agriculture for the Year 1886," *Sessional Papers* (1887), p. 75.

12 *The Emigrant* (October, 1886), p. 114.

13 *Emerson International* (April 29, 1886).

14 *Winnipeg Commercial* (June 22, 1886).

15 *The Daily Manitoban* (May 6, 1886).

16 *Emerson News* (May 20, 1886).

17 *Manitoba Daily Free Press* (July 6, 1886).

18 *Birtle Observer* (November 5, 1886).

19 *Idem.*

20 Canada, "Report of the Minister of the Interior for 1886," *Sessional Papers* (1887), p. 84.

21 *Minnedosa Tribune* (February 19, 1886).

22 *Winnipeg Commercial* (November 9, 1886).

23 *The Emigrant* (January, 1887), p. 244.

24 *Manitoba Crop Bulletin,* No. 10 (June 1, 1885), p. 18.

25 *Manitoba Crop Bulletin,* Nos. 14–17 (June-October, 1886).

26 *Manitoba Crop Bulletin,* No. 16 (August 1, 1886), p. 14.

27 See the report of the Brandon immigration agent in "Annual Report of the Minister of Agriculture for 1886," Canada, *Sessional Papers* (1887), p. 106.

28 *The Daily Manitoban* (September 2, 1886).

29 *The Nor'-West Farmer and Manitoba Miller* (October, 1886), p. 711.

30 *Birtle Observer* (March 5, 1886).

31 *Brandon Mail* (January 14, 1886).

32 *The Nor'-West Farmer and Manitoba Miller* (July, 1887), p. 900.

33 *The Manitoba Sun* (November 24, 1886).

34 *Manitoba Daily Free Press* (July 28, 1886).

35 *The Daily Manitoban* (October 27, 1886).

36 *Brandon Times* (November 25, 1886).

37 Though in actual fact St. Léon has grown in recent years with the aid of the motor car and truck.

38 *The Daily Manitoban* (June 1, 1886).

39 *Manitoba Daily Free Press* (December 31, 1886).

40 *Manitou Mercury* (February 19, 1886).

41 *Manitoba Daily Free Press* (January 28, 1886).

42. *Portage la Prairie Liberal* (February 19, March 5, 1886).

43 T. R. Weir, "Pioneer Settlement of Southwest Manitoba, 1897 to 1901," *The Canadian Geographer,* vol. VIII, No. 2, (1964), pp. 64–71.

44 *Manitoba Daily Free Press* (November 25, 1886).

45 *Ibid.* (August 2, 1886); *Regina Leader* (June 22, 1886).

46. *Manitoba Daily Free Press* (July 28, 1886).

47 *Manitou Mercury* (February 12, 1886).

48 *Ibid.* (April 2, 1886). In general, effective contact with American settlements was surprisingly slight along the 49th parallel, though occasional purchases or deliveries of products were made across the border. Settlers, too, crossed the boundary one way or the other to settle in the country, but generally this decision as to whether to settle in Canada or the United States had been made well before immigrants arrived on the land available for homesteading. Occasionally farmers would pull up stakes and try the greener country across the line.

49 Canada, "Report of the Minister of the Interior for 1886," *Sessional Papers* (1887), p. 14.

50 *Qu'Appelle Vidette* (January 14, 1886).

51 *Regina Leader* (December 7, 1886).

52 *Ibid.* (February 16, 1886).

53 *Brandon Times* (August 26, 1886).

54 *Regina Leader* (May 18, 1886).

55 *Qu'Appelle Vidette* (January 14, 1886).

56 *Regina Leader* (September 7, 1886).

57 *Qu'Appelle Progress* (July 16, 1886).

58 *The Manitoba Sun* (August 24, 1886).

59 *Ibid.* (August 18, 1886).

60 The origin of dry farming in western Canada is usually attributed to an involuntary summerfallow made on some lands in 1885 in the Qu'Appelle area by farmers who were absent teaming supplies to the troops quelling the Riel Rebellion. Next year some of the farmers observed that only the fallowed fields produced a crop despite the drought, and the idea of a deliberate fallow to conserve moisture was born. (See E. H. Oliver, "The Beginnings of Agriculture in Saskatchewan," *Transactions of the Royal Society of Canada,* vol. XXIX (1935), pp. 30–32. This account is correct as far as it goes, but the general adoption of fallow was a slow process. In 1886 only a few individuals saw the relationship between fallowing and conservation of moisture. Most farmers thought that the better cultivation made possible during the fallow year was the chief benefit to be derived from the practice.

61 No official figures are available on the size of these centres. My estimate is based on reports in various newspapers, particularly the *Winnipeg Commercial* (October 12, November 9, 1886).

62 *Regina Leader* (June 29, 1886).

63 *Qu'Appelle Vidette* (July 29, 1886).

64 *Regina Leader* (March 9, 1886); *Qu'Appelle Progress* (March 26, 1886).

65 *Regina Leader* (June 22, September 14, 1886).

66 *Regina Journal* (December 24, 1886).

67 *Manitoba Daily Free Press* (June 8, 1886).

68 *The Emigrant* (August, 1886), p. 60.

69 *Ibid.* (June, 1887), p. 15.

70 *Edmonton Bulletin* (April 24, 1886); *Saskatchewan Herald* (Battleford, July 19, August 16, 1886).

71 Some of the troops who repressed the rebellion of 1885 had, according to a correspondent of the Toronto Globe, looted and burned homes. (*Toronto Globe,* May 25, 1886).

72 *Qu'Appelle Progress* (March 5, 1886).

73 *Prince Albert Times and Saskatchewan Review* (June 19, 1886).

74 Based on news reports on the movements of steam boats in the *Selkirk Record, Prince Albert Times and Saskatchewan Review, Saskatchewan Herald* and *Edmonton Bulletin.*

75 *Prince Albert Times and Saskatchewan Review* (June 19, 1886).

76 *Saskatchewan Herald* (November 22, 1886).

77 *The Emigrant* (August, 1886), p. 61.

78 *Idem.*

79 *McPhillip's Directory of the District of Saskatchewan* (Qu'Appelle, 1886), p. 26.

80 *Prince Albert Times and Saskatchewan Review* (June 11, 1886).

81 *Edmonton Bulletin* (February 20, 1886).

82 *Ibid.* (April 17, 1886).

83 *The Emigrant* (February, 1887), p. 252.

84 *Ibid.,* p. 242.

85 *Edmonton Bulletin* (March 13, 1886); John Blue, *Alberta Past and Present* (Chicago, 1924), p. 309.

86 *The Daily Manitoban* (October 21, 1886).

87 *Ibid.* (November 20, 1886).

88 *Edmonton Bulletin* (August 14, 1886).

89 *Ibid.* (February 18, 1886).

90 Canada, "Annual Report of the Minister of the Interior for 1886," *Sessional Papers* (1887), p. 36.

91 *The Emigrant* (September, 1886), p. 95.

92 *Calgary Tribune* (May 29, July 31, 1886).

93 *Ibid.* (September 11, 1886); *Medicine Hat Times* (May 13, 1886).

94 *Calgary Tribune* (August 7, 1886).

95 *Manitoba Daily Free Press* (April 29,1886).

96 Canada, "Annual Report of the Minister of the Interior for 1886," *Sessional Papers* (1887), p. 19.

97 *Medicine Hat Times* (December 11, 1886).

98 *Lethbridge News* (February 5, 1886).

99 *Calgary Tribune* (December 10, 1886).

100 *Regina Leader* (September 28, 1886).

101 *Calgary Tribune* (December 17, 1886).

102 Canada, "Annual Report of the Minister of the Interior for 1886," *Sessional Papers* (1887), p. xxiv.

103 *The Nor'-West Farmer and Manitoba Miller* (November, 1886), p. 678.

104 *Calgary Tribune* (June 12, 1886).

105 *Lethbridge News* (February 5, 1886).

106 *Macleod Gazette* (August 3, 1886).

107 *Manitoba Daily Free Press* (August 25, 1886).

108 *Macleod Gazette* (July 20, 1886).

109 *Ibid.* (July 27, 1886).

110 *Ibid.* (August 3, 1886).

111 *Lethbridge News* (April 9, 1886).

112 Canada, "Annual Report of the Minister of the Interior for 1885," *Sessional Papers* (1886), p. 20.

113 *Macleod Gazette* (November 9, 1886).

114 *Lethbridge News* (February 5, 1886).

115 *The Daily Manitoban* (April 23 & 24, 1886).

116 *The Nor'-West Farmer and Manitoba Miller* (May, 1886), p. 541; *Manitoba Tribune* (November 19, 1886).

117 Canada, "Annual Report of the Minister of the Interior for 1886," *Sessional Papers* (1887), p. 23.

118 *The Emigrant* (January, 1887), p. 224.

119 *Medicine Hat Times* (October 16, 1886).

120 *The Nor'-West Farmer and Manitoba Miller* (November, 1886), p. 681.

121 *Regina Leader* (September 7, 1886).

122 *The Nor'-West Farmer and Manitoba Miller* (November, 1886), p. 681.

123 *Regina Leader* (November 2, 1886).

124 W. A. Mackintosh, "Some aspects of a Pioneer Economy," *Canadian Journal of Economics and Political Science,* vol. II, No. 4 (1936), pp. 457–63.

125 *Manitoba Daily Free Press* (December 28, 1886).

126 *Winnipeg Commercial* (February 8, 1887).

127 *Ibid.* (June 29, 1886).

128 *The Manitoba Daily Sun* (April 9, 1886).

129 *Winnipeg Commercial* (February 8, 1887).

130 *The Daily Manitoban* (October 6, 1886).

131 *The Manitoba Daily Sun* (September 4, 1886).

132 *Idem.*

133 *The Daily Manitoban* (August 10, 1886).

134 W. F. Butler, *The Great Land* (London, 1872).

135 *Moosomin Courier* (September 30, 1886); *Macleod Gazette* (December 7, 1886).

136 *Regina Leader* (February 16, 1886).

137 *Moosomin Courier* (April 22, 1886).

138 *Regina Leader* (November 9, 1886).

139 *Edmonton Bulletin* (July 31, 1886).

140 *Qu'Appelle Progress* (June 11, 1886).

141 *Regina Leader* (December 7, 1886).

142 One clear exception, however, is the example of the Montana ranching industry, which set the pattern of agricultural development in southern Alberta at this time.

143 In the first three-quarters of the nineteenth century there had been a close and more direct relationship across the border in the West as indicated by examples such as the annual buffalo hunt, and of trade with and through Saint Paul. Later on, in the twentieth century, the migration of many Americans to the Canadian West, the building of James J. Hill's railways into Canada, and the rise of the Dry Farming Congress and agricultural research institutions resulted in a closer contact again across the border all the way from the Roseau River to the Rocky Mountains.

144 *Macleod Gazette* (November 30, 1886).

145 *Regina Leader* (July 6, 1886).

146 *Edmonton Bulletin* (August 28, 1886).

147 *Macleod Gazette* (November 2, 1886).

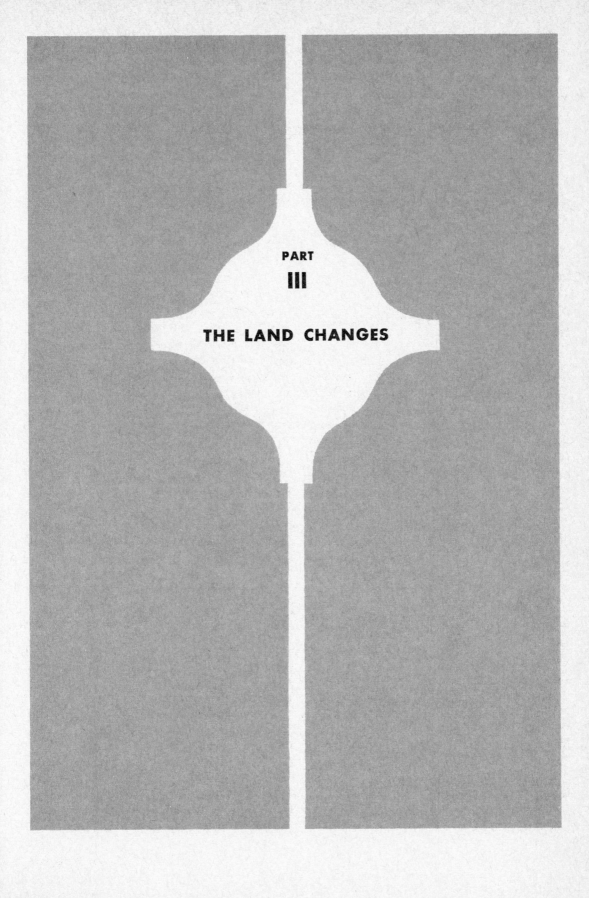

PART

III

THE LAND CHANGES

6

Agricultural Regions of Southern Ontario 1880 and 1951*

LLOYD G. REEDS

* From Economic Geography, Vol. 35 (1959), pp. 219–227. Reprinted by permission. Supplement by the author.

The economic development in Southern Ontario since 1940 has surpassed that of all other regions of Canada. Expanding cities and towns have reduced the area of agricultural land and have increased the demand for agricultural produce. Approximately 20 per cent of the total area of the Palaeozoic lowland[1] is now urban land or is occupied by roads, railways, parks, cemeteries, and provincial forests. In parts of the highly industrialized belt along Lake Ontario, the area of agricultural land has declined as much as 20 per cent since 1940. The most rapid urbanization is occurring in the areas with the highest proportion of good quality agricultural land. Land use planning on a regional basis is a prerequisite to future prosperity in this part of Canada.

Basic to an understanding of present agricultural land use patterns is the reconstruction of the agricultural geography of the past. Oftentimes, such an investigation will greatly illuminate the dynamic forces that initiate and give impetus to the changes. The purpose of this paper is to present the agricultural regions of 1880, to study the relation between these and those of 1951, and to explain the changes and to speculate regarding future trends.

In 1880, practically all of the suitable land had been occupied and improved. The acreage in wheat was three times what it was in 1950, though the livestock population was less than 40 per cent of the 1951 figure. The era of diversified and specialized farming had begun while the period of rapid exploitation and increasing farm population was drawing to a close.

The map of the 1880 agricultural regions has been constructed after a careful study of census data, the Ontario Agricultural Commission Report, and all other relevant historical source materials (Fig. 1). Wheat was the dominant cash crop. There was a very large part of Southern Ontario which could be classified as a general or mixed farming region with an emphasis on wheat production. Specialization and diversification were in their infant stages and even in areas where the trend was in this direction, wheat was still one of the most important crops. The traditional procedure in farming prior to 1800 was to clear as quickly as one could, as much land as possible, and to grow wheat year after year, until yields or prices declined. This was the pattern everywhere throughout the Palaeozoic lowland on all soil types regardless of their texture, drainage, or inherent capabilities. Wheat was grown on the flat, imperfectly-drained, and acid soils of the clay plains; on the steeply-sloping, light-textured soils of the terminal moraines; on the

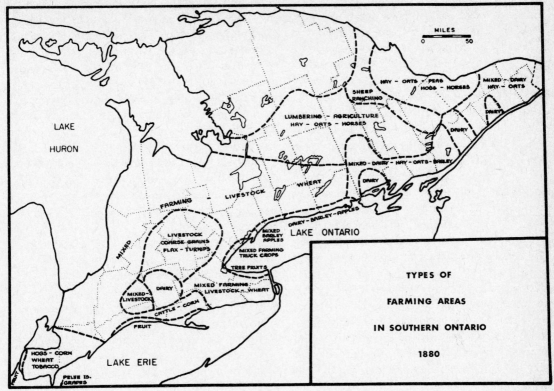

FIG. 1.

rolling drumlins with their highly calcareous till soils; and even on the shallow stony land of the limestone plains.[2]

Similarly, with regard to expansion of agricultural settlement generally, physical factors played a very minor role. All types of land and soil were occupied. Even the Pre-Cambrian upland, with its spotty pockets of good soil and its vast stretches of thin sterile podzols, did not provide a sufficient barrier to preclude its settlement.

For a considerable time, the poor land supported as many people as the good land.

Initially, farm depopulation was not generally due to the abandonment of sub-marginal lands nor to the physical deterioration of productive soils. Furthermore, the exodus from the poorer areas did not occur any sooner after settlement than it did in the more productive regions.[3] Thus, one should recognize the importance of tradition and the human factor in the earlier periods of Southern Ontario's agricultural development. Keeping this background in mind, let us examine more closely the 1880 pattern.

*

TYPES OF FARMING IN 1880

Because of improved transport facilities and markets, livestock was assuming a greater importance, while the increase in urban population was stimulating the development of dairying and market gardening. It is interesting to note, however, that other factors were involved in the early localization of these types of farming. The holding of fairs was very important in accounting for the initial development of livestock rearing in Western Ontario.[4] Flax was an important cash crop in areas where there was a large population of German origin. The introduction of dairy farming to Oxford Country, in the first instance, was due to the fact that a cheesemaker by the name of Harvey Farrington from Herkimer County, New York, visited friends in North Norwich township in 1863.[5] He decided to stay and in the following year erected the first cheese factory there. It is true that the physical conditions were propitious for dairying and that the market for cheese was excellent, but had his friends happened to have resided in another part of Ontario on a similar land type the present land use pattern might have been somewhat different. In Eastern Ontario, the cheese factory system was also introduced at an early date from nearby New York State.

By 1880, the outlines of the corn belt had taken shape. It had been discovered that climate and soils favored corn, wheat, and tobacco production in Kent and Essex Counties, and that local supplies of corn and wheat were advantageous to profitable hog-raising.

Fruit growing was in the experimental stage, as evidenced by the widespread distribution of apples, there being 300,000 acres of small orchards scattered throughout the peninsula. There was also a scattered distribution of pears, plums, and cherries. On the other hand, the areas of specialized fruit growing and market gardening were relatively small and were confined to those sections which had a long growing season, in Essex County and along the shores of Lakes Erie and Ontario. The commercial production was even more localized, since the bulk of the fruit being marketed came from a small section of the Niagara peninsula.

Higher prices for land in the south and the governmental policy of granting new immigrants free land along colonization roads encouraged the agricultural settlement of the Pre-Cambrian upland. However, even in the initial period of occupance, there were difficulties. As Lower stated so graphically, "Each year, the governmental hen would carefully count her chickens, to see how many the hawks, in the shape of sand and rock, had devoured."[6]

The shanty market was the chief determinant of the type of agricultural production in the Shield and in the Upper Ottawa Valley. Hay, oats, and peas were the important crops with hogs and horses the main types of livestock. The growing of peas in Renfrew County has continued ever since.

Between 1880 and 1951, a much closer adjustment of agricultural production to soil and climatic conditions developed. Production per unit area increased greatly by the application of scientific practices and by mechanization. Many farms were amalgamated or enlarged in response to increased costs of operation resulting from mechanization, higher labor costs, and competition from other industries. Production expanded in spite of a declining farm area and fewer farm residents. The rural population declined from 78 per cent of the total to 29 per cent between 1880 and 1951, while the actual farm population dropped to 15 per cent by the mid-century.[7]

*

TYPES OF FARMING IN 1951

The 1951 map shows 29 types of farming areas (Fig. 2). The chief differences in the two patterns include the development of the new tobacco belt in Norfolk and in parts of surrounding counties; the expansion of dairy farming in the Toronto hinterland, in Western Ontario, and in Eastern Ontario; the shift of wheat growing to and the upsurge of cash cropping in the southwest; the change in the center of hog production from

The Land Changes

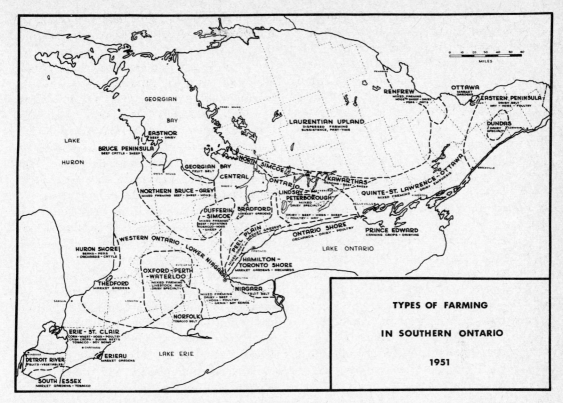

FIG. 2.

the corn belt to the dairy belt; the appearance of the Georgian Bay fruit belt; the growing contrast between the Pre-Cambrian and Palaeozoic areas; the development of bogs for market gardening; the emergence of central Western Ontario as the agricultural heartland; and the drastic decline in agricultural land in the "Golden Horseshoe" area.[8]

The development of the new tobacco belt in Norfolk County was initiated by the increase in demand for cigarettes following 1920. The old tobacco belt of Essex and Kent lacked large areas of light-textured soils essential for the production of the bright flue-cured tobacco. There was a very rapid expansion of production in Norfolk where both climate and soils were suitable. This region has the benefit of warm southern slopes and freedom from late spring frosts, though summer moisture deficiency and a tendency to drifting soil are handicaps. The slightly acid deltaic sands of Norfolk, with

their open structure, favoring aeration, root penetration, and decomposition of organic material, are highly desirable for tobacco. With increasing prices, the production expanded into the adjoining counties of Elgin, Oxford, and Brant, and more recently to the cooler regions of Simcoe, Dufferin, Durham, and Northumberland, though the acreage in northern areas, in 1951, was less than 5 per cent of that in the Lake Erie counties. The introduction of tobacco growing to Norfolk came at a time when general farming had languished. Depressed areas were restored to an unprecedented prosperity. The value of land increased from $10.00 to $300.00 per acre. The entire pattern of land use and the agricultural landscape were transformed. The large general farms were subdivided. Drying sheds and greenhouses sprung up alongside new farmhouses. New machinery and equipment and new people appeared. Workers came from the "Old Belt," from the United States tobacco-growing regions and from Belgium, Poland, Hungary, Czechoslovakia, and Romania. A more specialized type of farming developed in the "New Belt" since the Fox and Plainfield soil series do not possess the same inherent versatility as the Brookston series of Kent and Essex which can be utilized for general farming and for the production of corn, wheat, canning crops, soybeans, and sugar beets.[9] By 1951, the expansion of tobacco growing in Western Ontario had practically reached its limits while further extension of production in northern areas was dependent upon prevailing prices.

By 1951, dairying was widely distributed throughout the peninsula, though there was increasing specialization in certain locales. In 1880, there were three districts in Eastern Ontario with some specialization (Fig. 1). The industry was much more widespread in 1951. Winchester and Mountain townships of Dundas County and Russell and Finch townships of the adjoining counties had become the center of highest density of dairy cattle. This area has a higher proportion of productive land than other parts of the Eastern peninsula. For many years, the emphasis was on seasonal cheese manufacturing, but the use of supplementary feeds and the introduction of early-maturing cereals has enabled the farmers on the better lands to carry on a year-around production of milk.

In the Toronto region, the early growth of urban population provided a local market for butter and milk. Toronto's milkshed has expanded with the city's growth. Proximity to the large market is the outstanding control, though the highest densities of dairy cattle are centered in the clay plains.

The transitional zone between the Toronto milkshed and the Eastern cheese belt was, for a time, important for cheese production but as transport facilities were improved, the emphasis swung to whole milk and certain areas such as the Lindsay clay plain became specialized in this enterprise.[10]

In Western Ontario, the original core area was Oxford County where the cheese factory system and government creameries had been established at an early date. The undulating till plains with their medium to heavy-textured soils favored production of hay, forage, and grain while the growing season was sufficiently long to encourage the earlier advent of winter production. The 20th century has been marked by a great expansion of the dairy belt to meet the growing demands of the local cities and towns for fluid milk. The direction of this expansion has been westward and northward. These areas have similar land types which were capable of exploitation for this type of farming while competition from cash crops had limited expansion southwards.

The dairy belt and adjoining areas of the Central upland of Western Ontario has emerged as the "Iowa of Canada."[11] Part of this region had more than 150 animal units per square mile of farm land in 1951.[12] There was a heavy concentration of dairy cattle, hogs, and poultry and a high production of mixed grain, oats, hay, and ensilage corn. Hog raising has increased with the growth of dairying, the skimmed milk being used as an important source of feed. The capabilities of the soils for high yields of grain also favored the emphasis on hogs. In addition to the high livestock and crop densities, the landscape generally exhibited a greater uniformity of development than most parts of Ontario. This agricultural area had a fairly large urban population and a higher than average rural population density. Quality of land is the most important of the factors underlying this development. 80 per cent of the farm land of Middlesex, Perth, Waterloo, and Oxford falls into the first and second class categories as compared to 64 per cent in Halton, Peel, York, and Ontario and 42 per cent in Lanark, Carleton, Russell, and Prescott. However, one must also underline the human factor, since in parts of Waterloo County, particularly, the peculiar industry and efficiency of the farmers was largely responsible for the excellent development of mediocre land.

*

In 1880, there was a relatively small acreage devoted to cash crops other than wheat. The areas of specialized fruit growing were also small, and within the regions delineated on the map there was not the same intensity of land use as there was in 1951. The production of tree fruits was widely dispersed. By 1951, there was a contraction of production to the areas most favored climatically, near the ameliorating influence of Lakes Ontario and Erie and Georgian Bay. There were several areas in south-western Ontario which had become very important for a great variety of cash crops including husking corn, sugar beets, soybeans, tender fruits, and vegetables and canning crops (Fig. 2). The great increase in demand for these types of agricultural produce stimulated this development while the localization of production has been related primarily to the length of the growing season.

The contrast between the Pre-Cambrian area and the Palaeozoic lowland was much sharper in 1951 than it had been in 1880. This is one instance where bedrock accounts for the most striking differences in agricultural land use. This also leads one to suggest that these basic physical controls, though not necessarily as significant in the early stages of development, do eventually exert their full influence.

The drastic decline in agricultural land in the highly industrialized region along Lake Ontario and the rapid urbanization since 1940 has already been mentioned. The same trend has been evident in a much broader belt which extends northwards and westwards to include the agricultural heartland area. A high proportion of the total farm land in this region centering on Oxford and Waterloo counties is adaptable for cultivated crops. There is a high percentage of good quality land, the variable soils permit diversification, and the climate of the lakeshore part is especially suitable for tender tree fruits. The crucial problem is that of competition between land uses. As urbanization continues, an increasingly small area of this highly productive land will be available for agricultural use. For a time, more intensive use of remaining lands and a more complete application of scientific practices and technological improvements may be sufficient to maintain production at present levels. Much might be done to decentralize industry within the region and to direct urban growth onto the poorer land types. Eventually, however, there will be a movement outwards from this core area. A more intensive development of outlying regions will then take place. The trend toward increased cash cropping in the Lake Erie counties will continue.

*

CONCLUSION

By 1880, agricultural settlement of the peninsula was almost complete. In these early stages of development, it has been seen that tradition and human factors played the major role. The period between 1880 and 1951 was marked by a retreat from the less favorable areas and a much more intensive development of the productive lands. It is evident that economic factors were primarily responsible for initiating the changes in types of production generally, but that climate, relief, and soils have been the main determinants of the characteristic patterns, locally. It would appear that, in the latter half of the 20th century, the frontier of extensive land use will be rolled back, though one hopes that history will not repeat itself and that no attempt will be made to redevelop land which is inherently unsuitable for agricultural use.

Changing Patterns Since 1951

Ontario agriculture has been adjusting at a rapid rate to pressures of industrial and urban expansion. Farmers have been caught in a cost-price squeeze in which costs of production have risen more rapidly than prices received for produce. Increases in net farm income have not kept pace with increments in urban wage rates and other non-farm incomes. As a result, Southern Ontario has experienced a further substantial reduction in the total acreage of land in farms and in its farm population. Large acreages of sub-marginal land have been abandoned; other large areas of mediocre-quality land is being used less intensively, and in the most highly industrialized regions, considerable acreages have been transferred from agricultural to urban uses.

The bulk of the reduced acreage has occurred in the districts of Parry Sound and Muskoka and in the counties of Haliburton, Hastings, Frontenac and Renfrew. These areas have particularly severe physical limitations for agriculture, including frequent rock outcropping, excessive stoniness, and shallow and infertile soils. Occupied farm land constitutes only a small proportion of the total area. Individual farms have small crop acreages and low values. For many years, the continuation of farming depended upon the availability of cheap labour and a very low capitalization. Increasingly high labour costs and a dwindling labour supply have finally forced many of these operators out of business. Thousands of acres have been abandoned; other farms have been incorporated into much larger units and are being used as ranches.

While the bulk of the "fallout" has occurred in the fringe areas where there is a high proportion of sub-marginal or marginal land, a considerable acreage of good quality agricultural land has been diverted to industry, housing, highways and other non-farm uses in the highly industrialized regions. Areas undergoing the greatest losses are those along the St. Lawrence Seaway, around the rapidly expanding industrial cities of Oshawa, Toronto, Hamilton, London, Kitchener-Waterloo and in the Niagara Fruit Belt. Most of the land that has gone out of production has been of fair to good quality. The Lake Iroquois Plain between Toronto and Hamilton is almost a continuous string of low density housing, light industry and shopping plazas and may now be regarded as a non-agricultural area. The Niagara Fruit Belt which has soils and climate that are uniquely adapted for the production of tender tree fruit, is being reduced at the rate of 500 acres per year. It will eventually disappear as an important producer of these special crops, if the present patterns of uncontrolled urban sprawl are permitted to continue.

Areas in the northern parts of Western Ontario, in Central Ontario and in Eastern Ontario are being used less intensively than prior to 1951. Physical capabilities of the soils are generally lower than in the Toronto area or in south-western Ontario. The major land use hazards include poor drainage, steep topography, water erosion and excessive stoniness. The medium-sized family farm with a small acreage of high quality land can no longer be operated profitably on an intensive basis. Land that was formerly cultivated is now being used for pasture or is reverting to woodland.

Even in the mixed farming areas of the Niagara Peninsula, where over 80 per cent of the soils are classified as good arable land, and where climate and location with respect to markets are favourable, urban pressures have had a sharp effect on agricultural land use. In 1961, 56 per cent of the farms had gross incomes of less than $2,500. Most farms are too small and the volume of production too low to provide the owner with a satisfactory net income. As a result, many farms are being operated on a part-time basis, with the farmer deriving the major portion of his income from a job in the city. Acreages in crops have declined and large areas of potentially productive land are lying idle. Part-time farming and occupation of farms by urban workers have resulted in a greatly increased acreage of scrub grassland and weedy, unproductive pastures. The trend to further deterioration of the land's productivity is continuing at an alarming rate.

On the other hand, most of the remaining areas of south-western Ontario have experienced increasing specialization and a greater intensity of use since 1951. The acreage in farms has remained relatively static but yields per acre have increased dramatically. Production of such high value cash crops as early vegetables, tomatoes, soybeans, sugar beets, tobacco and corn has expanded greatly. A more intensive agriculture has also developed in the dairy farming and livestock areas of Oxford, Perth and Waterloo counties. Farms have been enlarged and are more efficiently managed.

The changing patterns of agricultural land use since 1951 continue to reflect the interaction of physical and socio-economic factors. Economic competition has accounted for the greatly reduced acreages of farmland and the more extensive uses in the poorer areas. The same forces have brought about increasing intensity of production in the most favourable regions. However, when location is most suitable for urbanization, there appears to be little that can be done to prevent even the best quality agricultural land from being put to this "higher" use.

*

FOOTNOTES

1 The Palaeozoic lowland is that part of peninsular Ontario to the south and east of the Pre-Cambrian Shield.

2 For a map of the physiographic areas of Southern Ontario, see L. J. Chapman and D. F. Putnam, *The Physiography of Southern Ontario* (Toronto: University of Toronto Press, 1951; Second Edition, 1966).

3 J. W. Watson, "Rural Depopulation in S. W. Ontario," *Annals of Assn. of Amer. Geogrs.*, Vol. 37 (1947), pp. 145–154.

4 R. L. Jones, *History of Agriculture in Ontario 1613–1880* (Toronto, 1946), pp. 159–161.

5 *Ibid.*, p. 254.

6 A. R. M. Lower, "Settlement and the Forest Frontier in Eastern Canada," *Canadian Frontiers of Settlement*, Vol. IX (Toronto, 1936).

7 *Census of Canada*, Vols. II and IX, Dominion Bureau of Statistics, Ottawa.

8 This term has been used to designate a highly industrialized area along Lake Ontario from Oshawa to Niagara Falls where over 25 per cent of the entire Canadian manufacturing production is now concentrated. Professor D. F. Putnam of the University of Toronto has named this area "Mississauga."

9 For soil maps and descriptions of soil types, see "Ontario Soil Survey Maps and Reports," published by Canada Department of Agriculture, Ottawa and the Ontario Department of Agriculture, Toronto.

10 For a map showing extent of clay plain see Chapman and Putnam, *op. cit.*

11 Iowa has the greatest density of livestock per unit area of any part of the U.S.A.

12 An animal unit is equivalent to: 1 horse, 1 cow, 5 hogs, 7 sheep or 100 hens.

7

Settlement Migration in Central Bonavista Bay, Newfoundland*

C. GRANT HEAD

* Based on Settlement Migration in Central Bonavista Bay, Newfoundland, *Unpublished M. A. Thesis, Department of Geography, McMaster University, Hamilton, Ontario, 1964. Thanks are due to the Province of Ontario, whose Ontario Graduate Fellowship during the academic year 1963–64 and the summer of 1964 made this study possible.*

A growing number of reports has pointed to the profound economic and social changes that must take place if the Canadian Atlantic Provinces are to bring themselves to the prosperity of Canada as a whole. In a large part of the Atlantic area, a rather sparse population strung along a great length of coast has made the provision of modern services, such as electric power, well-equipped schools, and medical attention, a difficult and costly task.

Recently, the Governments of Newfoundland and of Canada announced a joint $100 million, five-year fisheries development programme. An important part of this will be to encourage the abandonment of small fishing settlements by giving financial assistance to families who wish to move to larger centres. Each migrating householder will be paid $1,000 plus $200 for each member of his family as well as the actual expenses of moving. If, as it is hoped, 5,000 householders respond to this incentive, the total cost could amount to $12 million.[1]

Population migrations are nothing new for the Atlantic Provinces; a drift from the rural areas (and even small urban communities) to the larger centres has been common for many years. What the announced government scheme envisions, however, is large scale *settlement* migration—moving the people of whole settlements, not just individuals. This scheme is, in fact, an enlargement of a government programme that has assisted the moves of 1504 families from 112 settlements in the decade between 1954 and 1964 (Fig. 1).[2] The present state of research does not permit generalization about the moves. This paper specifically examines one of the first and most concentrated examples of settlement migrations, that of the Central Bonavista Bay area.

*

BONAVISTA BAY: SETTING AND SETTLING

Bonavista Bay is a broad mouthed, archipelago-choked bay on the northeast coast of Newfoundland. Just off its islands, streaming south from the barren coast of Labrador, is

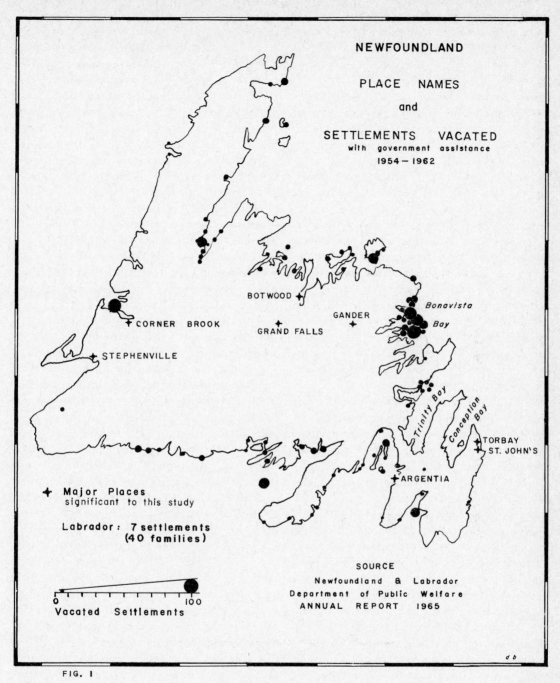

FIG. I

FIG. 1.

the cold Labrador Current. Bleak indeed seems the environment. But each March, the ice floes of the current are alive with the intensively sought whitecoat seals. By May, as the drift and bay ice clears from the coast and only the icebergs slide by, silently marking the Labrador Current, the bay waters warm; the lobsters become active along the shallow, boulder-strewn parts of the coast; and the salmon return from the sea to fight up the rivers to spawn. Then, in June, come the "caplin scull" and the cod.

The migrations of the cod are controlled, in part, by water temperatures and, in part, by the availability of food. They are a cold water fish, but are killed by temperatures below 30° F, so they spend the winters in the deeper waters offshore. In the spring they come closer to shore to feed upon the marine life at the lower junction of deep, warm waters and the shallower Labrador Current. As the vast schools of small silver caplin drive inshore to spawn, the pursuing cod break through the cold layer and swarm along the coast.[3]

In this June run of caplin, the cod can be taken in traps and nets along the shore. Later, glutted with caplin, they sink to the layers just above the cold water, and can be taken by jigging. As the water warms, the cod move deeper and farther off, and must be taken by handlining and lines of trawl. By mid-summer, the salmon and lobster seasons are over, and as winter sets in and the top layers of water cool, the cod return to the much deeper waters offshore.[4]

Toward the end of the seventeenth century, the pressures on the long used fishery resources of the eastern coast of the Avalon Peninsula, the western shore of Conception Bay, and about Cape Bonavista, were substantial. Both English fishing ships and the year-round "planters" moved north (and later, after the French were pushed from the south, in that direction as well) onto less used fishing grounds. As a contemporary noted, "it is certain, the fewer boats are kept in a place, the better the fishing."[5]

Whether these northern sea resources were to be exploited from ships or from small boats, a safe harbour near the fishery was essential. For the ship fisherman it would be a haven from storms, a base supplying water and firewood, and a place to dry fish; for the boatkeeper it would be all these and home as well.

The larger islands, closest to the Labrador Current and the sea resource, were settled first. From these, summer, and later year-round, settlement spread.[6] The headlands and islands of Bonavista Bay are almost everywhere rocky—granites to the north, and

basalts to the south. At the beginnings of settlement, on all but the smallest islands, stunted fir and spruce undoubtedly provided sufficient firewood, and either surface ponds or springs offered potable water. But it was the narrow, deeply gashed coves or the maze of fault line channels called "tickles" that provided the real focus of interest. The nature of sites for buildings of permanent habitation do not appear to have been considered important; if necessary, the settlement could climb from the water on stilts.

Thus, by the beginning of the nineteenth century, settlements grew on the archipelago islands of Bonavista Bay. As population continued to increase, the local cod resource was supplemented by the seal and salmon fisheries and by the second half of the century it had become traditional for many of the islanders, along with thousands of other Newfoundlanders, to set out each spring for a summer schooner fishery off the coast of Labrador.[7]

Until the last third of the nineteenth century, Bonavista Bay attention was focused almost solely on the resources of the sea. The dense fir-spruce-pine forests that clothed the land "up the bay" yielded only "rinds," or bark, for covering sheds and fish, some firewood, the timbers for a schooner, or salmon from their streams. There was no intensive exploitation. But from the long settled Avalon Peninsula, the forest frontier had been marching quickly northward. In Trinity Bay (Fig. 1), the number of saw mills rose from five in 1858 to 39 in 1884.[8] During the 1870's, four large mills were established beside the upper reaches of Freshwater Bay, one of the long, narrow secondary bays of Bonavista Bay (Fig. 2), to tap the pine of that watershed.[9] Settlements grew around them. The physical sites were far superior to those on the islands, for they were upon raised sea terraces, cut into glacial outwash sands and gravels.

By 1892, a narrow gauge railway line had been pushed from St. John's as far north as Bonavista Bay, and gave added impetus to the sawmilling settlements, whose earliest residents had come from the older "headland and island" communities of Bonavista Bay.

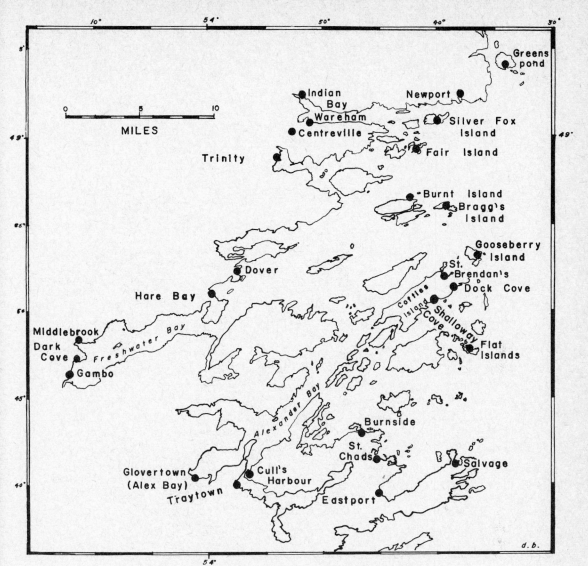

FIG. 2. Central Bonavista Bay place names.

In the two decades after the coming of the railway, more came from the archipelago to swell the established sawmill villages such as Gambo, Mint Brook, Dark Cove, Middle Brook, Alexander Bay (called Glovertown after 1900), and Traytown, and to found such new settlements as Hare Bay, Dover, and Trinity.[10] By 1901, the bay-head regions had a population of 1,200, which was to double in the next decade; the head lands and islands could still boast the much larger population of 5,000, but it remained almost static in the same period.[11]

As the virgin pine forests were exhausted,

the tempo of lumbering slowed somewhat but the establishment of a pulp and paper mill at Grand Falls in 1909, with an attendant movement into the Freshwater Bay watersheds for spruce and fir pulplogs after the 1920's, and a brisk demand for pit-props and butter-tub staves, guaranteed the continued vitality of the settlements "up the bay."[12]

The cold Labrador Current off the outer islands, then, helped provide an environment suitable for cod and clusters of population settled there to exploit it (Fig. 3A). But the same cold current limits tree growth and it

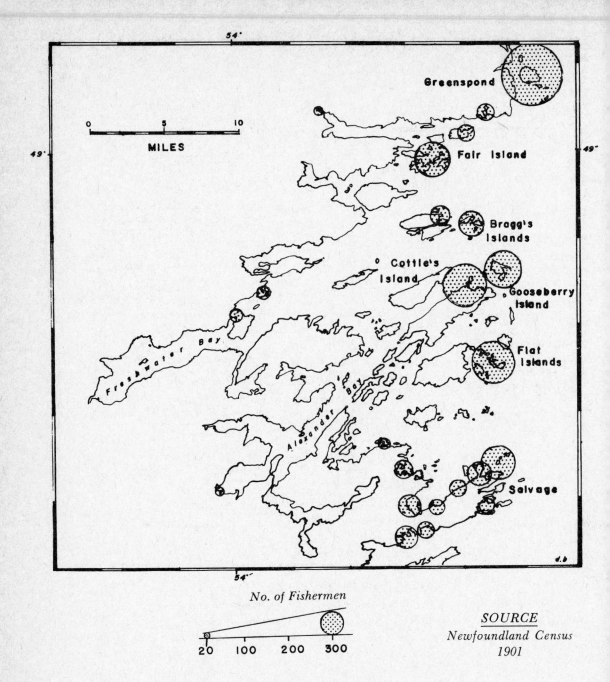

FIG. 3A. Central Bonavista Bay Occupations 1901

is not until one has moved well up the Bay and back from the coast that large trees are favoured; here were established the lumbering and logging communities (Fig. 3B). The archipelago settlements and the inner bay settlements were antithetical in their environments, and in these environments different economies developed. In the fringe land between, virtually no settlement was established.[13]

*

The Land Changes

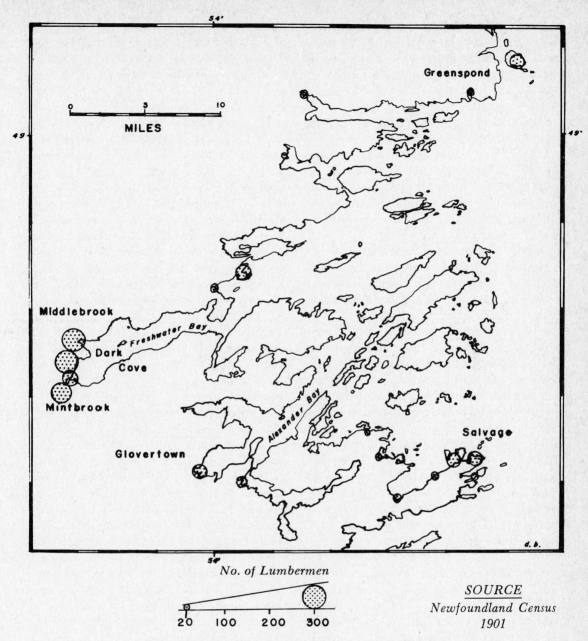

FIG. 3B. Central Bonavista Bay Occupations 1901

SOURCE
*Newfoundland Census
1901*

THE ISLAND WAY OF LIFE

Life in the archipelago settlements was strikingly tuned to the seasons. The period between the beginning of the break up of ice from the Labrador and its clearing from the harbours was one of almost complete isolation for the island settlements. Nearly all physical communication with the mainland ceased and medical emergencies had to be treated by the islanders themselves. But it was a period of considerable activity: seals were caught in nets or daringly hunted over the ice; nets were mended, trawl buoys painted and fishing stages put in order. In the outports that pursued the Labrador floater fishery, such as Fair Islands and Flat Islands[14] (Fig. 2), crews were chosen ("taken in collar," traditionally on May 1) and set to work to "haul over" the schooner (tip her on her side) so that she could be scraped and painted and fully checked out. By June 1, a voyage was made to St. John's to load salt for the summer's fishery, and to get provisions to carry the crew and their families at home until the fall. Shortly after the return to the islands, with all ready for departure, the rum would flow freely, and the schooner would slip from the *tickle* into the open sea with course set for the north.

Meanwhile, inshore fishing had begun around the islands. In the case of some communities, such as Bragg's Islands, most men stayed for the home fishery, but with others, such as Fair Islands and Flat Islands, only the old men and the boys did not go "down north on the Labrador." For those who would stay at home, the fishery began as soon as the ice went out, and each man thereafter put out salmon nets and about a hundred lobster pots until mid July or until the local cod-fishery began with jigging and handlining on the grounds just off from the land, during the last ten days of May. In early June, on days too "blowy" for the fishery, or between the morning and evening haul of nets and pots, or on days when the fish just didn't seem to be there, the men worked on their small potato and vegetable gardens. A site was selected on the few patches of soil or bog near the house, or even on an adjacent islet, and was carefully ditched and ridged, planted, and fertilized with kelp. The use of garden sites on adjacent islets, particularly notable at Flat Islands, dispensed with the necessity of fencing out the cows and sheep that had free run of the settlements.

By June 20, the "caplin scull' had begun as the small silver fish rolled by the millions on-to the beaches to spawn. They were taken by dip nets and by seine, spread upon the potato patches for fertilizer, and covered with earth. Until fall, the gardens would need little more attention than a Sunday afternoon inspection.

But far more important was the arrival of the cod inshore, following the caplin and feeding voraciously upon them. The cod would rush along the coast in great streams, and could easily be taken by the hundreds, in traps set out from the shore, and by trawls baited with caplin. By July 20, they were glutted on caplin—"too logy t'eat"—and fumbled blindly about. The cod traps were brought in and carefully laid out upon the grass or the rock to dry, while the fishing went on with cod gill nets and by jigging. With the warming of the water early in August, the cod moved offshore somewhat, and the nets too were brought in to dry; jigging entered its peak period. During August too, some of the activity shifted up the bay, where men from the islands were engaged in digging mussels, in jigging squid, or in netting herring to gain bait for the fall handlining and trawling. By the end of August, jigging was over; handlining and trawling lasted until rough weather, often in September, ended the year's fishery.

Throughout the summer the "home men" had salted their fish, laid it away in piles for about two weeks, then washed it out and spread it on the flakes to dry in the sun. But the return of the Labrador floaters by late August was the peak of activity for the schooner settlements such as Fair Islands and Flat Islands. Almost every man, woman, and child was engaged. Fish flakes lined nearly every open area of the shoreline, covered gulleys, and climbed cliffs. In a good season, drying fish lay on every foot of flakes, and spread to any available flat rocks. On sunny days the whole of the labour force was bent in a continual turning of the fish to prevent its burning by the sun. Each night, and whenever rain threatened, the fish had to be arranged in piles, and by some means protected from the dampness. A poor day for making fish offered no respite, for there were potatoes to be dug and stored in the turf-walled root cellars, and berries to be gathered from the barrens.

By mid-September, with luck, the fish would be cured, reloaded on the schooner

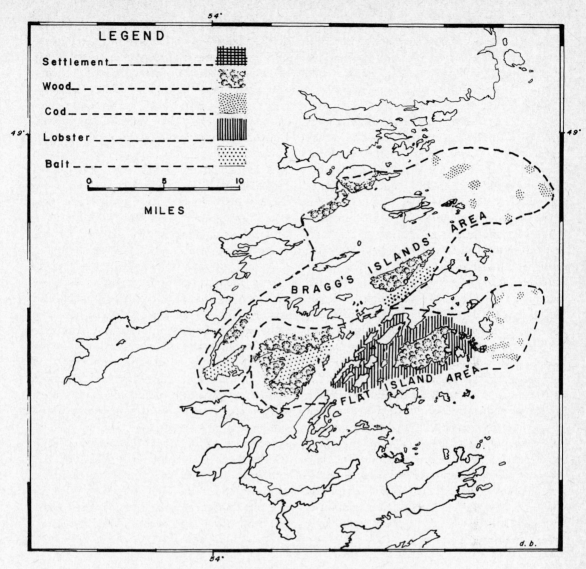

LEGEND

Settlement _ _ _ _ _ _ _ _ _ _ _ _ _

Wood _ _ _ _ _ _ _ _ _ _ _ _ _ _

Cod _ _ _ _ _ _ _ _ _ _ _ _ _ _ _

Lobster _ _ _ _ _ _ _ _ _ _ _ _

Bait _ _ _ _ _ _ _ _ _ _ _ _ _ _

0   5   10

MILES

FIG. 4. Gathering areas for two island groups.

(often with the production of the "home men") and taken to St. John's for sale. If space allowed, each fisherman would accompany his catch, in order to strike the best bargain he could; upon his work depended the greatest part of his family's winter food supply, which he brought back in place of the fish. This annual fall trip to St. John's was most common in the settlements that relied heavily upon the Labrador fishery; those that pursued the local fishery depended more upon their local merchant for supplies.

For the people of the islands least engaged in the Labrador fishery, such as Bragg's Is-

lands, late September was a slower time. Some washed out and dried the last of the fish; some cut a little firewood on the larger islands adjacent to the west; some cut timber for boats on the islands farther up the bay; some made ready to leave the settlement for winter work in the woods. Generally, this was a slack period when the house could be painted, or when a prediction of the severity of the coming winter could be advanced.

But for all the islands, the first of November saw the winter's work of gathering firewood begin in earnest. Whenever weather permitted, the men threaded their motor boats through the tickles and channels to the inner islands and unsettled parts of the local mainland, each settlement using its own distinct wood gathering area (Fig. 4). The balsam fir and white spruce, usually about 4 to 8 inches at the butt, were trimmed to sticks of 12 to 14 feet and stacked in teepee-like piles until the first big snow. With the snow, the men went again to the woods, to bring the wood to the shoreline on "hand-slides", small woodsleds hauled by either one or two men. (Only the mainland settlements kept horses). Slob ice drifted in from the Labrador in the early part of the year, and it was not until this had departed some time in May that this supply of next year's firewood could be taken by boat to the settlement. The women were kept busy with the spinning of wool and the knitting of socks, sweaters and caps. While waiting for the ice to go, the yearly round of activities started again with the preparation of gear for the coming spring's fishery.

The way of life of the islands illustrates the close ties of the island settlements to their physical environment, and the surprisingly large area over which a small population had to range for its commercial production and associated needs, and for subsistence materials. Each settlement had rather particular "gathering areas" (Fig. 4). The familiarity of the islanders with these areas would help direct their migrations of the 1950's.

The transportation ties between the islands and the outside world also were to give direction to the later settlement migrations. Early in the twentieth century, coastal steamers began to ply the Newfoundland bays with freight, passengers, and mail, and by mid-century, Bonavista Bay had weekly service. But this was supplied only during the ice-free season. In the winter months transportation was difficult; mail, for example, came by rail to Alexander Bay and Gambo, and from there it reached the other settlements variously through the years by a child's wagon pulled by the mailman, by ox cart, by dog team, by row boat, and by trap skiff.[15]

It was probably sometime in the 1930's[16] that a regular boat service began between the northern mainland settlements, the outer islands, and the bayhead communities. The more northerly communities sent passenger boats to the railway at Gambo, while the southerly islands were similarly connected with Glovertown. Hare Bay and Burnside became the nearest points of land accessibility, to the northern and southern island settlements respectively, and were used whenever the ice on the inner bays was too difficult for the boats. Glovertown, Gambo, Hare Bay and Burnside became familiar to residents of the islands, who were forced to wait for the ice to clear or the sea to calm, when returning from trips to St. John's.

*

THE PROBLEMS OF THE ARCHIPELAGO

The fishery of the archipelago became a marginal operation. The first move into the area had been to avoid the crowded fishery to the south; but population had continued to increase (both in Newfoundland as a whole and in Bonavista Bay in particular) and at an especially rapid rate since the opening of the nineteenth century.[17] The islands had expanded their resource horizons by embracing the Labrador floater fishery. Later, they spawned new settlements at the

head of the Bay to take out timber.

The move to the mill villages was a clear reflection of the marginal character of the shore fishery. The governor's reports of the 1880's and 1890's refer specifically to the pressures of population on Newfoundland's shore fishery, and to the acute depression caused by both poor catches and low market prices.[18] The railway that so spurred the mill communities was largely an attempt to open up the interior to reduce dependance upon

The Land Changes

the fisheries.

The staple of the fishing industry was salted dried cod, of which the majority was marketed in Spain, Portugal, Italy, and Greece—countries from which Newfoundland took virtually no produce. The necessary triangular trading connections were precariously balanced, and a great number of factors might operate, and indeed did so, to reduce Newfoundland's dried fish markets. During the depression of the 1930's the markets of Newfoundland's customers declined, and so too did their purchasing capacity. Many countries attempted policies of self-sufficiency. During the period also, other nations such as Iceland and Norway became powerful competitors with Newfoundland, as they developed newly-equipped, more efficient fishing industries. Partial compensation was found in expansion of markets in the Caribbean but in sum, by the 1930's, Newfoundland dried codfish had become extremely difficult to market.[19] Cod prices were unusually high during World War I, but by 1931 they were little more than one-quarter of the war years' levels. Even with government aids, the industry probably operated at a loss during much of the 1930's.[20] In such straits was the Newfoundland economy, that self-government was replaced by a British Commission in 1934. But, even in the face of such widespread depression, the islanders of Bonavista Bay were probably better off than, for instance, pulpwood loggers; at least the fisherman could produce his own food.

Newfoundland's strategic position marked it for prominence in World War II.[21] Canadian troops either established or manned air bases at Gander, Botwood, Torbay, and Goose Bay in Labrador, while the United States began developments at Stephenville, Argentia, and St. John's, (Fig. 1). At the peak of construction, these air and naval bases employed 19,000 Newfoundlanders, many of whom stayed on through the war, engaged in service, maintenance and expansion.[22] Furthermore, in order to supply primary industrial products to a western Europe whose normal supply lines had been interrupted, Newfoundland increased exploitation of pulpwood, pit-props, and base metals. In Bonavista Bay, for instance, Hare Bay became a centre of pit-prop extraction, and offered considerable employment. In 1944 and 1945, as a consequence, the whole settlement of Gooseberry Islands moved to the local mainland (largely to Hare Bay), thus foreshadowing by a decade the more extensive moves to come. But the other island settlements remained, though many of their men were working on the mainland. In the later years of the war, Britain's need for food created the Combined Foods Board, which allocated fishery production from Newfoundland, and thus enabled the trade to set minimum prices in advance each spring. Fish export prices rose by about three and a half times between 1938 and 1945.[23] With all of these factors operating, the economic condition of Newfoundland was profoundly altered. From an average yearly deficit of $1,600,000 before the war, the Newfoundland Commission of Government moved to an average yearly surplus of $7,000,000 following the war. In 1944–45, "not one dollar was required for able-bodied relief".[24]

The boom times continued to some extent after the war. The bases still employed many Newfoundlanders for maintenance and, in Bonavista Bay, pit-prop logging changed to logging for pulpwood, and continued at a high rate. Fish prices remained high.

The year 1949 marked two major events, the Confederation of Newfoundland with Canada and the devaluation of the Pound Sterling. With Confederation, Canada's scheme of social payments was applied to Newfoundland. Old-age pension rates were raised more than ten-fold and family allowance payments of more than $1,000,000 monthly were introduced.[25] Unemployment insurance benefits were welcomed by the Newfoundland workers since a large part of their employment was seasonal. But, importantly, unemployment insurance did not apply to self-employed fishermen until 1957. The fishery, largely consisting of self-employed men, was thus made considerably less attractive.

In September, 1949, Great Britain dropped

the value of the Pound Sterling from $4.03 (U.S.) to $2.80 (U.S.).[26] Newfoundland, like Canada, had never been a member of the sterling area; but her more important fish customers dealt in sterling and became highly uncertain markets.[27] It would seem that although there were years in which salt cod was difficult to market, financial arrangements by Britain and Canada prevented a much larger collapse of markets.[28] However, prices did fall somewhat; in the highly un-stable Labrador floater fishery, a large part of Bonavista Bay's island economy, they fell enough to cut profit margins drastically.[29] The heads-of-bays settlements at least provided seasonal employment (and off-season unemployment insurance benefits). Some with motor roads, offered the conveniences of the twentieth century, now well appreciated by Newfoundlanders to whom the bases had brought a taste of the life of urban Canada and the United States.

*

THE SETTLEMENT MIGRATIONS[30]

Young people had been leaving the island settlements to seek their fortunes elsewhere for years, but for the head of a family to undertake such a move was a major and serious undertaking. The real property a family must leave behind was of uncertain value; likely, they would be moving with little or no capital. For a man to start life anew was a big step, but each man's move was one that made it much easier for others to do likewise. The example of Gooseberry Islands in 1944 was important, and each move thereafter reduced the indecision caused by novelty. But in each outport it took the personal decision of one or two leaders to sway the community to the idea of moving.

The imbalance between the economic opportunity on the islands and that on the local mainland was basic to movement. But it was a combination of social factors that actually set the minds of the leaders: difficulties of obtaining school teachers; uncertain transportation to the mainland, especially during spring ice breakup; and unreliable medical services, due to transportation difficulties. For the islanders in the 1950's, these conditions compared unfavourably with the improving conditions up the bay. Since the timing and direction of movement of the islanders to the local mainland was dependant upon changing conditions in the latter area, we will consider each community in order of time of move.

Newport

Paradoxically, the first of the post-war settlement migrations of Central Bonavista Bay was not from an island, but from the local mainland (Fig. 2). Newport was small (maximum population less than 200) and isolated. It had few hopes of a motor road, and its men, from the war years on, had been working on the military bases. When, in 1950, the Newport merchant learned of an opportunity to take over a business in Hare Bay, then at the roadhead, he moved out. Others began moving, and the declining settlement had increasing difficulty in attracting teachers. By 1952, most of Newport had moved to Hare Bay and Dover, where pulpwood cutting was offering considerable employment. About half of the houses were floated intact to their new sites buoyed with empty oil drums (see Bragg's Islands, below), while the rest were dismantled, rafted and reassembled.

Bragg's Islands

During the war, Bragg's Islands had lost few men to the military bases. Most kept at work on the inshore fishing grounds, probably stimulated by the fixed minimum prices for fish. But with the much better living conditions developing in the post-war years in the settlements of the local mainland, well-qualified teachers no longer wished to take positions in small, isolated, island outports. Even some of Bragg's Islands' own young people went to teach in local mainland settlements, and their parents began to spend the winters there and the summers fishing from the islands. By 1953, two of the community's religious leaders moved to the mainland, one to Hare Bay, the other to Dark Cove, to take up the dual life of woods workers in the winter and fishermen from the islands in the summer.

Difficulties in education and loss of religious leadership were serious matters to a community that had sent out prominent people in numbers far out of proportion to its small population. A third Bragg's Islands merchant put the problem before the Newfoundland Government, who proposed that a petition be circulated on Bragg's Islands to gain the approval of *all* families to a proposal of *total* abandonment. If approval were gained, the province would supply all necessary equipment for the move, including tractors and cradles. In places where it was found impractical to move houses, a grant of costs up to a maximum of $600 was suggested.

Perhaps eighty percent of the Bragg's Islands people did not wish to move. But the merchant and community leader along with seven or eight other families decided to move anyway. They first considered a new settlement site at Cat Bay, their old mussel gathering ground (Fig. 4), which was on the local mainland, and thus offered the possibility of a motor road. It was felt better, however, to move to an established settlement, and after an unsuccessful attempt to obtain suitable land for a shop at Dark Cove, a place was found near relatives (brought by employment opportunities in the early decades of the century) at Glovertown.

By October of 1954, Bragg's Islands had lost three of their secular and religious leaders, and only one small shop remained. So heavily do the people of a Newfoundland outport rely on their traditional leaders and especially their merchant(s), that suddenly robbed of them, they would find it difficult to carry on. Most decided to vacate. They accepted the government offer of a cash grant (payable only if *all* in the settlement moved) and engaged a community contractor to carry out the move.

Of the more than eighty families that were to make the move—to Glovertown, Dark Cove, and Hare Bay—thirty homes were to be launched and floated to Hare Bay. So rough was the terrain of the island house sites, however, that all but six or seven were dismantled and rafted to their new mainland sites. The operation of floating an entire house was not novel; it had been done sporadically for years, but by now was being developed into an efficient system. First, a slipway of cribbing was built from the water's edge to the house. With the help of a block and tackle, both fore and aft, the house was moved to the shore. Furniture was either removed completely or stored on the second floor, while the downstairs floor was covered with empty, sealed oil drums, wedged in place by sticks from the ceiling. At low tide the house was moved to the tidal shore and was floated on the incoming tide. Leaving the islands as early as possible in the morning, and using eight or ten fishing boats as power, the house would usually arrive at its new harbour by dusk of the same evening. With high tide the next morning, the house would be dragged ashore and taken on skids to a prepared building site.

By the fall of 1955, the Bragg's Islands settlement sites were only broken bits of old lumber, among which, the church, long a reference for the mariner, had been left as a monument. For the first few years, many of the islanders went back to fish for the summer but gradually, new occupational emphases appeared. The Bragg's Islanders in Hare Bay continued to interest themselves mainly in fishing, with a secondary emphasis on logging; those in Dark Cove depended on logging, with a secondary emphasis on carpentry work; in Glovertown, fishermen and construction workers dominated the occupational lists of the islanders, but loggers and retired men were not far behind. Only a few years before, the vast majority of the Bragg's Islanders had voted against a move; now, they had moved, and most of them had taken landward jobs. In the process, they had helped establish the precedent for government financial assistance that would be developed into the so-called "centralization" programme.

Flat Islands

During the war, Flat Islanders began to find work off the islands, and by the mid-1950's fully one-half of the work force found its main income from non-fishing jobs. Houses were closed for the winter while the family was working away on the mainland; gradually fewer and fewer returned. The abandoned houses impressed those left behind with the settlement's decline; many began to talk of leaving.

In 1954, an island merchant moved to Conception Bay. In 1955 and 1956 two Flat Islands families who had friends or relatives in Glovertown and who had become familiar with the community through long waits for the boat to the islands, floated their houses to that mainland site. Here they could be close enough to friends and relatives and yet still be in constant touch with the road and railway.

In the summer of 1956 many more moved out; in 1957 great numbers prepared to leave, and total evacuation was accepted. It must be remembered that no one would receive government assistance unless every family agreed to move, and that those who moved first would not receive assistance unless the migration was completed within two years.

Of 199 families who received assistance for the move, more than half went to Burnside, St. Chad's, Glovertown, or Eastport— settlements that had communication ties with Flat Islands or where relatives lived. Of these, approximately a third worked as carpenters, especially in Gander, a third continued fishing, from Burnside and the islands, and a third retired. About twenty percent of those who moved went to St. John's and vicinity where they were employed as carpenters and other tradesmen. The remainder scattered. For those who went long distances their Flat Islands houses were worth little and were sold, if possible, for prices varying from $100 to $300 to be moved to another outport.

Fair Islands

As on Flat Islands, local mainland jobs drew many men away from Fair Islands during the war, and schooner skippers found it most difficult to get crews. But by the mid-1950's, half of the men were working away at construction, and almost all of the others were cutting and loading pulpwood at nearby Indian Bay.[31] The schooners were beached and left to rot.

At that time, the abandonment of the archipelago was obviously taking place. The Bragg's Islands settlements had gone and Flat Islands were being abandoned quickly. But all of these places had moved to settlements with motor roads. For the Fair Islanders, the move would be long, and there were few family ties with such settlements. Trinity, the settlement spawned by Fair Islanders early in the century, was as isolated as Fair Islands themselves.

However, by the mid-1950's the Government of Newfoundland determined to press roads to link the most populous outports as soon as funds became available. Cutting and grubbing on the road to the Badgers Quay— the Wesleyville area of northern Bonavista Bay—began in 1955, and by 1958 the last gap, between Trinity and Hare Bay, was closed.[32]

Between 1955 and 1958, almost a dozen families moved from Fair Islands without their houses, the majority of them to Hare Bay for woods work. In the latter year, the first house left Fair Islands, buoyed with 38 empty oil drums, to occupy a site on the new highway near Wareham. The owner was a Labour Union delegate whose work took him among the loggers of Fair Island working at Indian Bay. The next year twelve houses were floated in and strung along the

TABLE I

SETTLEMENT MIGRATION IN CENTRAL BONAVISTA BAY, 1951–1961[38]

Move from:	Wareham	Centreville	Dover	Hare Bay	Dark Cove	Glovertown	Eastport	St. Chad's	Burnside	Others	Outside	Total
Newport			11	18							2	31
Bragg's Islands				25	21	29				4	5	84
Flat Islands						17	12	12	23	13	42	119
Fair Islands	16	69		9						25	22	141
Silver Fox Is.	16		10	11						7	1	45
Burnt Island				11						10		21
Totals	32	69	32	63	21	46	12	12	23	59	72	441

Number of Families. Columns under "Bonavista Bay": Wareham, Centreville, Dover, Hare Bay, Dark Cove, Glovertown, Eastport, St. Chad's, Burnside. Columns under "Outside": Others. "Total" final column.

highway. By the end of July, 1959, initialled boards marked land claims for almost a mile along the road, and were beginning to appear in a second range back.[33]

The other island settlers had been absorbed by, or added to, established local mainland settlements, but the Fair Islanders had decided upon a completely new site on Crown land. The provincial planners agreed that the islanders had chosen both a good location relative to their work, and the best site as well, but they were unhappy about the impending strip development.[34] The islanders made it clear however, that each wanted his lot to front on a road. The planners drafted and laid out a planned settlement containing approximately one hundred residential lots 100′ × 200′, as well as a central area for church, school, and commercial establishments. A circular made the new plan known on the islands.[35]

By October, 1959, the Fair Islands settlements had been reduced to little more than thirty families, the majority of whom intended to remain. The new mainland settlement of Centreville, as it was called, had completed its school by the next fall, and settled down to the new life. But by May of 1961, all those left on Fair Islands agreed to move to Centreville through the summer. As they moved, they were joined by twenty fishing families from Silver Fox Island, who spurned the planned site, and squatted along the shore near Wareham, because the new site would not allow them to be near their fishing stages and boats.[36] Centreville held mostly Fair Islanders then, and Fair Islanders went mostly to Centreville. This was a full settlement migration, including the people, buildings and the spirit of the community.

Summary

By the summer of 1961, the outer fringe of Central Bonavista Bay, which fifteen years before had harboured 3,500 people in more than a dozen settlements, had only 1,550 people in the two communities of Greenspond and Cottel's Island (Figs. 5A and B).[37] During the settlement migrations of the decade following 1951, almost 500 families had moved from the now abandoned settlements of the outer islands. The majority had moved with all their belongings, including houses, shops, and sheds. Table I summarizes the magnitude and the direction of the moves.

*

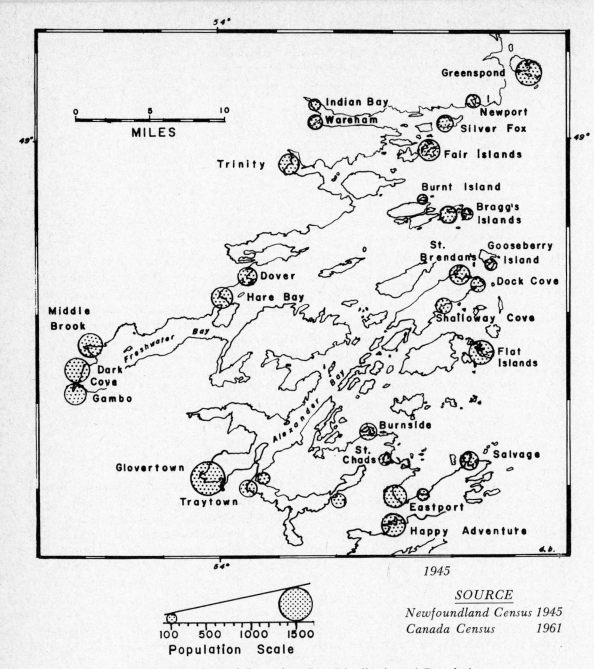

FIG. 5A. *Central Bonavista Bay Distribution of Population*

1945

SOURCE
Newfoundland Census 1945
Canada Census 1961

READJUSTMENTS OF 1964

Those who thought that the settlement migrations were to be a final outcome of the landward attentions, were to be mistaken. The pendulum of employment that swung between land and sea and that had pointed to the heads of bays settlements at least since World War II, has swung back to the sea. During the dry summer of 1961, a fire devastated one thousand square miles of the Bonavista Bay forest—almost the total resource north of Gambo. In many areas only sand and bare rock is left; in others, regeneration and

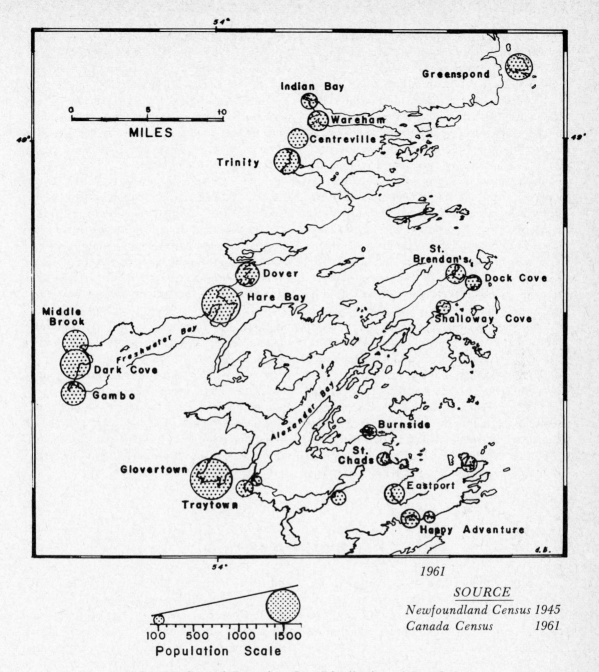

SOURCE
Newfoundland Census 1945
Canada Census 1961

FIG. 5B. Central Bonavista Bay Distribution of Population

growth to a commercial forest will take perhaps eighty years. Salvage operations of fire-killed timber occupied a good number of loggers until the summer of 1964, but after that it was understood that much of the logging in Bonavista Bay was finished. That which remained, south and west of Gambo, was being so highly mechanized that few men were needed. Furthermore, general labouring and construction jobs were becoming more and more difficult to obtain, perhaps because of greater competition. The migrant islanders then, had all modern conveniences, but too few jobs.

The lowered dried salt fish prices of the early 1950's, however, had yielded, by the

1960's, to the highest yet known. Salmon and lobster prices were also at a new high. A move back to the fisheries began. The islands and bays buzzed with small outboard motor boats, announcing a modernized salmon and lobster fishery. Abandoned houses and sheds on the islands were patched up and used as summer quarters for the codfishery, pursued with new and larger trap boats, many built with power tools during the winter on the local mainland. During the summer of 1964, Bragg's Islands had fifteen men fishing; Silver Fox, eight; Fair Islands, six; and Flat Islands, ten. Many brought their families with them. Whereas, in the move to the landward jobs, the women and children had turned happily from the back-breaking work of making fish, many now have returned to the islands in the summer to split and salt fish, to turn them on the flakes, and to work vegetable patches. "It is like a summer vacation," some have said, "for a change is as good as a rest."

A swing back to the Labrador Fishery has also begun. Whereas, in 1963 two schooners went to the Labrador with former Fair Islands men and one left from Glovertown, in 1964 four went with Fair Islanders from the Centreville area, three with Fair Islanders and Bragg's Islanders from Hare Bay, and one from Glovertown. Two more 130 ton vessels were under construction at Trinity and at Hare Bay. In 1963, 39 percent of the heads of families of Centreville were working in logging nearby, and 11 percent were fishing on the Labrador; in 1964, only 19 percent were logging but 27 percent were on the coast of Labrador.[39]

In the Cottel's Island settlement, (St. Brendan's, Dock Cove, Shalloway Cove), a similar shift of occupations back to the fishery has occurred. In 1955, 73 percent were engaged in labour, service and maintenance, mostly away from the community, while only 19 percent were fishing.[40] In 1964, only 42 percent were in the former occupations, but 40 percent were fishing. The men here are "stationers", travelling north by coastal steamer, and working in small boats from the shore.

In sum then, the fishing economy of Bonavista Bay, using local grounds, the Labrador floaters and Labrador stationers, is witnessing a rebirth. The bay itself is experiencing the uncrowded fishing from the islands that marked the beginnings of settlement more than two centuries ago.

*

CONCLUSIONS

Through more than two centuries, the population of Bonavista Bay has been making precise adjustments to exploit both its local resource bases and any opportunities available further away. Before they had been settled for a century, the archipelago islands had produced a population that far exceeded what the local inshore fishery could support; they had found it necessary to utilize the seal, salmon and Labrador fisheries, and had spawned new settlements at the head of the bay to take out timber. The pressures of population kept the island fishery marginal and, in times of low prices for fish, sub-marginal.

During World War II, and for a decade and more after, employment on the local mainland, especially in military, maintenance and logging was plentiful; the majority of the men of the Bonavista Bay Islands left their families for weekdays or for months to profit thereby. The much improved financial situation of Newfoundland after the war, and Confederation with Canada in 1949, helped make the local mainland more attractive. Unemployment insurance benefits were available in most of the landward jobs, but self-employed fishermen were not eligible; motor roads were being pushed to link the local mainland outports, providing reliable ties to job opportunities, to regional and consolidated schools, and to improved medical

The Land Changes

services; line electric power, television, and many more "modern conveniences" seemed sure to come to the local mainland.

But for the small island settlements, there was little hope of motor roads or line electric power. The improved conditions on the mainland were pulling teachers away, and the traditional medical services were unsatisfactory by local mainland standards. In 1949 too, the devaluation of the Pound Sterling lowered prices for salt dried cod, and the uncertainties of continued markets led to a seemingly permanent death for the long practised but long marginal Labrador floater cod-fishery, a mainstay of the Bonavista Bay fishing economy.

In the post war years then, most of the men of Bonavista Bay were finding their employment on the local mainland. Island leaders, especially merchants, saw that the improved social opportunities of the local mainland settlements could not be extended to their small islands, and began to move their families. The merchants or leaders of the Newfoundland outport are fundamental to its viability. As they moved, so the rest of the settlement soon followed. In 1954, the Newfoundland Government began offering assistance for the moves, or a cash grant of $600 per family, if the whole of the settlement would agree to move to a better location within two years. Though some members of a moving community wished to stay on the islands, social pressures were usually great enough to ensure a total settlement migration within the two year limit. Since buildings left on an abandoned island would be of little worth, they were usually taken to the new settlement site, either floated intact, or dismantled, rafted, and rebuilt. The local mainland settlement to which the islanders moved was determined by the direction of earlier migrations of relatives, familiarity gained through traditional activities such as wood gathering, communication or transportation ties, and employment.

It should be noted, however, that the moves of Bonavista Bay have not been consciously in response to the government's programme of"centralization". At the same time, many of the goals of the programme are being achieved. Consolidated and regional schools in local mainland settlements can offer, by means of specialized teachers and school buses, a better education to a wider area; shorter electric power and telephone lines can link greater numbers of people; hospitals can serve larger areas more efficiently by road than by sea.

The recent shift of employment back to the fishery is significant. It not only demonstrates how dependant the Newfoundlander is upon economic change beyond his control, but also, and more importantly, how quick he is to exploit these changes. Few New World people seem as tradition-minded as the outport Newfoundlander, but he is none-the-less surprisingly capable of adapting to large and sudden economic and social changes. Finally, it should be noted, that both economic and social changes were necessary to dislodge the islander from his old settlement. Though economic changes have taken him back to the islands to fish, it is unlikely that social changes will direct him there to live.

*

FOOTNOTES

1 "Bounty for Leaving Outports," *Financial Post* (June 19, 1965), p. 52; "Ottawa, Nfld., Set Up Program," *Hamilton Spectator* (March 5, 1965).

2 Newfoundland and Labrador, Dept. of Public Welfare, *Annual Report for the Year Ended March 31, 1965* (St. John's, 1965), pp. 77–80.

3 Newfoundland Fisheries Development Committee, *Report* (St. John's, 1953), pp. 25–28.

4 *Ibid.* and field enquiry. "Jigging" is a method of fishing in which an unbaited hook, weighted with a cast lead image of a caplin, is jerked rythmically in the water, hooking the curious cod. "Handlining" is similar but uses a hook baited with caplin, squid, herring, etc. "Lines of trawl" are long lines, suspended from buoys to which many baited hooks are attached.

5 Wm. Coch to Col. Norris, Sept. 7, 1698, cited in D. W. Prowse, *A History of Newfoundland* (London, 1895), p. 280.

6 C. G. Head, *Settlement Migration in Central Bonavista Bay* (*Unpublished M. A. Thesis, McMaster University*, 1964), pp. 12–14.

7 *Ibid.,* pp. 14–20.

8 Great Britain, Colonial Office; (Hereafter, C.O.), 199/54; 199/80.

9 Some material on the history of Newfoundland logging is found in Newfoundland, *Report of the Newfoundland Royal Commission on Forestry* (St. John's 1955), pp. 187–206.

10 Field enquiry.

11 *Newfoundland Census* (1901, 1911).

12 Field enquiry and *Commission on Forestry* (as in fn. 9 above).

13 The settlements of the Salvage Peninsula are possible exceptions to this. Before 1900 they were overwhelmingly sea-looking, but as fishery resources became overcrowded they looked more and more inland until today, with good road ties, they can be considered more a part of the inland settlement group than the headland group.

14 For the sake of clarity the name of the single largest settlement has been given to groups of settlements that can be thought of as "communities."

15 Field enquiry.

16 The writer was not able to find supplementary documentary material to better date the boat services described by local residents.

17 Population statistics for the eighteenth century are summarized in Great Britain, House of Commons, Second Report on the State of the Trade to Newfoundland, 1793, App. 6 H. (Reprinted in *Reports from Committees of the House of Commons),* Vol. X (1803), pp. 429–32, and for the nineteenth century in D. W.

Prowse, *op. cit.,* p. 702.

18 C.O. 199/82, p. 3.

19 R. A. Mackay, ed., *Newfoundland: Economic Diplomatic and Strategic Studies* (Toronto, 1946), pp. 140–45.

20 *Ibid.,* p. 142.

21 A. R. M. Lower, "Transition to Atlantic Bastion," Chapt. XIV of Mackay, *op. cit.*

22 *Ibid.,* p. 221.

23 Newfoundland Fisheries Development Committee, *Report,* p. 23.

24 A. B. Perlin, *The Story of Newfoundland* (St. John's, 1959), pp. 51–52.

25 J. W. Day, *Newfoundland, "The Fortress Isle"* (Gov't. of Nfld., The Brunswick Press, c. 1959) n. p.

26 The Bank of Nova Scotia, *Monthly Review,* New Series, No. 40, "Devaluation of the Pound Sterling" (Sept. 1949).

27 *Ibid.,* New Series, No. 37, "Newfoundland: An Economic Survey" (June, 1949).

28 *Monthly Review, op. cit.,* No's. 47, 60, 73, 84.

29 W. A. Black, "The Labrador Floater Codfishery," *Annals of the Association of American Geographers* (Sept., 1960), p. 295.

30 Unless otherwise noted, the material for this section was gathered through intensive field interviewing in the summer of 1964. The writer is indebted to Mr. K. M. Harnum, Assistant Director of Social Assistance and Old Age Assistance, Newfoundland Department of Welfare, for a compilation of families assisted in moving.

31 *Electors' Lists,* 1955, and field enquiry.

32 Personal communication, Newfoundland Dept. of Highways.

33 Personal communication, Newfoundland Dept. of Municipal Affairs, Provincial Planning Office.

34 *Ibid.*

35 *Ibid.*

36 *Ibid.*

37 *Census of Newfoundland* (1945); *Census of Canada* (1961).

38 The data for Newport was from field inquiry; that for the other settlements from source as in fn. 30, and does not, therefore, include families who moved prior to each settlement's two year period in which assistance was made available.

39 Field enquiry, 1964, and C. G. Head, *Community Geographical Surveys,* Institute of Social and Economic Research, Memorial University of Newfoundland (St. John's, 1963), p. 58.

40 Field enquiry, 1964, and *Electors' Lists,* 1955.

8

New Light From Labrador-Ungava[*]

F. KENNETH HARE

This paper is respectfully dedicated to Brian Haywood and André Grenier, of the McGill Sub-Arctic Research Laboratory, who lost their lives on the Korok River in northern Labrador-Ungava while engaged in field research.

[*] *From* Annals of the Association of American Geographers, *Vol. 54, (1964), pp. 459-476. Reprinted by permission. Revised by the author.*

What does a geographer do when confronted with empty, virgin territory? Does he have a function in a man-deserted world? Ackerman's systems-analysis concept of our field[2] is of little help in a country like Canada, where less than twenty per cent of the land surface supports any form of direct, nonsubsistence economic activity, and where there were still, only fifteen years ago, compact areas of 200,000 square miles without a single settler. Our answer at McGill has been straightforward. In such a country the geographer becomes once again an explorer. He reverts to an earlier mold, though with modern technology to assist him. He becomes not a social scientist, not a physical or biological scientist, but simply a scientist-in-the-round, concerned to discover the unknown in territories where ordinary scientific categories have little meaning. There are, of course, areas of Canada that are closely settled, and where modern economic and historical geography can be practiced. We have left these areas, for the most part, to others. At McGill, our objective has been to explore the empty areas.[3]

Most of these neglected lands are arctic or subarctic. Canada shares such environments with Alaska, the Soviet Union, and the Scandinavian countries (including Iceland and Greenland). Accordingly, our work has been along lines parallel to that of geographers in those countries. In strictly professional terms, I am in closer communion with the geographers of Finland and Sweden than I am with most of those of Britain or the United States. We have consciously tried to foster these northern connections. The head office of the Arctic Institute of North America is on our campus, and I would like to pay tribute to the help it has given us, especially in its magnificent library and map collection, and in the links it has provided with the scientific work in the northern lands.

My own special interest has been in the Labrador Peninsula, or Labrador-Ungava as I prefer to call it. This immense wilderness is an anomaly on the world map. All 500,000 square miles of its massive bulk lie in northern mid-latitudes, where Europe's population is densest. The heavily traveled St. Lawrence route to Europe parallels its southern shore, and it lies close to the main Atlantic air lanes. Yet in 1948, when I began to work on the area, it was empty and undeveloped. Goose Bay Airport was one of the loneliest stations in the hemisphere. We knew very little about the interior, as regards even its simple hydrography. Politically it lay in two countries, Canada and Newfoundland, the boundary between them tracing an arbitrary course across the interior,[4] although the subsequent union of the two countries in 1949 made the boundary merely interprovincial. Above all, Labrador-Ungava possessed a harsh climate, an ice-choked Atlantic coast, and a surface rendered so chaotic by recent glaciation, that it repelled all advances by the rising industrial economy of Canada. In 1948 it seemed that Canada still agreed with Cartier's disparaging comment: *"j'estime mieux que aultrement, que c'est la terre que Dieu donna a Cayn"*.

Now, of course, light has broken through. The interior is reasonably well known scientifically, though much remains to be done. The extraction of iron ore has moved Canada into the forefront of supplying countries. Railways penetrate deeply into the interior. And the peninsula's immense hydroelectric potential is at last being tapped. Labrador-Ungava still contains large stretches of wilderness. But it has become vital to Canada's economy, and is becoming increasingly important to the American. Hence, I want to do two things: to tell you something of the work my colleagues and I have done in exploring the interior, and to comment on the present economic developments. My punning title emphasizes these two points: I offer you intellectual light, in the shape of filled-in maps where formerly there was only blank paper; and light as Consolidated Edison understands it, since before long the Hamilton River power will probably be fed to New York.

*

EXPLORATION AS RECONNAISSANCE SURVEY

We were confronted with an almost unknown landmass equal in area to France, Spain, Portugal, and the British Isles. We were few in numbers, and poor in resources, especially financial support. It was imperative that we plan our attack wisely.

We decided that the exploration must involve these stages:

1) completion of topographic base maps adequate for mapping of the important distributions;

2) a selective program of fieldwork to establish a) the categories of surface type, physiographic, and vegetation, to be encountered; and b) keys for air-photo interpretation;

3) a peninsula-wide program of air-photo interpretation, based on the keys of stage 2), to be carried out at the National Air-photo Library, Ottawa, on scales appropriate to reconnaissance survey, and within our capacity in time and skill;

4) a synthesis of these results, involving a) the establishment of primary regional divisions and of generic relationships; and b) the identification of key problems and key areas for field study of these problems; and

5) a second field program aimed at the problems identified in stage 4). In practice these have included a) the history of deglaciation within the peninsula, and of the subsequent establishment of forest vegetation; b) the present extent and dynamic status of permafrost and peri-glacial processes; and c) the climatology of the peninsula, especially as regards the energy and moisture balances of its surface.

We were influenced in our choice of subject by the knowledge that both governmental and private geological exploration was already in progress, and that a second research group, under J.T. Wilson, was engaged in mapping the structural geology by similar methods. We also knew that the federal government of Canada was planning to extend high-altitude vertical photography to the southern and central areas of Labrador-Ungava in the summers of 1948, 1949, 1950, and 1951, and to rephotograph the remaining areas by trimetrogon methods. Accordingly, we decided to concentrate on natural vegetation and physiography, neither of which were to be fully covered elsewhere, and both of which were of high geographical interest.

Stage 1): Basic Topographic Survey

The National Topographic Series maps available in 1948 were simple eight-mile-to-the-inch (1:506,880) sheets showing streams, lakes, and coastlines—essentially the hydrography. There was no depiction of relief, and only a crude estimate (by spot heights) of altitudes of prominent hilltops. The southern and eastern sheets were based on photogrammetric interpretation of wartime trimetrogon photography. Substantial areas, especially in the northwest, were almost devoid of detail; on several sheets only sketches of the main watercourses, transcribed from travelers' notebooks, were available. The minimum basis for interpretive geographical survey did not exist.

In 1948-1951 the extensive program of vertical photography was carried out by the federal government, partly by a wing of the R.C.A.F., partly by private companies under contract. This photography covered all southern and eastern areas and the Labrador Trough. Trimetrogon coverage was revised. The vertical photography was carried out at heights between 20,000 and 35,000 feet corresponding (with six-inch lenses) to photo scales of 1:40,000 to 1:70,000. Trimetrogon photography was at 15,000 feet. High quality was maintained and, by 1953, when we began the interpretive phase of our work, virtually all areas had been covered, and the photographs filed under easy access conditions at the National Airphoto Library, Ottawa.

Since 1951, the Department of Mines and Technical Surveys has completed the eight-mile-to-the-inch hydrography series, and these served us as the indispensable base maps for our interpretation. We found it possible, even easy, to go directly, by visual plotting, from the 1:40,000 photograph to the 1:506,880 base map, although much training was required for adequate precision. Through much of the Labrador Trough and other mining areas, 1:50,000 sheets, fully

contoured, have been published and are suitable for more detailed work, although absolute altitude errors occur on some of the earlier of these sheets. Finally, it should be added that both the Geological Survey of Canada and the Quebec Bureau of Mines have published geological maps on various scales in widely scattered areas of the peninsula.

None of this base map preparation fell on our shoulders. It and the air photos from which it proceeded were the necessary raw materials for stage 2) of the work in which I and my colleagues were involved.

Stage 2): The Field Program for Key Preparation

We needed interpretation keys making it possible for the laboratory workers to identify physiographic types and natural vegetation types on the air photos. Such keys, to be useful, must be capable of use by workers who have never themselves visited the area. Hence, ground photography must play a major role.

It was first necessary to establish a classification of landforms and vegetative cover types, the latter term comprehending both vegetation, water bodies, and naked surfaces. We agreed with A. W. Küchler, who argued that such classifications must be neutral as to process of origin.[5] In the case of physiography, this is fairly simple, although use of categories such as drumlin, esker, and moraine partially begs the question. These are, however, readily identifiable by simple form; one does not need to postulate a particular mode of origin to use such terms. With vegetation the case is more difficult, since ecological ideas permeate most systems of nomenclature. We eventually settled on a classification suggested by Ilmari Hustich, a Finnish biogeographer who worked in Labrador with the 1937 Tanner expedition, and who subsequently revisited Labrador-Ungava on several occasions. He established a suitable physiognomic classification of vegetation types, and from these deduced the existence of three primary zonal divisions of the peninsula.[6] I myself, and to a far greater extent my collaborators R. N. Drummond, I. A. McKay, H. N. Lash, and Weston Blake, Jr., conducted field studies in the Goose Bay–Lake Melville–Mealy Mountain area, in the Romaine Valley of the southern Laurentide area, and in the Labrador Trough along the line of the Koksoak–Kaniapiskau. These studies established a suitable classification both for landforms and for cover types, and enabled Lash and Drummond to compile what are still among the best available interpretation keys for eastern Boreal Forest and Canadian Shield environments.[7]

All these field studies were carried out by small parties, chiefly in canoes, who were airlifted into the inaccessible areas chosen as most suitable for this sort of taxonomic work. Although the surface of Labrador-Ungava looks to the uninitiated like an appalling chaos, close study soon shows that it consists of countless variations on a limited number of themes. It was these themes that the field program was able to isolate, drawing heavily on previous experience in Scandinavia (especially Finland), Alaska, and the western Arctic and sub-Arctic of Canada. We must acknowledge our debt to the Swedish school of glacial geomorphologists, and to Professor Hustich. Little or nothing that we saw, classified, and documented had escaped their prior attention in the corresponding Fennoscandian landscapes.

I shall not discuss the physiognomic classifications here in detail, having set them out elsewhere.[8] I shall only re-emphasize the paramount importance in all such reconnaissance surveys of establishing a really sound and comprehensive classification before the detailed mapping begins. Once the map has begun to grow, it is too late to correct deficiencies.

Stage 3): The Reconnaissance Survey

Armed with the Lash–Drummond keys, we began mapping from the air photos at the National Airphoto Library, Ottawa (where prints of all the photos were directly and immediately accessible). In four months in the summer of 1953, I myself, P. S. Marchant, and Anne Pattison completed the mapping of about 200,000 square miles (the area of France) in southern and central districts. Pattison and R. G. Taylor completed the rest of the peninsula in 1954 and 1955, primarily by means of the trimetrogon photographs. In all cases the technique was the same: we plotted the flight lines on the 1:506,880 base maps, and interpreted the photographs strip by strip, purely by visual sketching. We made no use of mosaics, which are suitable only for more detailed work or for photogrammetry. The problems involved have been fully set out elsewhere.[9]

By 1955, we possessed a single working set of 1:506,880 maps of cover type, primarily vegetation, and a corresponding set of maps of physiography. These were working sheets: hand-colored, grubby, and tattered. In that year, however, Pattison and Taylor reduced them to a 1:1 million series which is still unpublished, through lack of funds.[10] I completed a further reduction to the 1:4 million scale in 1956-1957. These two maps have been published by the Geographical Branch, Department of Mines and Technical Surveys, Ottawa,[11] from whom copies are obtainable.

The unfolding of these maps was a scientific adventure more thrilling in its way than the fieldwork that preceded it. The patterns grew slowly: and as they grew they amazed us. The logic of the glacial morphology and the zonally organized forest vegetation became apparent. It was exploration of a new, safe, but very rewarding sort.

Stage 4): Generic Relationships

The finished maps, together with the experience gained in the field and during the interpretation program, enabled us to establish vegetation zones within the peninsula, to relate these generically to the circumpolar zonal organization of the arctic and subarctic vegetation, and to lay down the primary physiographic regions and the pattern of traces of the declining stages of Wisconsin glaciation. Comprehensive reviews of these

TABLE I

CIRCUMPOLAR ZONAL ORGANIZATION OF ARCTIC AND SUBARCTIC VEGETATION

Formation	Subzone	Vegetation
Arctic	1. Tundra	Treeless barren lands, usually dominated by the sedges, lichens, and scattered small shrubs. General permafrost.
	Arctic tree line	
	2. Forest-Tundra subzone	Interdigitation of tundra, primarily on interfluves, with forest or woodland of hardy conifers, primarily near watercourses. General permafrost.
Boreal	3. Woodland subzone	In eastern North America, characteristically open-structured coniferous woodland, with brightly lit, lichen-covered floor and a discontinuous shrub layer. Very widespread bogs. Scattered permafrost.
	4. Forest subzone	Closed-crown coniferous forests with shaded, mossy floor.
	Limes labradoricus or norrlandicus	

Source: Compilation from mapped field data

results have already been published, and I shall content myself here with a general discursive commentary on our conclusions.

Table 1 sketches, in extremely condensed form, my own classification of the northern vegetation ones, which I have attempted to trace around the pole.[12] As far as Labrador-Ungava is concerned, they correspond in all but nomenclature with the divisions proposed by Jacques Rousseau, greatest of the living explorers of the interior.[13] The description of the vegetation types is heavily weighted towards the special case of eastern Canada, but the basic structure proposed is identifiable all around the pole. The northern limit of the Boreal formation is the arctic tree line. The southern is marked by the northern limits of certain characteristic non-Boreal trees; North European ecologists call these coincident tree lines the *limes norrlandicus,* and Hustich's usage *limes labradoricus* for eastern Canada is a happy extension of European classicism. The key species for us are the white pine (*Pinus strobus*), the sugar and red maples (*Acer saccharum* and A. *rubrum*), and other hardwoods. Elsewhere I have shown that the arctic tree line, the boundaries of the Boreal subzones, and the southern *limes* all follow constant annual values of Thornthwaite's PE function.[14] The physical meaning of this function is not obvious, but it is known to correlate highly with annual net radiation (i.e., with the net energy supply due to emission and absorption at the earth's surface). I now think it probable that the zonal divisions of Table 1 are, in fact, reflections of the distribution of net radiation around the pole, although this hypothesis needs much more testing.

All four of the subdivisions of Table 1 are clearly visible on the map of Labrador-Ungava (Fig. 1). The arctic tree line is hard to find on air photos because the trees are stunted, and the division between the tundra of the Ungava and northeast Labrador peninsulas is approximate. The other boundaries are, however, well fixed, and are surprisingly clear-cut on the ground. The forest-tundra subzone is wide and homogeneous, except for the strip of so-called "coastal tundra" along the eastern and southern coasts some of which may be owing to man's activities. Tundra cover types are areally more extensive than forest in this subzone. The woodland subzone across the core of the peninsula is dominated by three cover types: open water (for the Lake Plateau is wholly within this subzone), bog and muskeg, and the celebrated lichen woodlands with their open crown and handsome lichen floor. There is little merchantable timber in this subzone, although most local constructional needs can be satisfied. Only the true forest subzone contains extensive areas of closed-crown coniferous forest of the sort pictured in textbooks. The main extent of this subzone is along the rugged Laurentide Massif, the heavily dissected and uplifted

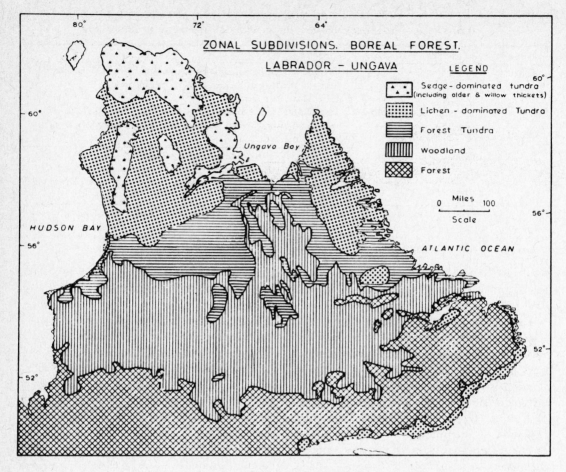

FIG. 1. The major vegetation zones of Labrador-Ungava.

plateau rim north of the St. Lawrence. A smaller outlier occurs on the low ground around the head of Lake Melville. Labrador-Ungava thus presents in classic form the typical subzones of the Boreal Forest, with the arctic tundra in contact with it along its northern flank. The *limes labradoricus* lies south of the area mapped.

Figure 2 shows the physiographic regions recognized following the interpretation program. Much of this map is already familiar, but the precise delimitation of the Lake Plateau, the great drift-strewn crescent of lake-studded plateau in south-central districts, is of interest. In the remaining plateau belts, drift is thin or absent, and bedrock structure controls the surface relief. Overwhelmingly, the peninsula is a featureless plateau between 1,000 and 2,200 feet above

sea level, developed on massive crystalline rocks. The uplifted southern and eastern rims, well known in the literature, are the only major exceptions to the drab monotony. The all-important Labrador Trough differs in being developed on closely folded sediments, and the relief is akin to that of the folded Appalachians. These sediments include the iron formation underlying the recent ore developments. The structural trough extends much farther north and south than does the physiographic Appalachian-type topography; hence, Figure 2 underestimates the extent of the structural province.

Upon this plateau surface, the drift sheets are primarily sandy morainic material, chiefly a thin drumlinized till, with an immense profusion of eskers (some running almost 100 miles unbrokenly). Drumlins and eskers

The Land Changes

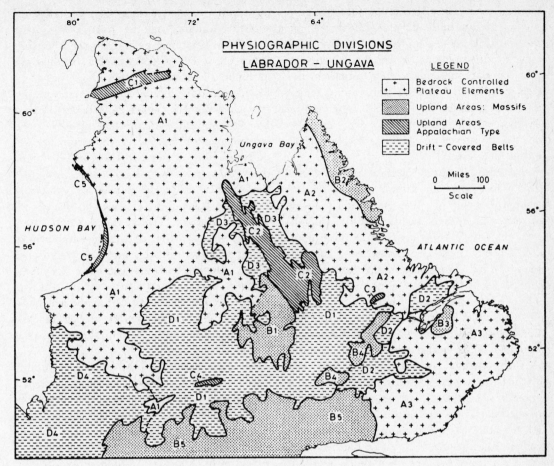

FIG. 2. *The major physiographic divisions of Labrador-Ungava; A 1–3, western, eastern, and southeastern plateaus; B 1, central massif, B 2, Torngat massif, B 3, Mealy Mts., B 4–5, Laurentide and Romaine massifs; C 1–5, folded belts, including C 2, Labrador Trough; D 1–4 drift-covered areas, including D 1, Lake Plateau.*

diverge from a center in the southern Labrador Trough, although in several localities there are drumlin fields and eskers following different trends. Many other late-glacial features, notably drainage channels, were identified and mapped.

Mention should be made, finally, of the stream pattern. Many parallel streams dissect all the rims of the plateau, typically reaching the sea after traversing lengthy gorges. Few have large catchment areas (20,000 square miles is unusual) but nearly all have interrupted profiles. The streams flowing southwards across the Laurentide Massif are all similar. The Peribonca, Bersimis, Outardes, Manicouagan, Moisie, and Romaine are of special interest for power development. The king of all, however, is the Hamilton, which drains the eastern Lake Plateau into the great Bowdoin Canyon, thereby creating the greatest single potential power source in eastern North America.

Stage 5): Later Research

In 1954 we built and opened the McGill Sub-Arctic Research Laboratory at Knob Lake (now Schefferville), near the railhead of the Quebec North Shore and Labrador Railway, in the heart of the peninsula. The Laboratory runs a full hourly synoptic reporting station for the Canadian Meteorological

Service, and the Dominion Observatory's seismic station, under formal contract. There are facilities for geophysical, geomorphological, and ecological research. The greater part of our subsequent field research has been conducted from the Laboratory, which is near a heavily used airfield. The annual reports of the Laboratory give a comprehensive survey of what has been attempted and achieved.[15]

The most elaborate of these research programs has been an assault on the glacial geomorphology of the peninsula, aimed primarily at unravelling the history of deglaciation. So far, work has been in three main areas. Ives, Tomlinson Løken, and Johnson have worked extensively in the great coastal mountains of northeast Labrador (the Torngats, Kaumajets, and Kiglapaits). Ives, Andrews, and Matthew have also worked in the George River valley west of this mountain axis. This work has established a tentative chronology of deglaciation in the Torngat area, and has correlated it with the variable sea levels. A vast system of proglacial lakes (Glacial Lake Naskaupi) in the George River valley has been mapped, and appears comparable in scale with Lake Barlow-Ojibway. Finally there has been much work in and northwest of Knob Lake itself, chiefly on the drainage channel system, by Ives and Derbyshire. This has established the last home of the Wisconsin ice near what Ives calls the Kivivik divide about twenty-five miles northwest of Knob Lake.[16]

A second major project has been aimed at a fuller understanding of the heat and moisture balance of the peninsula. Orvig and Nebiker have examined the moisture losses off a lichen cover, using installations at Knob Lake itself,[17] while Orvig has published the only available net radiation observations for the peninsula.[18] Jackson[19] and Davies[20] have investigated the albedo of the cover types for short-wave radiation. Davies' paper includes a detailed map of albedo for the entire peninsula. Knob Lake lies near the southern limit of permafrost; outlying but quite thick patches occur in the ridges of the Labrador Trough near Knob Lake, and at points farther south. The Laboratory has conducted research into the stability of these patches, and has extensive soil temperature installations in the vicinity of the Iron Ore Company of Canada's workings. The staff has made annual surveys of lake ice formation and the properties of the winter snow cover.[21]

All these investigations, and many others, have arisen fairly directly from the original reconnaissance survey, although it would be a mistake to assume that they have been carried out in accordance with a master plan. Each project has been launched as opportunity knocked: opportunity in the shape of competent investigators, financial support and, very often, available transportation. A common theme has nevertheless been maintained. The Laboratory is still very active, and we hope that in future much more ambitious work will be possible.

*

THE ECONOMIC AWAKENING

It was in our minds, as we began the survey, that economic development of the interior could not be long delayed. There were three signs that pointed that way. One was the growing postwar interest in new sources of iron ore, especially on the part of U.S. companies who knew that nearly three-quarters of the remaining Superior ores had been optioned by a single steel company.

That the deep interior of Labrador-Ungava was rich in iron formations, had been known since the late nineteenth century; and, as early as 1929, one of the writer's McGill colleagues, J. E. Gill, had discovered the large intermediate ore body at Ruth Lake, in the heart of what is now the Schefferville mining area. He also prospected the Carol Lake deposits, without reaching the final conclusion that they contained workable ores. It took World War II to bring the industry to the point where it was ready to develop such remote ores; but by 1948 that moment had arrived. The second portent of development was the desire of the Canadian Department of Defence to create a radar warning chain across the peninsula. This called for an elaboration of communications into the interior, the lack of which had been a stumbling block in the way of development. The third was the richness of the peninsula in hydroelectric power potential. The more accessible sites near the St. Lawrence, in both Quebec and Ontario, were approaching full exploitation. There remained Labrador-Ungava, with its rugged rims, its deep winter snow cover, and its enormous runoff, yielding nearly two cubic feet per second of water for every square mile south of about 55° N. Obviously, with Canada in the midst of her postwar boom, development was just around the corner.

*

The Iron Ore Development

The first step was taken by the Iron Ore Company of Canada, which was formed in 1949 to exploit the ore bodies in the south-central Labrador Trough, very near the center of gravity of the landmass. I have discussed elsewhere the early history of this venture.[22] The construction of the town of Schefferville, of the 357-mile railway to the St. Lawrence shore at Sept-Iles (Fig. 3), and of the necessary terminal and processing facilities, began shortly after incorporation, and mining began in the summer of 1954, the year in which the railway was completed. This railway, the Quebec North Shore and Labrador, was constructed to high standards, and from the first was operated under centralized traffic control from Sept-Iles. It has a common-carrier charter, so that it could serve, and has so served, as a public highway into the interior. This was the crucial first step in all that has since happened. McGill University built its Sub-Arctic Research Laboratory at Schefferville to take advantage of the new access facilities, and has since enjoyed excellent relations with the Iron Ore Company.

The Schefferville ore bodies lie on the flanks and crests of the low ridges (relative relief about 500 feet) of the Labrador Trough. They consist of large masses of intermediate ore (mostly 52—54 per cent iron content) readily mined by open-cast truck and shovel methods. In all, over 500 million tons have been located. Permafrost occurs in some of the bodies, but specialized techniques permit mining in these patches. Because the mined ore freezes in stock piles and in freight cars, production and shipping have been confined to the period May–October, the winter being used to strip off overburden.

The ore bodies are distributed on either side of the Quebec–Newfoundland interprovincial boundary, and production comes in roughly equal amounts from both provinces. In recent years, technology in the steel industry has changed drastically, and the demand for ores has shifted towards higher iron contents (63 to 65 per cent). In Labrador-Ungava no such ores have been found. On the other hand, there are vast deposits of leaner iron formations, mostly in the Labrador Trough. In the belt stretching 100 miles south and southwest from Schefferville, 10 billion long tons of potential ores have been located, and a further 10 billion tons will probably be found after further exploration.[23] Along the western shore of Ungava Bay, at the other end of the Trough, another 4 billion tons have been located or inferred. The Labrador Trough has thus been shown to contain one of the world's largest reserves of low-grade iron ores, most of which are readily mined and beneficiated. Such beneficiation consists of raising the iron content to about 64 per cent, rendered into hard pellets about one cm. across. Both processes require to be carried out near the mines, and both require considerable power. The pelletized ores can be shipped throughout the year.

Three major developments have already been started in the southern Trough area. The Iron Ore Company of Canada, faced with a declining market for the Schefferville-type ores, has developed a major mining area at Carol Lake, near Wabush Lake, about forty miles west of mile 224 on the Quebec North Shore and Labrador Railway. Production began in 1962, and by 1963 both concentration and pelletizing plants were in operation. Efforts to beneficiate the Schefferville ores have not yet succeeded, but are being actively sought. The Iron Ore Company has built a new town, Labrador City, near Wabush Lake, to house the workers. It has collaborated with Wabush Mines, the second producer in the area, in building the forty-mile Northern Lands Railway to mile 224 on the QNSLR. Wabush Mines has developed a similar ore body near Wabush Lake, and has also constructed a concentrating plant. Production began early in 1965. Separate port facilities have been built at Pointe Noire, near Sept-Iles. This single mining district has thus created two new townsites in the deep interior, and now has a productive potential close to twice Canada's domestic ore requirements.

The third producer in this southern Trough area is the Quebec Cartier Mining Company, a wholly owned subsidiary of the U.S. Steel Corporation. The deposits being worked are at Lac Jeannine, about ninety-five miles southwest of the Wabush area, and well west of the QNSLR in the drainage basin of the Manicouagan River. The *Compagnie de Chemin de Fer Cartier* (Fig. 3) threads its way through the dissected rim of the plateau from the new town of Gagnon to harbor facilities at Port Cartier, near the hamlet of Shelter Bay. This railway has a private charter. The ore body (of specular haematite) is 8,000 feet long, 2,300 feet wide, and 1,000 feet deep. It is of low grade, and feeds its output into a concentrator and pelletizer. Production began in

July, 1961, and in 1964, 9,141,964 long tons of beneficiated ore were shipped from Port Cartier. All-winter navigation is being practiced at this port.

The remaining producer in Labrador-Ungava is the Quebec Iron and Titanium Corporation, which mines an ilmenite deposit near Havre Saint-Pierre, with which it is connected by the peninsula's third short railway. The primary object of this venture is to ship the titanium and iron ores to Sorel at the Richelieu-St. Lawrence confluence. Titanium oxide and a small quantity of highly refined iron alloys are the output. Production began in 1950.

It is hard to overestimate the importance of these iron ore developments. They have opened up the interior in a most dramatic fashion. They have also transformed Canada's position as a producer of ores, both direct-shipping and beneficiated. National production leapt forward in 1954 with the opening of the Schefferville mines. It is probable that by 1970 annual shipments will have reached 45,000,000 long tons; 25,456,526 tons were shipped from Quebec and Newfoundland in 1964 (a total of about 24,000,000 tons coming from Labrador-Ungava). Thus, in less than a decade, the seemingly barren interior has been made to yield at a rate of about a quarter of the entire U.S. national output. Canada is now the world's fifth largest producer.

In round figures, Canadian domestic consumption of iron ore has attained about 8,000,000 tons, of which over half is imported from U.S. Superior fields. It follows that practically all the Labrador-Ungava output is exported. In fact, of course, the development has been aimed at captive U.S. markets, with some more recent British and West German interests. Canada is now the world's second largest exporter of ore, and is easily the largest supplier of the U.S. market. Table II shows the disposal of ores from Sept-Iles and Port Cartier in 1964.

Water Power

The potential richness of Labrador-Ungava

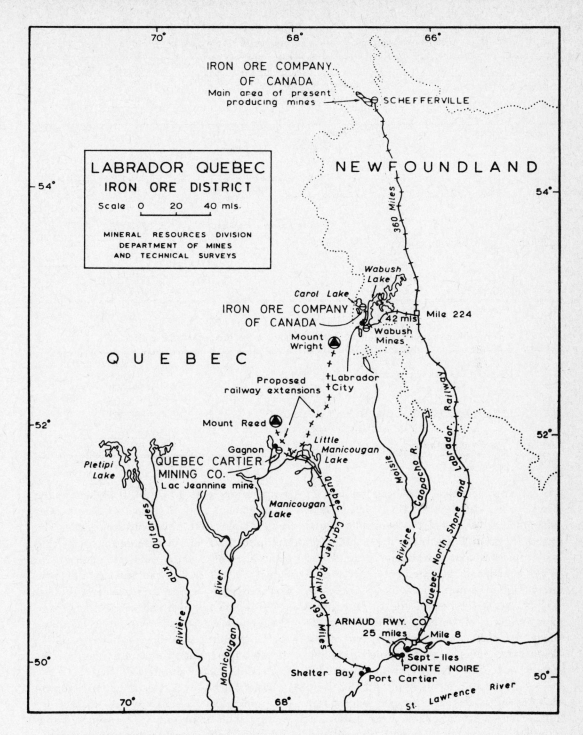

FIG. 3. The central iron-ore mining districts, with 1964 producers in capitals. Wabush Mines will come into production early in 1965 (Courtesy Mineral Resources Division, Department of Mines and Technical Surveys, Ottawa).

TABLE II-A)
DESTINATION OF IRON ORE SHIPPED FROM SEPT-ILES IN 1964

		Long tons	
Receipts	Schefferville origin	7,795,719	
	Carol Lake origin	6,406,655	
Total receipts		14,202,374	
Shipped overseas	Britain		2,895,082
	West Germany		186,662
	Netherlands		99,414
	Total to overseas	3,181,158	3,181,158
Shipped to Eastern Seaboard	Canada		228,109
	U. S.		4,542,120
	Total to Eastern Seaboard	4,770,229	4,770,229
Shipped via St. Lawrence Seaway	to Canada		47,061
	to U. S. ports		6,163,608
		6,210,669	6,210,669
Total shipments		14,162,056	

TABLE II-B)
DESTINATION OF IRON ORE SHIPPED FROM PORT CARTIER IN 1964

		Long tons
Shipped to Canadian points		8,069
Shipped to Europe		48,000
″ to Bahamas		5,000
Main flow to U. S. ports	(a) Great Lake ports	4,308,342
	(b) East Coast ports	4,772,553
Total shipments		9,141,964

Source: G.E. Wittur, op. cit.

in hydroelectric power has been known for many years. In 1950–1951 I prepared a climatological survey of the peninsula which suggested that, if anything, the runoff had been underestimated, largely because of errors in snowfall measurement.[24] An annual precipitation of approximately 30 inches in 55° N., of 45 inches on the St. Lawrence North Shore, of perhaps 50 to 55 inches along the main Laurentide rim, and about seventy-five miles inland, seemed probable long-term means. These correspond roughly to average water incomes of 2.2, 3.3, and 3.7–4.1 cubic feet per second per square mile. There were no reliable evapo-transpiration data, but measured runoffs showed that the annual moisture surplus corresponded to 1.91 c.f.c./sq. mile on the upper Manicouagan (latitudes 50° to 53° N.), and to 1.88 c.f.c./sq. mile on the upper Hamilton (latitudes 52° to 55° N.).[25] These implied

evaporation losses of 7 to 10 inches on the Lake Plateau, and of 10 to 15 inches farther south. These were physically reasonable. The southern half of the peninsula was thus established as a source of water close to two cubic feet per second per square mile, with large natural storage areas, and with over 1,000 feet of fall available on all the streams draining to the St. Lawrence. The Hamilton River, draining as it did the northern slopes of the precipitation-rich Laurentide rim, shared this happy situation.

Distance, however, was a major deterrent to production. There was no market for power closer than the St. Lawrence Valley industrial belt extending from the Saguenay to Montreal. The latter city was about 300 miles from the Manicouagan River, and over 600 miles from Grand Falls on the Hamilton River. In 1948 there remained several sites within southern Quebec awaiting develop-

The Land Changes

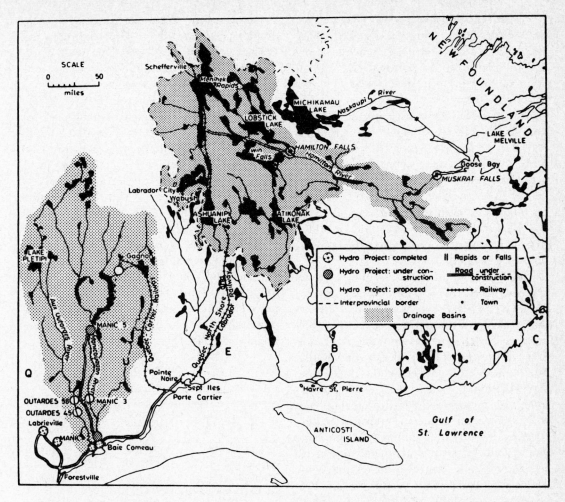

FIG. 4. The Manicouagan-Outardes and Hamilton drainage basins in relation to exist-ing road and rail links. Potential power sites are named. Those of the Manicouagan-Outardes basin are given the names used in Table 3 (Courtesy, Bank of Montreal).

ment. There was, moreover, the uncertain future of hydroelectricity in the face of nuclear power.

So fast did the Quebec demand for power increase, however, that by 1952 it had be-come apparent that the Labrador-Ungava source would have to be tapped. Nuclear power for electricity generation, although now a serious competitor in the making and the vastly improved efficiency of thermal generation, have not destroyed the market for large hydroelectric installations produc-ing power in the vicinity of five mils per kilowatt hour. In the past two years, more-over, a change in Canada's political climate has once again made possible the export of

power to United States markets. This change, coupled with great advances in the tech-nology of transmission at high tensions, has brought New England and New York State within the potential reach of Labrador-Ungava power.

The Bersimis Project

The streams of the Lake St. Jean basin—essentially the Saguenay and the Peribonca—are the westernmost developd streeams that can be considered part of Labrador-Ungava. Their story, however, belongs to an earlier phase of Canada's recent expansion. The first major use of the peninsula's power came in

1956, with the opening of the first station on the Bersimis River (sometimes spelled Betsiamites) at the new town of Labrieville, about 350 miles northeast of Montreal, the ultimate destination of the produced power (Fig. 4). By 1960, a second station had been installed nearer the coast. Between them the two stations used 1,252 feet of head, the profile of the river permitting a very simple development. Installed capacity from the thirteen generators now rates at 2,100,000 horsepower. The completion in 1961 of the remaining units of the Beauharnois plant on the St. Lawrence near Montreal, meant a further accession of power into the growing industrial region.

The Bersimis project was the work of Hydro-Quebec, the Quebec provincial government's public corporation in the electric-power field. Hydro-Quebec has been very active in seeking to develop the Labrador-Ungava sources. The exuberant nationalism now typical of French Canada rightly sees the peninsula's power as the key to Quebec's industrial expansion. Hydro-Quebec has thus become an agent in French Canada's modern revolution. In 1963, at immense cost, the provincial government proceeded to the politically controversial expropriation of most of the private producers (none of which was yet active in Labrador-Ungava). One of the largest was the Shawinigan Power Company, almost all of whose capacity was installed on the St. Maurice, outside our field of interest. The Shawinigan Company, however, was a shareholder in the British Newfoundland Corporation, within whose rights lies the development of the Hamilton. Hydro-Quebec has thus emerged as one of the western world's most ambitious, competent, and aggressive power producers. The Bersimis project, which added 2,100,000 horsepower of installed capacity to Quebec's network in four years, was French Canada's first wholly autonomous venture into massive resource development.

The Manicouagan Project

The next major river system beyond the Bersimis, as one advances along into Labrador-Ungava, is the Manicouagan; the Outardes, though it reaches the Gulf of St. Lawrence independently, does so only a few miles away. The two basins can thus be regarded as a unit having an area of 25,060 square miles (and hence a probable yield of about 50,000 cubic feet per second). Both rivers rise on the interior plateaus, and fall 1,500 to 2,000 feet in reaching the Gulf. Most of this fall is concentrated in a few major falls and rapids. The total potential yield in power is estimated at 33 billion kilowatt hours annually.

Hydro-Quebec surveyed the basins in the 1950's, and concluded that development was feasible, and could be conducted on a very large scale. Work began in 1959, with first power scheduled to flow in 1966. The proposed sites are shown in Figure 4, and are listed in Table III.

TABLE III

MANICOUAGAN POWER SITES

Site	Capacity to be installed (hp.)	Head (feet)	Construction began
Manic 5	1,800,000	505	1959
Manic 3	1,505,000	310	
Manic 2	1,360,000	240	1961
Manicouagan Power	580,000*	124	
Outardes 58	800,000	425	
Outardes 45	1,040,000	425	
Outardes Falls	500,000*	208	
Total	7,585,000		

* Expansion of existing privately owned plants.
Source: See footnote 25.

There is as yet no final timetable on the projects for which no beginning date is given; Manic 5, the most important work, is scheduled for complete installation by 1970. When all three Manicouagan projects are installed, the entire head between the storage reservoir above Manic 5 and the Gulf will have been used; nothing of the original profile will survive. The main storage reservoir above Manic 5 will be four times as large as Lake Mead above the Hoover Dam.

The power from the Manicouagan project,

like that of Bersimis, will flow to Montreal. Transmission voltages of 735,000 are planned, the largest in the western world. The St. Lawrence Valley industrial belt thus continues to collect power from an increasingly large "catchment."[26]

The Hamilton Falls Project[27]

There are several other St. Lawrence North Shore streams that may ultimately be developed after the Manicouagan project is fully installed. Immediate interest has shifted, however, to the Hamilton, whose drainage basin is wholly within Newfoundland-Labrador. The British Newfoundland Corporation (BRINCO, incorporated in Newfoundland in 1953) has the development rights on the Hamilton, under an agreement with the provincial government that lapses in 1973 (though the rights have been greatly extended for the Hamilton Falls Power Corporation, the BRINCO-sponsored operating company).

The headstreams of the Hamilton are the Ashuanipi and the Atikonak, which thread their way northwards from the hilly Laurentide rim across the bogs and shallow lakes of the eastern Lake Plateau. Both rivers appear to be, in origin, truncated headstreams of the Kaniapiskau, in the Ungava Bay drainage basin. Instead, however, both are now collected into Lobstick Lake, from which the Hamilton flows southeast to fall 1,000 feet into the remarkable system of gorges that carry it to Lake Melville and the Atlantic Ocean. Power sites exist at various places along the gorge (see Fig. 4), but only the Grand Falls site, where the main river falls into the gorges, is of immediate interest.

In brief, the Hamilton Falls Power Corporation proposes to construct control dams above Grand Falls, so as to create large increases in storage; to divert the outflow of Lake Michikamau into the Hamilton; and to construct an underground powerhouse through which the entire flow will be discharged into the gorge below Grand Falls.[28] The head will be 1,055 feet and the flow 49,000 c.f.s. This will permit the installation of ten 600,000 hp. turbines generating 6,000,000 hp. at full gate. When constructed, the Hamilton Falls Power Station will thus at least equal in capacity the world's largest existing station, that of Bratsk on the Angara River, in the U.S.S.R. (about whose full installation there has recently been indecision).

The project has not yet begun, but engineering surveys have been completed. A road (built in 1956) connects the site with mile 286 on the Quebec North Shore and Labrador Railway. In order to meet the power requirements of the Carol Lake mining area the Atikonak River has been temporarily diverted into the gorge of the Unknown River at Twin Falls, twenty miles southwest of Grand Falls. The Twin Falls Power Corporation is jointly owned by Wabush Mines, the Iron Ore Company of Canada, and BRINCO. Its 240,000 hp. is now fully installed (Mr. P. S. Marchant, the McGill group's first photo interpreter, is Vice-President and Director of this Corporation). There is thus a nucleus of development, even though the main site remains untouched.

Development of the Hamilton power can proceed only if the power is sold outside Quebec and Newfoundland, neither of whose economies can absorb the output in the immediately foreseeable future. The obvious markets are southern Ontario, New England, and New York State. There are difficulties in the way of sale to Ontario, and until recently, this was also true of export to the U.S.A. Until 1959, Canadian policy had been increasingly restrictive to such exports. In that year, however, the National Energy Board Act established new procedures, and made possible the granting of export licenses for periods up to twenty-five years, provided that the Canadian national requirement could be fulfilled within the foreseeable future. More to the point, perhaps, is the change in political atmosphere engendered by the ambitions of the British Columbia, Manitoba, Quebec, and Newfoundland governments, all of whom stand to gain from sales to the U.S. In any event it is now possible to negotiate long-term supply contracts with U.S. agencies.

In the case of Hamilton Falls, negotiations of considerable delicacy are involved. The power will be produced in Newfoundland by a company with many corporate shareholders, among whom is Hydro-Quebec (who acquired the equity by expropriating the Shawinigan Company). It will be sold at the Quebec border (never overtly accepted as legal by the Quebec government) to Hydro-Quebec, who will then transmit it to the U.S. border near Rouses Point, N.Y. Consolidated Edison of New York will then build the transmission lines south from the border. Extremely high voltages will be required. This is the plan, although it is far from realization at present; it is rumored that a six mill rate is unacceptable to the U.S. consumers. Several governments are involved in the negotiations, as well as two large private corporations.

I have no doubt that the project will go forward in one form or another, although things may be materially different from the plan just sketched. There is heavy pressure in New York State from those interested in nuclear power generation, and in thermal production from coal. In Canada, it is never easy to write long-term agreements involving both Quebec and Newfoundland governments, which have a tradition of hostile bickering over the legality of the Privy Council's 1927 decision assigning the Hamilton drainage to Newfoundland.[29] Yet the logic of what is proposed is as clear as that of the St. Lawrence Seaway. One hopes for a quicker and more adequate solution, if new light is indeed to come from Labrador-Ungava.[30]

*

CONCLUSION

The peninsula of Labrador-Ungava has thus arrived in the North American scene. For several hundred years it remained a vast emptiness on the continental map, a bewildering shadow land on which, in recent years, travelers from Europe via Goose Bay could look down with distaste. Now it has been opened up both scientifically and economically. There are prosperous, well-appointed towns in the very heart of the landmass, heavily traveled railways, a few roads, deep sea harbors, and scheduled airlines. For a decade, highgrade iron ore has been exported to the steel makers of North America and Europe. And now the snowy interior may yield the western world's largest supplies of hydroelectric power. All this has been achieved in less than twenty years, in spite of fluctuating prosperity and political uncertainities.

What role has the professional geographer played in this unfolding? Not, I hope, a negligible one. Certainly our physiographic and vegetation maps have been put to good use by government and private industry. Several of my colleagues have stepped into jobs in which they are actually involved in the present economic development. I have myself served intermittently as a consultant on some of the larger projects. But our role has been much smaller than it might have been. We chose, as categories for our survey, things primarily of scientific interest. It never occurred to us that we were in an excellent position to contribute to the practical developments. Many of the things done by consulting engineers were within our competence, and we could have done these things better and much more cheaply than they did. Unlike geologists, geographers are not habituated to the idea of being useful.

And what lessons can be learned about the pattern of economic development? Essentially, it seems to me, that there is little scope for small-scale action, for the little investor. All the major activities described above have involved a similar type of corporate organi-

The Land Changes

zation. The typical development corporation working in the Canadian sub-Arctic is a joint venture, or a company whose shares are not sold on the open exchanges. The equity is purchased, before work begins, by corporate or institutional shareholders, most of whom are potential purchasers of the eventual product, or who see the prospect of profitable future work. Thus, the Iron Ore Company of Canada is largely owned by a number of U.S. steel companies and financial interests associated with the steel industry; its shareholders contract to buy much of its output, the so-called "captive market." Wabush Mines is a joint venture involving another group of steel companies, including Canadian, Italian, and West German firms. It has become the practice for the large steel producers to diversify their sources of ore, and to draw their requirements from several parts of the world. In this way they are able to escape the consequences of temporary disruption of supplies owing to unrest or calamity in one or more of their supply areas. They are also remarkably resistant to governmental pressures and to adverse fiscal policies. All that has happened in Labrador-Ungava in the iron-ore field is a result of this industry-wide policy.

The second point concerns the vital role of pugnacious governmental policy in achieving development. This is especially true as regards geological survey and other forms of resource appraisal. I have already spoken of the vital role of Hydro-Quebec, and of the nationalist fervor with which it is pushing forward with one of the world's largest power developments. In Newfoundland territory, the pattern has involved, as chosen instrument, the British Newfoundland Corporation. At the time of its incorporation in 1953, it had seven corporate shareholders, including N. M. de Rothschild and Sons, Rio Tinto, and several other large international paper, power, and mining corporations. Since then it has gained many other corporate shareholders and part of its equity has been quoted on the stock exchanges. It was given vast powers by the Newfoundland government and has pushed its exploration forward in a vigorous fashion. As each new development prospect matures, it has organized new corporations to undertake the specific work required.

The small shareholder has thus little chance of participating individually in these new ventures, which are in any case too risky to attract him. Moreover, most of the large companies who have joined in the development work have been controlled outside Canada, and the captive markets are mostly American. Canadian companies and individuals have had much to do with the work of exploration, survey, and management. But they have not, for the most part, figured heavily as sources of capital, or as buyers of the product. U.S. interests in Labrador-Ungava are overwhelming, and are inevitable. Only the U.S. market can absorb the ore and power of the peninsula on a scale large enough to justify the minimum feasible development.

Thus, our two countries are thrown together in this, as in so many things. There has been much anxiety in Canada about the loss of her natural resources to external control. But, a country capable of such massive production with so few people cannot hope to escape involvement in the export trade; and trade in bulk ores, or in power is usually with shareholder customers. The Canadian sub-Arctic is in a state of rapid awakening. In that awakening U.S. participation is essential.

*

FOOTNOTES

1 Address given by the Honorary President of the Association of American Geographers at its 60th Annual Meeting, Syracuse, N.Y., April 1, 1964.

2 E. A. Ackerman, "Where is a Research Frontier?" *Annals,* Association of American Geographers, Vol. 53 (1963), pp. 429–440.

3 First and foremost I must thank the small army of colleagues who worked with me on this project, especially Professor R. N. Drummond and Dr. J. D. Ives (Director of the Geographical Branch, Department of Mines and Technical Surveys, which provided extensive field help). Financial support was provided by Defence Research Board of Canada. I am indebted to Mr. P. S. Marchant, himself an important member of the group, for much help, and to Mr. W. J. Bennett, Vice-President, Iron Ore Company of Canada. M. René Therrien of Hydro-Quebec, Mr. E. J. Mapes of Pickands, Mather and Company, Mr. R. L. Boudreau of Quebec Cartier Mining Company, and Mr. W. L. Walsh of Quebec Iron and Titanium Corporation all provided invaluable help, as did Mr. W. Keith Buck of the Department of Mines and Technical Surveys, Ottawa.

4 F. K. Hare, "The Labrador Frontier," *Geographical Review,* Vol. 42 (1952), pp. 405–424; H. Dorion, *La Frontière Québec–Terreneuve* (Québec: Les Presses de l'Université Laval, 1963), 316 pp.

5 A. W. Küchler, "A Physiognomic Classification of Vegetation," *Annals,* Association of American Geographers, Vol. 39 (1949), pp. 201–210.

6 I. Hustich, "On the Forest Geography of the Labrador Peninsula," *Acta Geographica,* Vol. 10, No. 2 (1949); see also "Photographical Regions of Labrador, *Arctic,* Vol. 2 (1949), pp. 36–42. The zonal divisions in these two papers do not precisely correspond.

7 R. N. Drummond, I. A. McKay, and F. K. Hare, "Investigations in the Boreal Forest of Labrador-Ungava, 1948–51," *Proceedings of the 17th International Geographical Congress,* Washington (1952), pp. 248–254. The master key is on the file in the library of the Joint Intelligence Bureau, Defence Research Board, Ottawa, Ont.

8 F. K. Hare, "Mapping of Physiography and Vegetation in Labrador-Ungava," *Canadian Geographer,* No. 5 (1955), pp. 17–28. For the complementary work of J. T. Wilson's group, see M. Vibert Douglas and R. N. Drummond, "Air Photo Interpretation of Glacial and Physiographic Features of Quebec-Labrador," *Canadian Geographer,* No. 5 (1955), pp. 9–16.

9 Hare, 1955, *op. cit.,* and Douglas and Drummond, *op. cit.*

10 The master series, consisting of eleven sheets mounted in wall-map form, is on deposit with the Quebec Command H.Q., Canadian Army, Montreal.

11 F. K. Hare, *A Photo-Reconnaissance Survey of Labrador-Ungava,* Memoir 6, Geographical Branch, Department of Mines and Technical Surveys, Ottawa (1959), 83 pp. The 1:4 million maps are included as inserts.

12 F. K. Hare, "The Boreal Conifer Zone," *Geographical Studies,* Vol. 1 (1954) pp. 4–18.

13 Jacques Rousseau, "Les zones biologiques de la péninsule Quebec-Labrador et l'Hemiarctique," *Canadian Journal of Botany,* Vol. 30 (1952), pp. 436–474.

14 F. K. Hare, "Climate and Zonal Divisions of the Boreal Forest Formation in Eastern Canada," *Geographical Review,* Vol. 40 (1950), pp. 615–635.

15 McGill Sub-Arctic Research Laboratory, *Annual Reports,* 1955–1956 to date Department of Geography, McGill University, Montreal).

16 J. D. Ives, "Glacial Geomorphology of the Torngat Mountains, Northern Labrador," *Geographical Bulletin,* No. 12 (1958), pp. 47–75. See also "Glacial Drainage Channels as Indicators of Late-Glacial Conditions in Labrador-Ungava," *Les Cahiers de Géographie de Québec,* No. 5 (1958–1959), pp. 57–72; and "The Deglaciation of Labrador-Ungava—an Outline," *Les Cahiers de Géographie de Québec,* No. 8 (1960) pp. 323–343; E. Derbyshire, "The Identification and Classification of Glacial Drainage Channels from Aerial Photographs," *Geografiska Annaler,* Vol. 40 (1958). pp. 188–195. See also "Fluvioglacial Erosion near Knob Lake, Central Quebec-Labrador, Canada," *Geological Society of American Bulletin,* Vol. 73 (1962), pp. 1111-1126.

17 W. A. Nebiker and S. Orvig, "Evaporation and Transpiration from an Open Lichen Woodland Surface," *Comptes Rendus et Rapports Généraux, Union* géophysique internationale, (Toronto, 1957), pp. 379–384.

18 S. Orvig, "Net Radiation Flux over Sub-Arctic Surfaces," *Journal of Meteorology,* Vol. 18 (1961), pp 199–203.

19 C. I. Jackson, "Estimates of Total Radiation and Albedo in Sub-Arctic Canada," *Archiv für Meteorologie, Geophysik und Bioklimatologie,* Serie B (Allgemeine und biologische Klimatologie), Vol. 10 (1960), pp. 193–199.

20 J. A. Davies, "Albedo Investigations in Labra-

dor-Ungava," *Archiv für Meteorologie, Geophysik und Bioklimatologie*, Serie B (Allgemeine und biologische Klimatologie), Vol. 13 (1963), pp. 137–151.

21 There has also been work on the synoptic climatology of the peninsula. See, for example, R. G. Barry, "A Note on the Synoptic Climatology of Labrador-Ungava," *Quarterly Journal of the Royal Meteorological Society*, Vol. 86 (1960), pp. 557–565.

22 F. K. Hare, "The Labrador Frontier," *op. cit.*

23 G. A. Gross, *The Iron Ranges and Current Developments in New Quebec and Labrador, Canada* (Ottawa: Geological Survey of Canada, Reprint 10, 1960), 17 pp; G. E. Wittur, *The Canadian Iron Ore Industry in 1964* (Ottawa: Mineral Information Bulletin MR 80, Mineral Resources Division, Department of Mines and Technical Surveys, 1965), 110 pp. I have drawn heavily, and without further acknowledgement from this excellent memoir. Table 2 is drawn wholly from this source.

24 F. K. Hare, *The Climate of the Canadian Arctic and Sub-Arctic and Its Influence on Accessibility,* (Ph.D. thesis, Université de Montréal, 1950), 440 pp. The part of this thesis dealing with Labrador-Ungava was rewritten and revised (with much benefit) by R. W. Longley, and issued by the Canadian Department of Transport as *The Climate of Quebec and Labrador* (Toronto, 1953), 134 pp.; "The Present-Day Snowfall of Labrador-Ungava, American Journal of Science, Vol. 249 (1951), pp. 654–670.

25 Computed from data supplied to the writer by British Newfoundland Corporation and Hydro-Quebec. Most engineering estimates, although agreeing on the runoff figures, assume much lower values of evapo-transpiration. This is because they are based on weather station precipitation data, which I believe systematically underestimate the regional snowfalls, probably by several inches of rainfall equivalent. (An inch of annual precipitation is equal to 0.0739 cubic feet per second per square mile; one cubic foot per second per square mile equals 13.54 inches per annum.)

26 I am indebted for the unpublished materials used in these paragraphs to Mr. René Therrien, Director of Public Relations, Hydro-Quebec.

27 Since this article was written the name of the project has been changed to Churchill Falls.

28 E. N. Webb, "Hamilton Falls Hydro-Electric Scheme," *Proceedings of the Institution of Civil Engineers,* Vol. 11 (1958), pp. 313–332. There have been amendments since this paper was published, chiefly owing to an upward revision of the estimate of available runoff.

29 As if to prove my point, Premier Lesage of Quebec announced a breakdown of negotiations with Newfoundland on July 8, 1964, three months after this article was written, *Montreal Star* (July 9, 1964).

30 An agreement has since been signed for Hydro-Quebec to purchase Churchill Falls power. Construction of the project began in October 1966.

9

The Future Colonization of
Northern Canada*

TREVOR LLOYD

* From V. W. Bladen (ed.): Canadian Population and Northern Development, *Royal Society of Canada*, *"Studia Varia"* series (Toronto, University of Toronto Press, 1962), pp. 148–158. Reprinted by permission.

When seeking to draw conclusions concerning the large-scale colonization of northern Canada, it is important to keep in mind the extent and character of the region we are discussing. The North is vast in area, just how vast, it is not easy to appreciate unless one has travelled it on the ground as did Camsell, Tyrrell, and Low and not a few veteran Fellows of the Royal Society of Canada. Its scale may be illustrated by a circle centred on Montreal and passing through Alert at the northern end of Ellesmere Island. It also passes through the delta of the Mackenzie River, cuts the Pacific well to the west of Vancouver Island, then touching San Francisco, Trinidad and Iceland. Those geometrically minded may care to remember that an approximate equilateral triangle can be formed by joining Vancouver, the Bay of Fundy and Alert, N.W.T.; the sides of the triangle would be approximately 2,500 miles long.

*

PHYSICAL CHARACTER

In character, the enormous land mass of northern Canada is diverse. It may be usefully divided into regions based on the nature of its bedrock types and their surface manifestations. In some areas, the landforms were recently modified by glaciation and a few higher parts are still beneath the ice. Within the one-and-a-half million square miles of northern Canada, lies scenery as diverse as are the Rockies and the western plains, the Laurentians and the St. Lawrence lowland, the sandy beaches of Prince Edward Island and the fjords of British Columbia.

The climate is almost equally varied. This is a consequence of the interrelated influence of latitude and elevation, and of location with respect to oceans, seas and other land masses. A map of natural vegetation emphasizes the striking distinction between east and west. Thus, the treeline, significant as an indicator of summer temperatures and also of great ecological and economic importance, reaches north of 68° N. Lat. in the Mackenzie Valley, but on the Labrador coast lies south of the 55th parallel, a difference of a thousand miles. The soils, which have been dismissed rather cavalierly by some, may, it is true, be of limited extent and fertility but in a few areas, particularly the northwest, are of real local significance. The seas, a major topic for study in themselves and one all too long neglected in Canada, serve both as a reservoir of food and as a means of travel, though obstructed by ice for much of the year.

On the basis of these and other physical characteristics, the Canadian North is divisible into five main regions—the mountain ranges and plateaus characterized by much of Yukon; the Mackenzie Valley; the mainland area extending from Churchill northward and westward to the seacoast, devoid of trees, with severe winters and short cool summers, and underlain by Pre-Cambrian rocks; the region from New Quebec northward to Lancaster Sound, loosely termed the Eastern Arctic; and to the far north, the region which includes the Arctic islands. In physical characteristics and the means needed for development, each of the five regions has within itself a certain degree of unity. An important physical characteristic lacking in southern Canada but widespread in the North is perennially frozen ground, the so-called "permafrost." New to engineers, miners and community planners, its presence must be taken seriously if disaster is to be avoided.

Such then is the background against which human activities in the Canadian North must be considered.

*

TRANSPORTATION

It is universally recognized that efficient and economical transportation holds the key to much of northern development. So, it may be useful to recall the main lines of communication between the settled areas of southern Canada and the Far North. For ocean-going vessels, there are two main routes: the lesser is based on coastal British Columbia and passes around Alaska into the western Arctic, a frequently hazardous route; the other is based on the St. Lawrence region or the Maritimes and passes northward to enter Hudson Bay or continue through Davis Strait to the Arctic islands. The "Northwest Passage" famous in history is not significant as a "through" route, although parts of it are used regularly. Hudson Bay, Baffin Bay and the western Arctic coast are readily navigable in most summers, but sea-ice conditions vary from year to year. No part of the Canadian North is as favoured as is West Greenland south of the Arctic Circle where navigation is possible all year.

The Canadian railway network sends lines northward at several points, the two most significant being that based on Edmonton and tapping the Mackenzie Valley, and that based on southern Saskatchewan and reaching eventually to Churchill on Hudson Bay. Two highways are similarly significant, the one leading from Edmonton to Alaska by way of Yukon, and the other reaching the Mackenzie Valley at Great Slave Lake and recently continued to Yellowknife.

The pattern of commercial air routes is very similar. An eastern "flyway" extends to Frobisher on southern Baffin Island, a central one, by way of Churchill, penetrates to Resolute Bay and thence to the Arctic islands, while a third route from Edmonton follows the Mackenzie Waterway to the coast. The Yukon is served by a route roughly paralleling the Alaska Highway.

*

By customary standards, the total population of northern Canada is negligible. There are a few pockets of concentration, some areas where semi-nomads roam, and a vast area with no one at all. Yukon, a relatively populous area, has fifteen square miles for each person. The Mackenzie District, with an area of half a million square miles, provides a home for only 14,400 people, or thirty-five square miles for each one. North of the treeline each person has about seventy-six square miles.

Apart from the native Eskimos and Indians, most of the residents retain close ties with "the outside," being in the North for a more or less brief tour of duty and, even if settled there, looking to the south for supplies and periodical refreshers. The Indian and Eskimo populations are small in number. Until the 1941 census, the total was not known with even fair accuracy. It is a measure of the improved administration of northern affairs that the modern census combined with "family allowance" records provides today a reasonably true picture of Eskimo numbers and distribution. The population is rising, health is improving (the death rate from tuberculosis dropped to one-seventh in the last ten-year period) and infant mortality is declining. In fact, a coming population bulge is a new and unexpected hazard facing administrators.

Small though the northern population is, it includes diverse groups, ranging from exiled city dwellers, haunted by all the problems of suburbia, to semi-nomadic hunters not far removed from the Stone Age. So when considering the problems of northern development, along with the diversity of physical geography, account must also be taken of the wide gulfs that separate northern residents. To grant "self-government" to such a region may in fact mean to place the economic future of native Eskimos and Indians in the hands of white residents such as miners and traders.

*

SOVEREIGNTY

Occasionally, one still hears of uncertainty about Canada's sovereignty over the Arctic. While there may at one time have been grounds for doubt concerning the effectiveness of this country's title to all its Arctic possessions, and there may even have been some fear that parts might be lost by default, there is no such risk today. Canada's title is universally recognized. The area of national responsibility was increased recently when the right to extract minerals from the submerged Continental Shelf was internationally recognized. This explains in part the present hurried search to locate the outer limit of the Shelf lying north of the Queen Elizabeth Islands.

*

DEVELOPMENT COMPARED

The complaint is often heard that northern Canada has been neglected and that its development has proceeded slowly in comparison with Greenland, northern Scandinavia, or the Soviet Union. Such comparisons may be misleading, particularly because they seldom take account of significant differences in the physical characteristics of the several areas. An obvious case of this is the frequently contrasted development of the Canadian Eastern Arctic and Danish West Greenland, on the other side of Davis Strait. Along the Greenland coast between Cape Farewell and Melville Bay is a string of large and small communities certainly not duplicated across the water in Canada. There is, however, a fundamental difference in physical geography between the two areas, based primarily on climate supplemented by the influence of nearby waters. It is this that makes possible the plan to export Ungava iron ore by way of an ice-free transit harbour on the Greenland coast. West coasts are always milder than east coasts in high latitudes, as is apparent from a comparison of the climates of Norway and Pacific U.S.S.R., or the Alaskan Panhandle and Labrador. Thus, Murmansk in northwestern U.S.S.R., with a population of a quarter of a million, is at a latitude approximating that of the coast of the Canadian Arctic mainland. But the climates are entirely different. Other contrasts between physical conditions in northern Canada and those in northern U.S.S.R. are apparent when one compares the extent of territory which lies north of the treeline in both cases. The Canadian area is far more extensive and complex, and there are other important distinctions. Nevertheless, some useful circumpolar comparisons may fairly be made. The large river valleys flowing northward to the Arctic Sea are a case in point. In Canada, the Mackenzie, together, with its tributaries, is located much as are the Lena, the Yenesei, and the Ob of Siberia. All of these rivers are used by shipping that links the railroad systems of the South with the Arctic Sea coast. There is no doubt that the tonnage of freight moved on the Mackenzie does not compare with that on the Siberian rivers. The difference gives some indication of the relative development of the two areas. There is nothing in Canada to compare with the mining city of Norilsk, where over 100,000 people live at almost 70° N. Lat. some miles east of the Yenesei.

One great and unique physical asset Canada does have in the North is Hudson Bay, a gateway to the heart of North America. That it has been utilized far less than it might have been in the past thirty years, is a fair commentary on Canada's attitudes towards northern expansion.

*

THE ECONOMIC BASIS FOR CANADIAN ARCTIC SETTLEMENT

There appears to be a widely held view that the primary purpose of developing northern Canada is to supply raw materials needed by southern industries or, if these are adequately served from elsewhere, to secure foreign exchange by exporting the resources. The future of the North is thus seen as that of an economic colony of the already industrialized South. My own view, expressed often in the past, is that this provides no basis for a permanent northern population. Such can only come about if a reasonably self-contained society can be established there. In any event, there is little in contributions to this symposium to encourage those who await impatiently a far northern industrial boom. Information provided about the economics of northern mineral exploitation suggests that it may be a very long time indeed before large-scale mining operations are likely, except possibly in a few favoured and strategically placed locations. The obvious lack of enthusiasm shown by southern industry for venturing into the Far North is not peculiar to Canada. It seems to be universal along the northern frontier. Since the state trading monopoly in Greenland was lifted a decade ago, there has been no appreciable rush of private capital anxious for investment there. So too elsewhere in Scandinavia. A Norwegian businessman at Hammerfest, one of the most northerly cities in the world, told me recently that "Bankers don't lend money north of Trondheim" (a city which lies one-third of the way up the long Norwegian coast). And even in the Soviet Union it is now authoritatively reported that "economic laws" govern the exploitation of Arctic resources. This is revealed in a recent paper on the economics of Soviet Arctic development, which states:

The development of natural resources will be economically expedient only under two conditions:
1. When the special value of these resources justifies the high outlays necessary.
2. When the resources in question are generally scarce in the country and their development is essential for the pressing needs of the national economy and for strengthening the country's military preparedness.[1]

If a considerable population is to be settled in the Canadian northland, what resources are likely to be available to attract it and support it?

Lumber is far from negligible—at least in the Yukon and the Mackenzie Valley—and is likely to prove adequate for all local needs. About one hundred million board feet per annum are available for cutting in the Yukon, while less than one-twentieth of this is at present used.[2]

Agricultural lands are not to be overlooked, particularly in areas where urban centres grow up and there is a demand for fresh vegetables, milk, and eggs. Land awaits use in the Yukon and Mackenzie Valley every bit as good as that now being broken for new settlers in northern Finland and Norway. There are believed to be a quarter of a million acres of arable land available in Yukon and five times that amount in the Mackenzie Valley.[3] Persons familiar with the area can vouch for the usefulness of the small-scale farming operation long carried on there and now encouraged by agricultural research stations. Of course, when the soils and the climate are compared with those of more smiling lands, they are not impressive but they are still capable of making life

healthier, pleasanter and less expensive for those who must live there. Where local coal, oil or natural gas exist, hothouse cultivation of vegetables could be undertaken.

There has been earlier mention of the fish resources of lakes and seas.[4] While these may, in a few cases, be able to serve the luxury markets of New York, Chicago, and Montreal, they may elsewhere be an important source of food for the local population.

However, today—as almost fifty years ago when Charles Camsell first wrote about it[5]—the development of the Far North is generally considered to depend upon the exploitation of minerals. It is for this reason that the contribution by Henderson and Buck is included in this symposium. The magic of the Pre-Cambrian Shield and of the oil and gas presumably hidden in the strata to its west and north, is the basis for most of the hopeful forecasting about the future of the North. Yet the record as seen today is not impressive. We are still far from being able to justify, on the basis of returns from minerals produced there, the large public investment made in northern Canada. Gross revenues from minerals amount to about twenty-three million dollars a year for the Northwest Territories and twelve million dollars for the Yukon, and the amount has fallen in recent years. The publicly owned mining operation on Great Bear Lake has, perhaps conveniently for some critics, ended with the petering out of the ore supply, and the company has agreed to give up the search for more. A small nickel mine on the west coast of Hudson Bay may prove to have had only a brief, if meteoric, career. There are no other truly arctic mines in Canada. In the Northwest Territories there remains only the Yellowknife area to demonstrate what mining can do for northern development after forty years of intensive effort. The small oilfield at Norman Wells, first detected fifty years ago, is now used to barely half of its capacity and is the lone producer in northern Canada. The vast flow of petroleum products which constantly pour northward at enormous cost for freight and non-returnable oildrums, originates on the Prairies or

The Land Changes

in Venezuela, and the Near East. When given the "cold, hard look" customary in trade and commerce, the mining industry of northern Canada today, despite the large sums and enormous effort spent on it, offers a singularly fragile foundation on which to build a new northern empire.

In striking contrast, there can be no doubt that one public agency has been notably productive as a basis for arctic development both in Alaska and Canada. I refer of course to defence enterprises. These alone have commanded the public financial resources, the priorities, and the technical knowledge to achieve more northern development in a decade than had seemed likely in a century. From Northeast Greenland to the outermost Aleutians, there are now well-equipped settlements, provided with first-class communications, often with year-round airfields and in many cases with access by sea. A remarkable concentration of scientific expertise and industrial "know-how" has gone into their location, construction and maintenance. The personnel occupying them are not only highly trained in their special skills but in some cases have become expert at working under arctic conditions.[6]

Much though one may regret the reasons for its being there, and deplore the enormous cost to the community, it remains true that without the DEW line and associated development, the hope of effective occupation of the Far North would be even more remote today than it is. Such far-ranging enterprises have made possible elaborate programmes of research and development with have speeded the solution of many problems in logistics, housing, and communication. When the military men eventually evacuate their settlements, as is beginning to happen at some arctic sites, they will leave behind them an invaluable group of well-endowed oases in the northern wilderness.

*

SETTLEMENT OF THE FAR NORTH

This brings us to the fundamental question —what kind of settlement or type of colonization of the Far North is desirable and also possible? In answering this I shall repeat views I have expressed elsewhere, reinforced by the contributions of other authors of this study.

1. There is not likely to be, in the near future, a large movement of permanent settlers to the North. The present resident labour force there totals about 8,500 men, and is likely to increase to about 14,500 in the next decade.[7] Sufficient employment at a living wage for this group is not now available. As standards of health rise, as a result of better social services, northern Canada will presumably become a labour surplus area. The first obligation on the authorities is to provide the Eskimos and Indians with useful occupations in the part of Canada where they choose to live. This is presumably the main reason for the present drive to educate northerners, to provide many of them with economcially useful technical skills, and also to help those not capable of such a revolutionary change to maintain themselves by traditional occupations supplemented by small-scale craft industries. In the absence of the kind of profit enterprises common in the south, co-operatives and other modest community ventures are being encouraged to make possible developments of local resources as, for example, the fish and timber of Ungava Bay.

2. The possibility of developing northern minerals on a commercial scale lies in a co-partnership of private industry (if it desires to participate) and public enterprise. This has been demonstrated in other arctic areas of the world (a Canadian mining company has shared in a Greenland government mining project and a Canadian airline may adopt a similar technique there). Such "joint operations" are far from impossible in northern Canada, because there is a long tradition of

comparable public enterprise in the provinces. However, in the case of mining, it has become customary for public funds to be expended by subsidies or other devices without in return retaining a share in title to the industry. In this matter other nations such as Denmark, Norway, Sweden, and Finland appear to be more hard-headed, seeing to it that the capital invested by the state also earns its share of the profits (as it bears a proportion of the losses) along with private capital.[8] Cases have been cited of mining industries in the Canadian northwest where the contribution from public funds has been or may be expected to be very high indeed. The railway to Great Slave Lake to be built with public funds is likely to cost far more than the mine it is designed to serve. There would seem to be sound reasons to ensure that the public interest will be protected by joint ownership of such enterprises. Some might consider that Canada should go even further, and enable the state itself to take the initiative in determining *when* a valuable national resource should be developed. A case in point might be the valuable lead and zinc deposit on Great Slave Lake, which will apparently continue to lie idle until the smelters at Trail, B.C., need concentrates to keep them going. On such a basis, any ores, oil or gas there may be in the north will continue to serve as a "strategic reserve" to be called on when thought appropriate in London, New York or the Hague. This would seem to be a less than satisfactory way for Canada to develop its resources and to people its frontiers.

3. Since rapid development of the Far North based on mineral resources is not to be expected in the near future, there is still time to ensure that when such development does take place, it will be rational, and in the best interest of the country as a whole. The time made available to us should therefore be utilized in such ways as these:

(*a*) To explore and study the Canadian North thoroughly to determine with reasonable accuracy its extent and main characteristics, in other words "to map it" scientifically (on a scale of about four miles to the inch), to show bedrock geology, terrain types, forests, soils, and biological resources. Such an inventory-taking can be carried out far more speedily today than was possible even a decade ago, and particularly in the 1920's and 1930's when a similar undertaking was initiated in the Soviet Union.

(*b*) To provide, at strategic locations in the North, a network of permanently-manned scientific stations for regular observation of the various geophysical phenomena and to serve as bases for the scientific study of surrounding areas.

(*c*) To initiate a long-term, systematic study of all aspects of the arctic seas, including the Polar Basin. Little has been done as yet by Canada along these lines. There is still only very limited knowledge of sea-ice conditions, for example, vital though this is to secure and dependable navigation.

(*d*) To undertake long overdue social and economic studies related to development of the natural and human resources of the North. Success or failure of settlement there may well depend upon them.

A large-scale scientific stocktaking of northern Canada of the kind envisaged here will be very expensive. There can be no place in it for waste, or for duplication of effort. There will need to be genuine coordination, a balancing of work between the traditional scientific disciplines and an absence of interdepartmental rivalries in government agencies. An expansion of the co-operative system being tested by the Polar Continental Shelf Project would seem to have much merit.

So pressing is the need for scientific activity in the north, that all available means should be employed. Generous help should be provided from public funds for the universities and for such private agencies as the Arctic Institute of North America. This is essential, not only to speed the work itself but also to ensure production of the new generation of arctic scientists and administrators so urgently needed.

Some developments in northern Canada cannot, however, await completion of this gigantic scientific stocktaking, for economic and social improvement is long overdue. When planning new industries, better com-

The Land Changes

munities, modern transportation, and greater use of the local resources, the authorities will need to take into account the following:

(i) The role of the native people should be paramount. They have been dispossessed of their inheritance without fair compensation, and are entitled to adequate education and training to allow them to play eventually a leading part in their native land. My own view is that Canada should follow a policy of absorbing the Eskimos and Indians, at present isolated from other Canadians, into the general community. There is no need for compulsion in this; there are many examples from other lands of the effectiveness of equality of opportunity in education and employment for bringing it about. There is, however, much lost ground to be retrieved. At Canadian universities one is aware of the presence of peoples welcomed from many a distant, under-developed land. I have, however, yet to encounter many students from the not-so-distant under-developed territory of Caughnawaga or the remoter colony of Pangnirtung.

(ii) The wildlife and other renewable resources must be carefully preserved for posterity.

(iii) Strict control over non-renewable resources should be retained for the benefit of the community as a whole, and not alienated for the short-term enrichment of speculators, Canadian or not.

(iv) No appreciable development of the Far North is likely without large public investment, whether in scientific surveys or for construction of harbours, airfields, radio aids, roads, railways, towns, schools and churches. This enormous investment of public funds will surely need to be safeguarded. It seems to me incontrovertible that the common good requires that companies operating in the Far North must include an appreciable proportion of public capital in their financial structure. Such may, in fact, be the only way of ensuring that control over company policies is employed in the interest of this country.

Nothing I have said suggests that the immediate future of the Canadian north is a particularly rosy one. Large outlays must be anticipated before there is much income, for the road to national development is always expensive. All we can determine at present is that the resources that may exist in the North will be wisely utilized, that the local residents shall not be exploited, and that planning for the future must be based on a broad, systematic and thorough scientific appraisal.

*

FOOTNOTES

1 S. V. Slavin, "Management of the Socialist Development of the Soviet North: Methods and Forms," *Problems of the North* (Ottawa: National Research Council, 1960), pp. 247–262. (Translation of *Problemi Severa*, no. 1 [Academy of Sciences of the U.S.S.R., 1958].)

2 B. G. Sivertz, "The North as a Region," *Resources for Tomorrow* (Ottawa, 1961), I, p. 571.

3 *Ibid.,* p. 569.

4 M. J. Dunbar, "The Living Resources of Northern Canada," *Canadian Population and Northern Colonization,* Royal Society of Canada "Studia Varia" series (Toronto: University of Toronto Press, 1962), pp. 127–137.

5 Charles Camsell, "The Unexplored Area of Continental Canada," *Geog. J.* (September, 1916), pp. 249–257.

6 The United States Air Force base at Thule, Greenland, is in effect a city devoted to defence operations based largely on scientific research and development.

7 Sivertz, *op. cit.,* 576.

8 A recent Canadian recognition of this need may be cited from the Province of Quebec. See interview with Premier Jean Lesage concerning provincial financial collaboration in developing natural resources, *Montreal Star* (September 1, 1961).

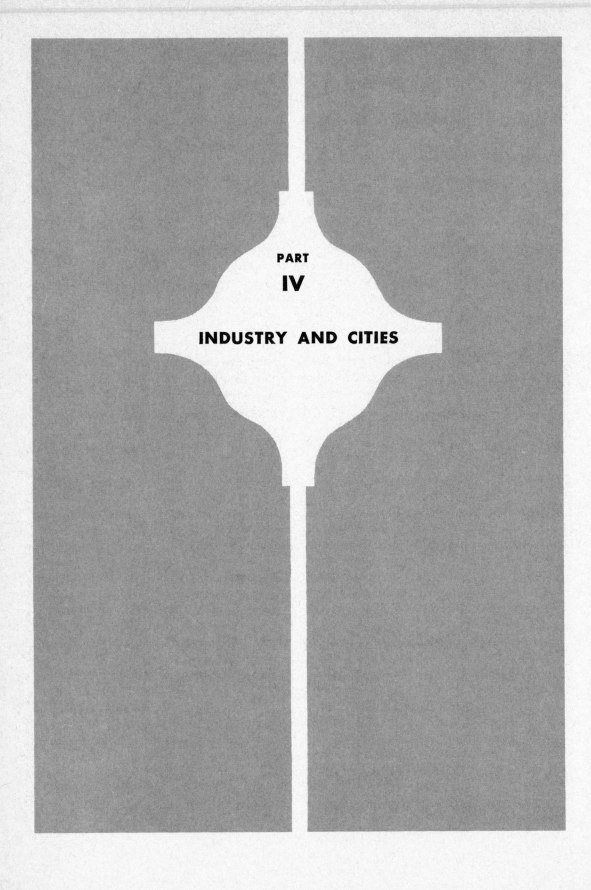

PART

IV

INDUSTRY AND CITIES

10

The Spatial Organization of the Iron and Steel Industry in Canada*

DONALD KERR

* Previously unpublished. Printed by permission of the author.

Since the turn of the century, three widely spaced cities, Sydney in Nova Scotia, and Hamilton and Sault Ste. Marie in Ontario have accounted for nearly all of the production of pig iron in Canada and about 90 per cent of the steel ingots and castings.[1] As production increased from just less than one million tons of steel on the eve of World War I to over three million tons in the late 1940's and ten million tons in the mid-1960's, the relative importance of each centre has changed. Whereas in the first decade of this century, Sydney produced about half of all the steel, at present it turns out less than 10 per cent. By way of contrast, the mills at Hamilton account for over 55 per cent and

the one at Sault Ste. Marie almost 25 per cent. The remaining 10 per cent is produced mainly from scrap in electric furnaces, most of which are located in the Montreal-Sorel region, the Niagara Peninsula and major cities in Western Canada.

The purpose of this paper is to describe the spatial distribution of the primary iron and steel industry in Canada. In doing so, it will, hopefully, throw some light on basic patterns of economic geography and lay the groundwork for a more rigorous, historically-oriented and quantatively-based study which must follow. A discussion of the development and current status of steel manufacturing at each of the three centres is followed by a commentary on the overall influences of resources and markets on the locational pattern.

*

SYDNEY, NOVA SCOTIA

Although the origins of steel manufacturing in Nova Scotia go back to the 1870's the beginnings of an integrated works at Sydney dates from 1901. Unquestionably, the existence of large deposits of coal on eastern Cape Breton Island proved to be attractive, but the generosity of the Sydney Council in making property available to the company

and exempting it from taxes for thirty years were added incentives.[2] By 1928, the financial reorganization of some units and the merging of others brought the steel and coal operations at Sydney under the control of one company. Units affected ranged from those engaged in the mining of iron ore at Bell Island to those engaged in the fabrication

TABLE I

CAPACITY OF STEEL FURNACES OF PRIMARY PRODUCERS (INCLUDING SUBSIDIARY PLANTS)
IN THOUSANDS OF NET TONS PER YEAR * ON JANUARY 1, 1957 AND JANUARY 1, 1966

Primary Producer		Open Hearth	Oxygen	Electric	Total
ALGOMA	1957	1,120			1,120
Sault Ste. Marie	1966	1,150	1,450		2,600
DOFASCO	1957	100	365	185	650
Hamilton	1966		2,100	50	2,150
DOSCO	1957	820		116 †	936
Sydney	1966	979		120 †	1,099
STELCO	1957	2,040		110	2,150
Hamilton	1966	3,750		200 ‡	3,950

Primary Producers
Total 1957–4,856,000 tons
Total 1966–9,799,000 tons

All Steel Producers
Total 1957– 5,500,000 tons
Total 1966–10,800,000 tons

* Equipment considered obsolete, or not in use for some other reason, not included.
† Includes two furnaces in Montreal (annual capacity approximately 90,000 net tons)
‡ Includes two furnaces of the Premier Steel Works in Edmonton (annual capacity approximately 200,000 net tons)
Source–*Metallurgical Works in Canada* "Primary Iron and Steel", Mineral Resources Division, Department of Mines and Technical Surveys, Ottawa (annual reports) with modifications and brought up-to-date from information supplied by companies

of steel at Montreal. The Dominion Steel and Coal Corporation (Dosco) emerged as a very large industrial empire operating not only the steel mill at Sydney but also ships, shipyards, finishing mills and distributing facilities.

On the surface, it would appear that Sydney is a splendid location for the production of iron and steel. Coal is mined close by and iron ore and limestone can be brought in by low cost water transport, the former from Bell Island (the Wabana mine) off the coast of Newfoundland,[3] the latter from Aguathuna off the west coast. Further, the Sydney harbour is open for year-round shipping, placing, at least, no physical obstacle in the way of an expanding trade. In spite of what is apparently a favourable juxtaposition of raw materials, capacity of steel furnaces at Sydney has increased very slowly to one million tons (Table 1) and its relative position, as mentioned earlier, has declined sharply.

At the turn of the century, when at least four times as much coal as today was needed to produce a ton of steel, and before the by-product oven had become an economical way of manufacturing coke, coal-fields continued to exert a powerful attraction for primary iron and steel manufacturing. Subsequently, changes in technology in blast furnace operations and coke manufacturing have greatly reduced the consumption of coal per ton of steel and consequently its locational pull has been weakened. This disadvantage has been compounded by the fact that Cape Breton coal contains a relatively high percentage of sulphur (just over two per cent) and is very volatile, so that it makes coke inferior to that which is manufactured from Appalachian coal at Hamilton and Sault Ste. Marie.[4] Further, it is expensive to mine and the delivered cost at the mill is no lower than that of U.S. coal at Hamilton. Iron ore from the Wabana mine contains more silica and phosphorus than is desirable for the open hearth furnaces at Sydney, and it must be mixed with varying amounts of ore brought in mainly from Labrador and Brazil. Thus, the mill's accessibility to coal and ore is only apparent; it is offset in an economic sense by the very nature of these materials which, in turn, make steel manufacturing costs somewhat higher than at the Ontario mills.[5]

In the early years of this century, the Sydney mill began to specialize in the production of rails to support the expansion of Canadian railways, especially in the Prairie Provinces. Following World War I, the demand for steel rails fell off greatly and other markets

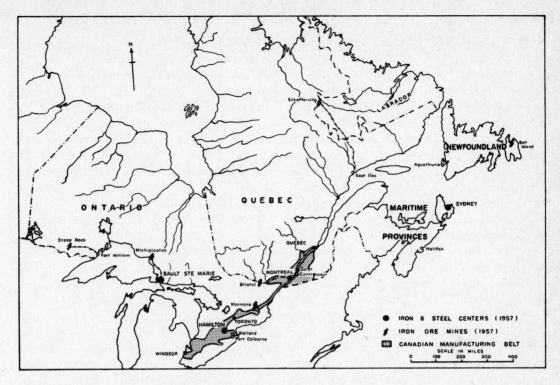

FIG. 1. Location of primary iron and steel mills and iron mines in eastern Canada.

were difficult to develop. Expectations that a number of steel-consuming industries would cluster in Sydney to form an industrial complex were not realized. To find at least a partial solution to the problems of marketing, subsidiary plants in Montreal, Toronto, Windsor and other centers in the St. Lawrence Lowlands were gradually acquired to absorb a great deal of the production. The recent planning and completion of rolling and finishing mills near Contrecoeur, Quebec points up the continuation of this policy. The handicap of high freight charges is partially overcome by shipping blooms, billets, wire rod, etc. to fabricating mills in southern Ontario and Quebec for further processing. To cite one example only, freight charges on nails from Sydney to Toronto are approximately twice those of wire rod from which the nails are manufactured.

Subsidiaries in the Maritime Pronvices, such as the Halifax Shipyards and the Trenton Steel Works (railway cars, wheels and axles), normally take less than 20 per cent

of the steel production at Sydney. The mill is admirably located to export steel but relatively high costs of production and, to some extent, the lack of facilities for manufacturing a greater variety of products, restricts overseas trade. On the other hand, rails make up 40 per cent of the total production, some of which is exported, and the reconstruction of the rail-finishing mill at Sydney in the early 1950's made it one of the most efficient on the continent.[6]

In summary, Sydney's distance from the market, its poor quality coking coal and the general lack of local supplies of scrap are serious disadvantages which are only partially offset by reasonable access to iron ore, specialization in certain products (rails), subsidiaries, cheap ocean transport for the export of steel and fully integrated operations. Undoubtedly, the persistence of production in such a marginal location is due to inertia,[7] for today it would be uneconomical to build a steel mill so far from the main market.[8]

By any yardstick, Hamilton is by far the most important steel-producing centre in Canada. Two of the four primary producers, Stelco and Dofasco, have appropriated large tracts of land on Burlington Bay for their operations and each year account for approximately 38 per cent and 19 per cent of the Canadian production of steel ingots and castings, respectively. The regional location resembles that of Cleveland or Buffalo or other Great Lakes cities; it is market-oriented and in terms of transport costs, half way between coal and iron ore.

Although the origins of iron working at Hamilton are obscure, the roots of the modern complex go back to the building of a blast furnace in 1895, followed by a steel mill two years later. These decisions were influenced to a large extent by the local council's generosity in providing a free site for the plant, a long term exemption from local taxes and a cash payment if expansion proceeded at a determined rate.[9] However, it was not without competition. By 1900, at least six blast furnaces had been built in Ontario, in response to the Federal Government's policy of 1883, to pay a cash bonus for the production of pig iron from domestic ore.[10] Problems in the smelting of low grade Ontario ore proved to be insurmountable and in the long run, all operations except those at Hamilton were closed down. In fact, it was probably the government's decision in 1897 to pay a similar bounty on the processing of foreign ore that saved the American-owned Hamilton operation from bankruptcy. From that time on, expansion continued and was based entirely on the import of high quality hematite from Minnesota.

In 1910, the Hamilton Steel Company, which had become Canadian-owned, merged with four other companies (Montreal Rolling Mills, Dominion Wire of Lachine, Quebec, Canadian Bolt of Toronto, Gananoque, Belleville and Brantford, and Canadian Screw of Hamilton) to form Stelco.[11] From this union, Stelco has grown to be, without question, the largest steel company in Cana-

da, having a steel furnace capacity of almost four million tons (see Table 1). Dofasco was founded in 1917 but did not become a fully integrated works until 1951, when its first blast furnace was built. Since then, it has grown at a remarkable rate, achieving a steel furnace capacity of two million tons in 1965.

In retrospect, decisions to build and expand steel mills at Hamilton proved to be well taken, for, approximately one third of all manufacturing in Canada lies within a radius of about 100 miles of Hamilton. Even more relevant, is the concentration of large consumers of high quality steel, including industries which produce automobiles, farm machinery, domestic appliances and electrical goods. The questions may be asked: to what extent did the availability of steel at Hamilton help to stimulate this industrial development, or has steel production simply followed the expanding market demand? Perhaps the question is more important than the answer for it serves to draw attention, at least superficially, to the systems of industrial interconnections which have grown up around the western end of Lake Ontario and beyond. Clearly, a process of circular causation, set in motion in the early part of the century, has been remarkably well sustained.

Not only is Hamilton central in the market sense, but also in terms of distance from raw materials and thus in the cost of assembling such materials. High quality coking coal comes from properties in Pennsylvania and West Virginia, owned, in part or outright, by the Canadian steel companies. The freight costs to Hamilton from the coal fields have progressively diminished as the consumption of coal per ton of steel has declined. For example, twenty years ago, approximately 1.5 tons of coal were needed to produce one ton of steel; in 1965 only 0.5 tons were needed in the operations at Dofasco.[12] Until very recently, practically all of the iron ore consumed at Hamilton came from mines in Minnesota, jointly owned with

American steel companies. Shipped most of the way in lake carriers, the ore can be assembled at a cost which, in the aggregate, closely approximates that of coal. This emphasizes Hamilton's position half way between coal and iron ore. Further, it lies midway between the old mines in the Superior Uplands and the new ones in Labrador-Quebec, the costs of shipping ore from Wabush to Hamilton not being significantly different than those from Mesabi to Hamilton. Consequently, its competitive position, with respect to ore, will not change as larger amounts of Canadian ore move from Labrador and Quebec through the Seaway to the Hamilton mills. To complete the picture, limestone is quarried nearby and normally, a surplus of scrap accumulates in southwestern Ontario.

From the outset, the Hamilton mills have manufactured a greater variety of steel products than their competitors, but in turn, have never produced rails or rail fastenings. Although precise figures on shipments are not available and although they vary from year to year, it may be estimated that at least 55 per cent of the production is sold in southwestern Ontario within a radius of 100 miles; about 30 per cent is shipped to the rest of southern Ontario and Quebec (mainly Montreal) for sale; another 8 per cent is shipped west and about 7 per cent is exported.

*

SAULT STE. MARIE

A fully integrated iron and steel works, accounting for about one quarter of all steel production in Canada, has grown up on the northern bank of the St. Mary's River at Sault Ste. Marie. The building of a mill on this site can be explained only in terms of the personal initiative of Francis Clergue, a most remarkable entrepreneur.[13] While reconnoitering the area in 1894, he noticed a half-completed hydro-electric power plant on the St. Mary's River. Sensing the possibilities of the region, he convinced the town council of Sault Ste. Marie that he could not only finish the abortive power development but add other industries as well. Subsequently, a pulp mill and a ferro-nickel plant were built. The discovery of iron ore at Michipicoten, about 120 miles north of the Sault, was followed by the building of a steel mill in 1902. Early expansion was based on the demand for steel rails. In 1909, American properties, such as limestone mines at Fiborn, Michigan, and coal mines in West Virginia were acquired; they are still controlled by the company. As high grade hematite diminished at Michipicoten, ore was imported in increasing quantities across Lake Superior from Minnesota. In 1921, the Canadian mines were closed down and the mill became entirely dependent on American raw materials, until the outbreak of World War II. Mainly because of Algoma's marginal location to markets in southern Ontario and Quebec and declining sales in rails, production during the 1920's and 1930's was small and intermittent. Bankruptcy in 1932 was followed by financial reorganization in 1934.

In 1939, the ore bodies at Michipicoten were reappraised and because the province of Ontario had for many years agreed to pay a bounty on domestic production, the company decided to develop the low grade siderite deposits. Two mines, containing ore with a 35 per cent iron content, but also a very significant manganese content, were brought into operation and a sintering plant was built. Production of Algoma sinter averages 1.8 million tons a year, of which 85 per cent is consumed by the mill at the Sault and the remainder exported to the United States. In return, modest amounts of red ore and iron pellets are brought in from Minnesota. Because of the increasing demand for iron ore, Algoma reached an agreement with Steep Rock Iron Mines in 1965 to take delivery of at least one million tons of iron pellets annually beginning in 1967.

As noted, the most serious historical, and in fact contemporary, problem is Algoma's marginal location to the main Canadian market of southern Ontario and Quebec, where about two-thirds of all its steel production is sold. Entrance to this market is gained in one of three ways: by absorbing freight charges on those products and product sizes offered by Hamilton competitors, by specializing in the manufacture of products such as wide flange beams which are not made elsewhere in Canada and on which freight costs do not have to be equalized, and by shipping some products on chartered vessels to Lower Lakes ports. The remaining one-third of the steel production is sold throughout the rest of Canada but mainly in the west. Pig iron, mostly from the Port Colborne works, and small amounts of steel are shipped to the United States.

In spite of its marginal location, Algoma has more than doubled its capacities of steel furnaces from just over one million tons in 1956 to 2.5 million in 1965, by installing three L-D oxygen furnaces. Consumption of coal and scrap iron per ton of steel ingots has been reduced, that of sinter and iron pellets increased. Algoma, being situated closer to iron ore fields than Hamilton, has been able to benefit accordingly. Finally, Algoma has been able to take advantage of the substantial increase in the demand for steel in the west to a greater extent than its competitors.

*

OTHER MILLS

In addition to the primary works, a number of small to medium-sized mills produce about 1¼ million tons of steel and almost 750,000 tons of pig iron annually. Typically, these small steel mills turn out products for a local market, and in turn depend very heavily on local supplies of scrap, most of which is processed in electric furnaces. Clearly, production costs are higher than those in the large integrated works but in turn can be offset either by specialization, which, in the case of the Atlas Steel Company at Welland, supports an export trade of high quality stainless steel, or by market proximity. The significance of the latter is well illustrated in Western Canada where steel mills with an aggregate capacity of approximately 600,000 tons are found in every major centre, namely, Vancouver, Edmonton, Calgary, Regina and Winnipeg. In Eastern Canada, mills having a capacity of approximately 400,000 tons have been built on the margins of the Toronto-Hamilton conurbation and those having just over 300,000 tons in the Montreal-Sorel region.

For a variety of reasons, pig iron is produced at Kimberley, B.C., Port Colborne, Ontario, and Sorel, Quebec. The basis of production at Kimberley is the existence of at least 13 million tons of "iron tailings" which have accumulated from the mining of lead and zinc. Recently, steel-making facilities have been added to the iron works and about 100,000 tons are produced annually. The Algoma Steel Corporation maintains a subsidiary plant at Port Colborne where the the capacity of the blast furnace is 240,000 tons of pig iron a year. Most of the iron ore and all of the coal are brought by low cost water transport from the United States and in turn, varying amounts of pig iron are shipped to the United States. At Sorel, approximately 400,000 tons of pig iron are produced by the Quebec Iron and Titanium Corporation as a by-product of the manufacture of titanium dioxide concentrate. Finally, at the time of writing, the Quebec Government was planning an integrated iron and steel works at Bécancour, just across the river from Trois Rivières.[14] It should be noted that further upstream, in the vicinity of Contrecoeur, both Dosco and Stelco have quite recently built or have planned to build large finishing mills. In short, the St. Lawrence Valley below Montreal, and including the mills at Sorel and Contrecoeur, may emerge as an important steel producing and steel fabricating region.

*

RESOURCES

Domestic resources have had a minimal influence on the location of Canadian steel mills. Canadian coal is consumed only at the Sydney mill and it is very unlikely that either Nova Scotia or Alberta coal will ever be used in any of the Ontario mills. The quality is inferior to that obtained from the Appalachian mines; in fact, recognition of the importance of coal fields in Pennsylvania and West Virginia brought about their purchase in part or outright by the Canadian companies.

Dependence on American ore, somewhat more variable than that of coal, has in recent years been diminishing. In 1956, 75 per cent of all ore consumed in Canada came from the United States; in 1965, the proportion was one-half. By far the largest consumers have been the two mills at Hamilton, which, until the summer of 1965 when first shipments were received from Wabush, imported almost all their ore from the United States. In fact, Stelco, like its American counterparts, invested many years ago in the development of iron mines in Minnesota and more recently in plants processing taconite.

In view of the absence of tariffs, ore can flow freely across the border, the direction of shipment being determined mainly by the patterns of ownership, and to a lesser extent by the nature of the ore and the transportation costs. Most ore is captive, its production and marketing being controlled by one or a number of steel companies. Thus, unlike other commodities, most of the production is not offered for sale on the open market. It is not surprising, therefore, that ore should flow from Minnesota to Hamilton or in turn from Labrador to the American Midwest.[15] During the last 25 years, the search for new sources of iron ore has focussed largely on the Canadian Shield. Developments have been noteworthy; in 1939 Canada produced no iron ore; in 1964 it produced almost 35 million tons (Table 2). As Canadian steel companies continue to invest more heavily in the development of Canadian properties, the proportion of domestic iron ore consumed by Canadian mills will increase. For various reasons, however, American ore will continue to be imported into Canada but in diminishing amounts.

*

MARKET PATTERNS

In the decade between 1956 and 1965, production of steel in Canada doubled, increasing at a rate exceeding that in the United States. The upshot has been a sharp decline in imports, especially from the United States. In fact, in a few products, a modest surplus for export has appeared. Whereas in the past only basic steel shapes such as rods and rails and bars were manufactured, at present an incredible variety of all sizes and shapes of steel is produced and only very highly specialized steel must still be im-

TABLE II

PRODUCTION OF USABLE IRON ORE IN 1964 BY MINE OR MINING DISTRICT AND
DESTINATION OF SHIPMENTS (IN MILLIONS OF TONS*)

Mine or Mining District	Total Production†	Domestic	Shipments U.S.A.	Other
NEWFOUNDLAND				
Wabana	1.2 (C)	0.4		0.8
LABRADOR-QUEBEC				
Schefferville	7.7 (D.S.)		6.2	1.5
Carol Lake	6.5 (C & A)	0.2	4.6	1.7
Wabush‡				
Cartier	9.1 (C)		9.1	
OTHER QUEBEC				
Hilton	0.9 (A)	0.45	0.45	
SOUTHERN ONTARIO				
Marmora	0.6 (A)		0.6	
NORTHERN ONTARIO				
Lowphos	0.6 (A)		0.6	
Algoma	1.8 (A)	1.5	0.3	
Caland-Steep Rock-Charleston	3.5 (D.S. & A)	0.5	3.0	
BRITISH COLUMBIA				
Vancouver Island	1.4 (C)			1.4
Queen Charlottes	0.4 (C)			0.4
By-product in Ontario and British Columbia	0.9 (C & A)	0.4	0.5	
Total	34.6	3.45	25.35	5.8

* *Source:* Wittur, G.E., Canadian Iron Ore Industry 1964, Mineral Information Bulletin No. 80, Mineral Resources Division, Department of Mines and Technical Surveys, Ottawa, 1965 (with modifications).
† D.S. refers to direct shipment ore (varying percentage of iron—on the average 50%).
  C refers to concentrates (ore content—on the average 60 per cent)
  A refers to agglomerates (ore content—on the average 64 per cent)
‡ Wabush mines began producing ore in 1965—at time of writing no figures on production were available.

ported.[16] Now that the gap between consumption and production on a national scale has virtually disappeared, a meaningful commentary on regional disparities is possible.

At the outset it is useful to assume that all mills turn out the same variety of products (which in fact they do not) and the F.O.B. selling price of each product does not vary from one mill to another. In such a hypothetical case, any price variation from one consuming centre to another would be determined by transportation charges alone.[17] On this basis, Hamilton mills can sell steel at a price lower then any competitor in a belt from Chatham in southwestern Ontario to Trois Rivières in the northeast. Disregarding tariff charges, Buffalo becomes competitive along the eastern fringe of the Niagara Peninsula, Detroit in the Windsor-Sarnia area, and both Sydney and European seaport mills downstream from Trois Rivières. It is apparent that on the basis of transport charges, Sydney can sell steel more cheaply than any domestic or overseas competitors through the Maritime Provinces and extreme Eastern Quebec. Consumption of steel in this region, however, is only about 3 per cent of the Canadian total or less than half the production at Sydney. On the other hand, Hamilton can sell steel within the most highly industrialized and densely populated part of Canada, at prices lower than any domestic or foreign competitor. Within this region, consumption of steel, which is extremely difficult to calculate, is estimated to be approximately 75 per cent of the Canadian total; production is just over 60 per cent of the national total, the deficiency being filled by shipments from Dosco, Algoma and foreign mills.

In terms of transport costs, Sault Ste. Marie has advantages over Hamilton northward and westward from approximately

North Bay to Alberta, an area, however, which accounts for only about 14 per cent of the Canadian consumption. In British Columbia, where consumption averages about six per cent, transportation charges from Hamilton and Sault Ste. Marie are equal on most products. However, disregarding tariffs, it may be noted that the mills at Fontana, California; Geneva, Utah; and European seaports can reach much of British Columbia and parts of the western Prairies at costs lower than those for the Ontario mills.

In summary, domestic producers have transportation advantages over all foreign competitors throughout Canada except in the far west, extreme southwestern Ontario, the eastern fringe of the Niagara Peninsula, and the lower St. Lawrence estuary. Among the domestic producers, it is quite clear that Hamilton has by far the most favourable location.

*

CONCLUSION

In conclusion, this study confirms generalizations about the location of primary steel manufacturing which have been brought forth by Isard,[18] Rodgers[19] and others. The Hamilton location represents an almost perfect adjustment to the geographical organization of materials and markets. Half way between coal and ore and in the heart of a diverse and large market, Hamilton's location is unexcelled. Further, Hamilton Bay facilitates the assembly of raw materials at relatively low cost and provides access to cold water for cooling.

By way of contrast, Sydney is very much off-centre and Sault Ste. Marie less so. The fixity of these two centres for over 60 years in the face of serious problems is testimony to the importance of the law of inertia. As the consumption of coal and to a lesser extent, iron ore, has declined per ton of steel ingots, and as transportation rates have risen on finished products, the geographical position of Sydney has worsened. And yet it is extremely unlikely that this mill will ever be closed down and dismantled; its importance in the economy of Nova Scotia is too great. In short, investment in plant equipment, and economic and social and, therefore, political significance in the region, have emerged as the major contemporary locational factors in the Sydney steel industry.

The survival of the mill at Sault Ste. Marie, particularly during the critical years between 1919 and 1939 can only be explained in terms of investment in the site and astute financing. The law of inertia, however, has only historical relevance, for Algoma, at present, is in a very healthy financial condition and is, in fact, planning further expansion. Of the changing external relations of Sault Ste. Marie, those of increased consumption of steel in the west and greater accessibility to the St. Lawrence Lowlands through the shipment of non-competitive steel products such as wide flange beams, are the most important.[20]

In addition to market orientation and inertia, community attitude is the only other explanatory variable necessitating emphasis. As noted, decisions to build mills at each site were greatly influenced by the policies of the respective city councils in providing land and tax exemptions. Obviously, within each region, a considerable choice of suitable sites was available, the final selection of which was determined by the vigour of the community. Nor has the political factor in the location of mills diminished.

The location of a steel mill in the province of Quebec, if such a mill is to be built, will be decided, in part, by political considerations.

*

1 For the early history of the iron and steel industry in Canada see: W. S. Donald, *The Canadian Iron and Steel Industry* (Boston, 1915); and Donald Eldon, *American Influences on the Canadian Iron and Steel Industry* (Ph.D. Thesis, Harvard University, Cambridge Mass., 1952). The writer has drawn heavily on the excellent publications of the Mineral Resources Division, Department of Mines and Technical Surveys (See Reference 20) for contemporary data.

2 W. Keith Buck and R. B. Elver, *The Canadian Steel Industry—A Pattern of Growth,* Mineral Information Bulletin No. 70, Mineral Resources Division, Department of Mines and Technical Surveys (Ottawa: Queen's Printer, 1963), p. 7.

3 The Wabana mine has been closed down permanently: see Obituary for Bell Island, *Toronto Globe and Mail* (April 30, 1966), p. 8.

4 *The Steel Industry of Nova Scotia:* Report No. 11 by the Arthur McKee Co. to the Royal Commission on Provincial Development and Rehabilitation of Nova Scotia (Halifax, 1944), p. 47.

5 L. Morgan, *The Canadian Primary Iron and Steel Industry,* a special study for the Royal Commission on Canada's Economic Prospects (the Gordon Commission) (Ottawa, 1956), pp. 16–17.

6 *Ibid,* p. 11.

7 Allan Rodgers, "Industrial Inertia—A Major Factor in the Location of the Iron and Steel Industry in the United States," *Geographical Review,* Vol. 42, (1952), pp. 56–66.

8 Walter Isard, "Some Locational Factors in the Iron and Steel Industry since the Early Nineteenth Century," *Journal of Political Economy,* Vol. 56 (1948), pp. 203–217.

9 William Kilbourn, *The Elements Combined, A History of the Steel Company of Canada* (Toronto, 1960), page 48.

10 Buck and Elver, *op. cit.,* pp. 6–7.

11 Kilbourn, *op. cit.,* pp. 79–96.

12 Correspondence with management at Dofasco (March 1966).

13 Donald Eldon, "The Career of Francis H. Clergue," *Explorations in Entrepreneurial History,* Volume 3, No. 4 (1951), pp. 254–267.

14 A change of government in June, 1966, has resulted in a re-examination of these plans.

15 Donald Kerr, "The St. Lawrence Seaway and Trade on the Great Lakes, 1958–63," *The Canadian Geographer,* Volume 8, No. 4 (1964), pp. 191–2.

16 "Growth of Canadian Steel," Monthly Review of the Bank of Nova Scotia (Toronto, May 1963).

17 In an earlier paper, Donald Kerr, "The Geography of the Canadian Iron and Steel Industry," *Economic Geography,* Volume 35, No. 2 (1959), tables giving precise data on freight charges were presented on pages 160 and 161. Although these figures are out-of-date and have been deleted from this paper, they still have validity in showing the relative costs between centres.

18 Isard, *op. cit.*

19 Rodgers, *op. cit.*

20 The reader who wishes to keep up to date on developments of the iron and steel industry in Canada and those of the iron ore industry is referred to the excellent annual publications of the Mineral Resources Division, Department of Mines and Technical Surveys, Ottawa, in particular: "Primary Iron and Steel" (in the series *Metallurgical Works in Canada*), and "The Canadian Iron Ore Industry" (in the series *Mineral Information Bulletins*), (Ottawa: Queen's Printer).

11

The Location of United States Subsidiaries in Southern Ontario*

D. MICHAEL RAY

* Research supported by a (United States) Social Science Research Council fellowship 1964–1965. A more complete report is presented in Market Potential and Economic Shadow "Chicago: Department of Geography, Research Series No. 101, University of Chicago, 1965. Professors Chauncy D. Harris, Brian J. L. Berry and Harold M. Mayer of the University of Chicago offered many stimulating comments and constructive criticisms during the course of the research. Printed by permission of the author.

One-half of the manufacturing in Canada is owned and controlled by United States nationals. American ownership of the auto-mobile and rubber industries is almost complete, although, by contrast, American ownership of the beverage, textile, and steel industries is neglibible. What factors influence the location of American subsidiaries in Canada? What is their geographic pattern of location and what is their influence on regional economic development? This paper develops a general concept of industrial location to answer these questions and it focuses attention on Southern Ontario where American subsidiaries are concentrated.

*

THE INFLUX OF UNITED STATES CAPITAL

The United States replaced the United Kingdom as Canada's main source of foreign capital investment after World War I. American investment in Canada rose during and after World War II, and since 1948 has provided a substantial proportion of the total investment in Canadian industrial and resource development.

American investment has tended increasingly to take the form of direct investment in particular firms rather than portfolio investment. Direct investments are defined as:

Those investments in business enterprise which are sufficiently concentrated to constitute control of the concerns.... Direct investments are usually in the form of equity ownership. The investors supply the capital assuming the largest burden of risk, technical knowledge and skills.... In general, portfolio investments have a passive character in contrast to the more dynamic influences of direct investments.[1]

Americans, consequently, have played an increasingly important role in the location of manufacturing enterprises in Canada.

149

The location of United States branch plants is related to their need to maintain close contact with the parent company, particularly in the early stages of their organization. The parent company is generally represented by its own board of directors or senior executives at branch plant board meetings. Among larger, wholly-owned United States subsidiaries in Canada, for instance, more directors live in the United States than in Canada (see Table 1). American branch plants, "tend, therefore, to be located in regions which are near the parent company and the main industrial centres of the northern United States from which, in many cases, they draw complex parts, technical services, or management and supervisory advice."[2]

The location of those industries which are predominantly United States owned and controlled is concentrated, therefore, in Southern Ontario, the closest and most accessible part of Canada to the United States manufacturing belt. Industries, in which United States investment is most concentrated, have had the highest industrial growth rates since 1948 and have provided Ontario with the largest post-war industrial growth rate in Canada, as well as a substantial proportion of the province's total manufacturing employment. A survey of the larger United States controlled firms

in Canada showed that they provided nearly one-third of the manufacturing employment in Ontario compared with less than one-twentieth in the Atlantic Provinces.

The effects of American ownership of Canadian manufacturing on economic development have caused considerable political concern. Nevertheless, the influence of external factors on regional economic development is not a problem unique to Canada.

Almost every fear and complaint expressed in Canada about the inflow of American funds and the dominance of American corporations can find its counterpart in the southern region of the United States. There, too, there are complaints about "absentee ownership", about the absence of research facilities in the region, about the fact that able men must leave the region in order to hold the higher positions in the companies, and about the fact that under certain conditions, the companies may tend to "drain profits" from the region. These facts seem to indicate that the problem is not a political or national one, but rather that it is purely economic in origin.[3]

The location of American subsidiaries in Canada must be explained not in terms of political factors but in terms of economic factors which are combined to form a new concept, *economic shadow*.

TABLE I
RESIDENCE OF DIRECTORS OF 105 DIRECT
INVESTMENT COMPANIES

Residence of Directors	Wholly-Owned Subsidiaries	Partially-Owned Subsidiaries	Total
United States	219	155	374
United Kingdom	11	38	49
Canada	199	284	483
Total Directors	429	477	906

Source: Canada, Royal Commission on Canada's Economic Prospects (RCCEP), Canada-United States Economic Relations, by Irving Brecher and S.S. Reisman (Ottawa: Queen's Printer, 1957), p. 134.

*

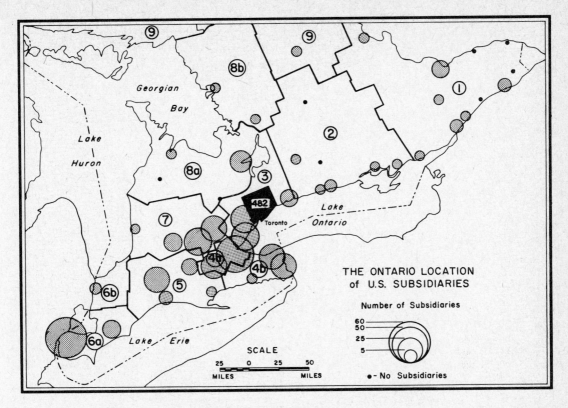

FIG. 1. *The Ontario Location of United States Subsidiaries.*

THE ELEMENTS OF ECONOMIC SHADOW

The basic data from which the concept of economic shadow has been developed are tabulations giving the locations of all subsidiaries in Ontario controlled by each of the sixty-two largest industrial centres in the United States. Some of these tabulations are presented in Table 2. Examine first the relationship between the number of Ontario subsidiaries and the number of manufacturing establishments in, and the distance of each Standard Metropolitan Statistical Area (SMSA) from Toronto. The larger the SMSA, the more Ontario subsidiaries it tends to have. New York and Chicago have 210 and 147 subsidiaries respectively. Boston, about the same distance from Toronto as New York and Chicago but with many fewer establishments, has only 14 Ontario subsidiaries. The number of Ontario subsidiaries is also strongly influenced by the distance of the SMSA from Ontario. The

further a United States city is from Ontario, the fewer the number of Ontario subsidiaries it tends to control. Compare Los Angeles, Chicago and Buffalo. Los Angeles, with more establishments than Chicago, has 35 Ontario subsidiaries, that is, only one more than Buffalo.

In general, the number of Ontario subsidiaries controlled from any United States city is directly proportional to the number of establishments in that city and inversely proportional to its distance from the province. Stated another way, the interaction between United States cities and Ontario, as measured by the establishment of branch plants, is analogous to the force of gravity which is also proportional to mass and inversely proportional to distance. A mathematical equation can be written that estimates the number of Ontario branch plants that are likely to be established by any United States

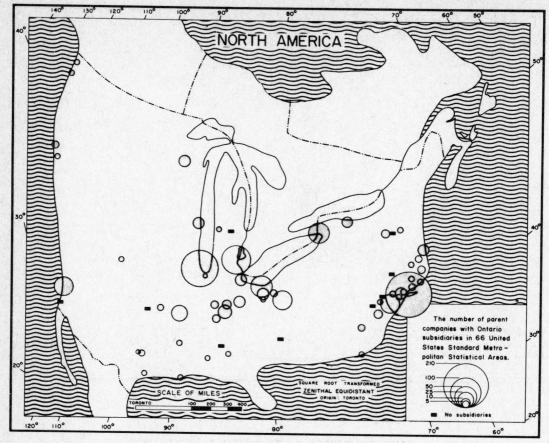

FIG. 2. *The Location of United States Parent Companies with Ontario Subsidiaries.*

city. Such an equation is called a gravity or *interactance model*.[4] The validity of this concept has been demonstrated by the accuracy with which the model estimates the actual number of subsidiaries.

As a corollary of this interactance model and the reduction of interactance with increasing distance, it follows that economic development within Ontario must closely reflect the economic health of those United States regions contiguous to the province. The importance of this corollary may be seen by comparing the map of the Ontario locations of United States subsidiaries and the map of the location of United States parent companies (Figs. 1 and 2). Note the proximity of the American Midwest industrial concentration to Southwestern Ontario, compared with the distance of the New York region to Eastern Ontario. This geographic pattern is reflected as a contrast between the number of subsidiaries in Southwestern and Eastern Ontario.

The location of United States subsidiaries in Ontario cannot be explained adequately in terms of the interactance model alone. Two other factors are evident. Examine Figure 3 which links by straight lines, termed "desire lines," the location of a hundred Ontario subsidiaries, drawn at random, to their parent companies in the United States. The map reveals a pattern of geographic *sectoral affinity*; that is, subsidiaries tend to be located in the geographic sector that links the parent company to the primary Ontario market centre, Toronto. Of 35 Ontario subsidiaries with parent companies in Los Angeles, 28 are in Toronto Metropolitan Region, and 7 are in Southwestern Ontario. Of 210 Ontario subsidiaries with parent com-

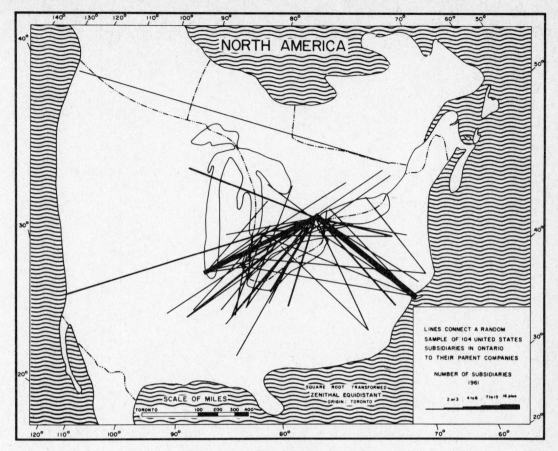

FIG. 3. Industrial Desire Lines.

panies in the New York Metropolitan Area, 179 are in Toronto or locations closer to New York.

Toronto provides the optimal market location for American subsidiaries and few subsidiaries locate beyond it. In general, industrial interactance between a city within a region and an external city is severely restricted whenever the primary regional market centre becomes an *intervening opportunity*,[5] terminating sectoral affinity. An "economic shadow" is thus cast over the area lying beyond the sector that links the parent company to the primary regional market centre. An Ontario city, for example, suffers economic shadow whenever Toronto constitutes an intervening opportunity between it and a United States city. Toronto impedes Eastern Ontario's interactance with all United States industrial centres except those in New England and adjacent states. Hence, sectoral affinity parallels the effect of economic interactance, to augment the contrast between the number of subsidiaries in Southwestern and Eastern Ontario.

A third element is apparent from an examination of Table II and Figure 3. Compare the Ontario location of the 35 Los Angeles and the 34 Buffalo subsidiaries. Buffalo has 10 subsidiaries in the Toronto Region compared with 28 for Los Angeles. Seventeen of Buffalo's subsidiaries are in the adjacent Niagara Region. The contrast between the location of Chicago and Detroit subsidiaries is equally striking. Detroit has more subsidiaries in its border satellite, Windsor, than in the four-county Toronto Region; Chicago subsidiaries are concentrated in Toronto with a fairly even scattering of the remainder between Toronto and Windsor.

TABLE II

THE LOCATION OF UNITED STATES SUBSIDIARIES IN SOUTHERN ONTARIO BY SUB-REGIONS

United States SMSA	Number of establishments 1958.	Distance from Toronto by air (km).	Eastern Ontario	Lake Ontario	Metropolitan Toronto	Burlington	Niagara	Lake Erie	Lake St. Clair Border	Lake St. Clair Lambton	Upper Grand River	Georgian Bay	Northern Ontario	Total Ontario
Akron	698	336			9	2	1	1			1			14
Boston	5,665	690		2	8	4								14
Buffalo	1,820	96		1	10	2	17	1			3			34
Chicago	13,508	702	5	7	98	11	3	6	5	6	4	2		147
Cincinnati	1,776	660	2		12	2		2						18
Cleveland	3,898	306	1	1	28	9	6	1	1		2	1		50
Columbus	835	506			7			1		1		6		15
Detroit	6,468	340	4		26	6	1	3	37	3	9			89
Los Angeles	16,910	3,496			28	1		1	1	1	3			35
Milwaukee	2,298	693			10	1			1			1		13
Minn.-St. Paul	2,433	1,111	2		13			1				1	2	19
Newark	4,425	539			14		1	1		2		2		20
New York	39,396	557	7	7	145	12	8	11	3		11	3	3	210
Philadelphia	8,124	534	1	2	19	5	1	2			2	1		33
Pittsburgh	2,479	363			19	4		5	2		7		1	38
Rochester	1,015	152			10		2				1			13
St. Louis	3,150	1,065	2	1	13	2	1	4	1		5			29
Toledo	742	409		7		1	1		3	2		1		15
Total			24	28	469	62	42	40	54	15	48	18	6	806

Source: Compiled from a list of parent company addresses supplied by the Ontario Department of Economics and Development.

Note: These regions are mapped in Figure 1 which shows the distribution of subsidiaries by county.

TABLE III

ONTARIO AND TORONTO SUBSIDIARIES CONTROLLED BY UNITED
STATES PARENT COMPANIES LOCATED WITHIN TEN
DISTANCE BANDS FROM TORONTO

Distance Band Road Distance of Parent Company From Toronto	Total Number of Subsidiaries Controlled by Parent Companies Located in Each Distance Band	Toronto Metro. Area Subsidiaries	
		Number	Per cent
0 — 200	47	20	43
201 — 300	165	68	41
301 — 400	76	41	54
401 — 500	467	312	67
501 — 750	67	35	52
751 — 1000	56	32	58
1001 — 1250	5	4	80
1251 — 1500	11	8	73
1501 — 2000	0	0	—
2001 +	49	38	85
Total Sample	943	558	59

A pattern of *sectoral penetration* occurs in which the distance that a parent company penetrates into Ontario to locate a branch plant is directly proportional to the distance of the parent company from Ontario. The Detroit manufacturer can evade the Canadian tariff barrier and prejudice against foreign products by locating a branch plant across the St. Clair River. The marginal benefits of locating closer to the centre of the Canadian market may not compensate for losing the convenience of operating the subsidiary close to the parent company. The marginal effort required by the Los Angeles manufacturer to locate in Toronto rather than near Windsor is negligible for land and negative for air. By extension, the Chicago manufacturer should tend to favour an intermediate location.

The corollary of sectoral penetration is that the more distant the United States centre from Ontario, the greater the proportion of its Ontario subsidiaries that are located in Toronto. This corollary is illustrated by Table III. United States cities closer than 400 miles to Toronto have a relatively low concentration of subsidiaries in Toronto. There is a sharp increase in the percentage of all subsidiaries in Toronto for cities located more than 1,000 miles from Toronto.

These three elements, (i) interactance, (ii) sectoral affinity, and (iii) sectoral penetration, determine the locational pattern of branch plants. They state that the chances of a city within a region attracting a branch plant controlled from an industrial centre outside that region, (1) are proportional to the size of the industrial centre and inversely proportional to the distance between the industrial centre and the city, (2) are seriously reduced whenever the primary regional market centre becomes an intervening opportunity for location, and (3) are influenced by any intervening barriers, whether political or physical, such that there is a direct relationship between the distance of the industrial centre from the barrier and the distance beyond the barrier it will likely penetrate in establishing a branch plant.

*

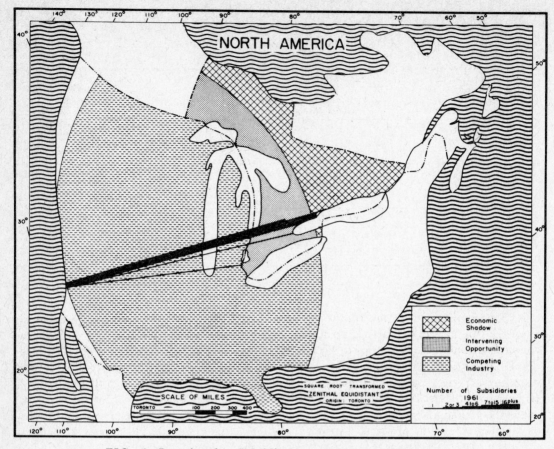

FIG. 4. *Los Angeles Subsidiaries and Economic Shadow.*

AREAS OF ECONOMIC SHADOW, INTERVENING OPPORTUNITY AND COMPETING INDUSTRIES

The three elements, which together constitute the economic shadow concept, may be reviewed by examining the maps of the location of the Ontario subsidiaries controlled from six United States cities (Figs. 4 to 9).[6] Ellipses have been produced on these maps by drawing one arc, with its centre at Toronto, through the United States city and the second arc, with the United States city as centre, through Toronto. These ellipses are used to define areas of economic shadow, intervening opportunity and competing industries.

The area of economic shadow is the area in Ontario which lies beyond the ellipse and hence beyond the area of sectoral affinity. This is termed the economic shadow area

because it appears unlikely that any Ontario subsidiary will be located farther from the parent company than Toronto, or farther from Toronto than the parent company.

The intervening opportunity area is the part of Ontario falling within the ellipse and, therefore, closer to the United States city than Toronto. It is the area of sectoral affinity.

The competing industries area is the area in the United States part of the ellipse; it is closer to Toronto than a particular United States city. Compare Figures 4, 8 and 7; the closer the United States city is to Ontario, the smaller is the concentration of the subsidiaries in Toronto. Los Angeles subsidiaries (Fig. 4) are almost all in Toronto. The

Industry and Cities

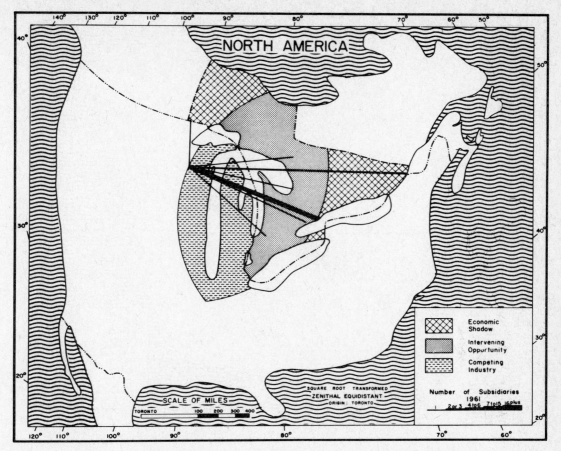

FIG. 5. *Minneapolis-St. Paul Subsidiaries and Economic Shadow.*

widest bar from Detroit (Fig. 7) points away from Toronto and to Windsor.

The more widely spaced the United States cities, the less satisfactory is any interchange of ellipses. The Minneapolis-St. Paul ellipse (Fig. 5) would exclude most Syracuse subsidiaries (Fig. 9). Minneapolis-St. Paul is the only city shown with subsidiaries in Northern Ontario. One of these, located in Rainy River, is further from Toronto than is Minneapolis-St. Paul, but is much closer to the parent company than any other part of Ontario.

The area of intervening opportunity changes with each United States city. Only ellipses from the Northeastern United States include Eastern Ontario (see Figs. 8 and 9). No ellipses cover Eastern Ontario exclusively, although most of the Niagara Peninsula is included in all ellipses. Many ellipses include only Southwestern Ontario and exclude Northern and Eastern Ontario (see Figs. 4, 5, 6, and 7). Compare these six figures with Figure 3 showing industrial desire lines and note how few desire lines cross Eastern Ontario compared with Southwestern Ontario. The impact of economic shadow on regional economic development in Southern Ontario is evident.

*

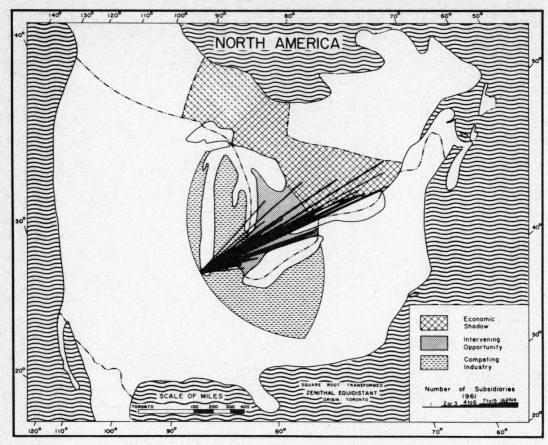

FIG. 6. *Chicago Subsidiaries and Economic Shadow.*

THE PATTERN OF ECONOMIC SHADOW IN SOUTHERN ONTARIO

The impact of economic shadow on Southern Ontario's regional economic development is measured by combining the elements of economic shadow into a single mathematical equation or model and computing the economic shadow values for each county. The higher the numerical rating, the greater the possible contacts with United States industrial centres and the lower the economic shadow. Figure 10 is a simplified measure of economic shadow taking account of the size and air distance of each United States city from every Ontario county, and of whether Toronto is an intervening opportunity. No account is taken of sectoral penetration or of the population of the county. The regional contrast between Southwestern and Eastern

Ontario is marked; high numerical values, indicating low economic shadow, are restricted entirely to Southwestern Ontario and Georgian Bay.

Compare this pattern of economic shadow with Figure 2, which shows the location of the parent companies in the United States with Ontario subsidiaries. The New York concentration of large industrials reduces the economic shadow within a peripheral belt including the Niagara Peninsula and the shore of the Upper St. Lawrence. This area is the intervening opportunity area for New York industrials (see Fig. 8). The interactance is weakened because of their distance from Ontario. A narrow wedge of moderate economic shadow extends northward from

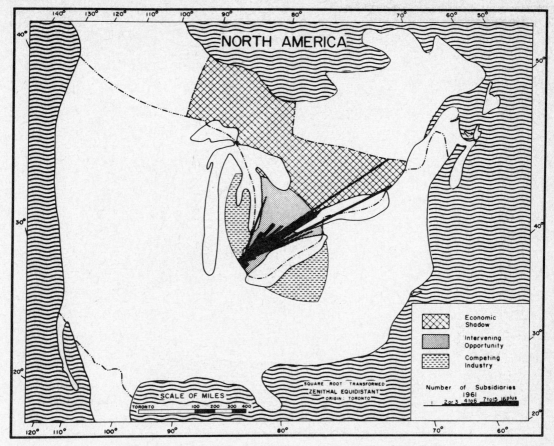

FIG. 7. Detroit Subsidiaries and Economic Shadow.

Kingston to Renfrew and reflects the proximity and intervening opportunity for Syracuse and adjacent industrial centres (see Fig. 9). Elsewhere in Eastern Ontario, economic shadow remains high.

Economic shadow is generally low in Southwestern Ontario because of its proximity to the concentration of Midwest industrials. The ellipses, demarcating the area of intervening opportunity for the industrial centres from Detroit (Fig. 7) to Minneapolis-St. Paul (Fig. 5), exclude increasingly larger areas of the Niagara Peninsula which is the only area of high economic shadow in Southwestern Ontario.

*

ECONOMIC SHADOW AND REGIONAL DEVELOPMENT

The contrast between Eastern and Southwestern Ontario is not confined to the difference in the number of American subsidiaries they contain. A similar contrast occurs in post-war growth of all manufacturing as well as in a wide range of other economic and many social characteristics. There is a significant association among the growth of manufacturing, population growth, post-war immigration and the age and value of housing. The sharp contrast between the accelerated growth of Southwestern Ontario and the retarded growth of the remainder of the Province is the basic factor in the

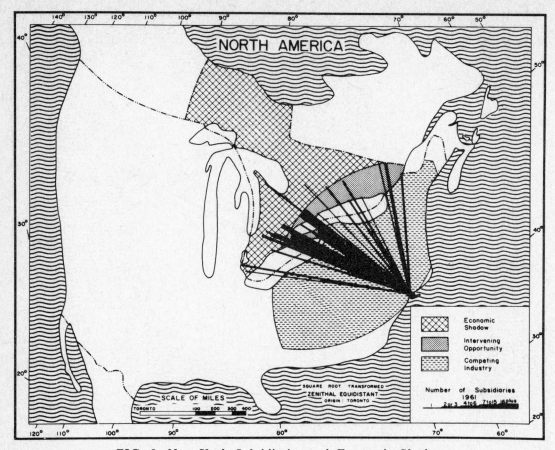

FIG. 8. New York Subsidiaries and Economic Shadow.

geography of the area. This contrast cannot be explained in terms of internal economic factors.

Take the case of Eastern Ontario where accessibility to markets combines with relatively low labour costs and high labour stability to present an environment very suitable for industrial expansion. Yet recently, its industrial growth has lagged behind that of other regions. On the other hand, certain communities in Southwestern Ontario, having a market accessibility somewhat less favourable than that of Eastern Ontario, higher labour costs and higher labour instability, have experienced a remarkable post-war expansion.

It is obvious that other factors exert a great influence on industrial location.[7]

These other factors, exerting a great influence on industrial location and economic development, are the elements of economic shadow. The geographic pattern of investment of American finance capital and entrepreneurship in Ontario that is expressed in the location of branch plants has played a primary role in Ontario's economic development.

*

CONCLUSION

Post-war industrial expansion in Southern Ontario, the main part of the Canadian Manufacturing Belt, has been concentrated in Toronto and Southwestern Ontario. The

Industry and Cities

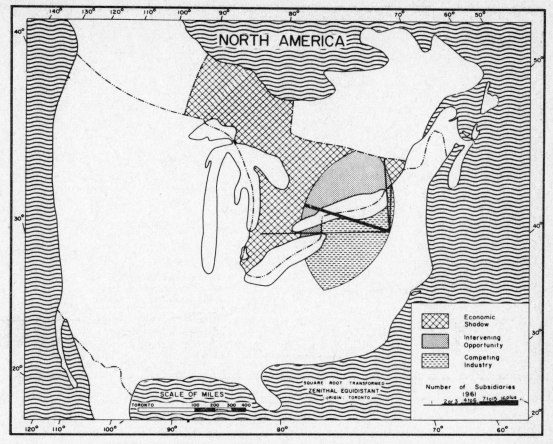

FIG. 9. Syracuse Subsidiaries and Economic Shadow.

marked contrast in manufacturing growth between Southwestern and Eastern Ontario is associated with similar contrasts in other economic and in many demographic characteristics; these contrasts are the basic factor in the geography of Southern Ontario.

These geographic contrasts are not explained by internal location factors but by the location of subsidiaries of United States parent companies. About half of all manufacturing in Canada is owned and controlled by parent companies in the United States. These subsidiaries have a distinct locational pattern that is independent of Canadian plants, and is explained by economic shadow.

Economic shadow measures a region's inability to supplement locally-controlled manufacturing with branch plants controlled from outside the main market area. Economic shadow weights the importance of

external manufacturers to a city within the region, by their distance from the city in accordance with the gravity or interactance model. Nevertheless, the primary element of economic shadow is sectoral affinity, which introduces the intervening opportunity notion to location theory. Sectoral affinity states that subsidiaries are generally established in the geographic sector between the parent company and the main regional market centre. The part of the region beyond this geographic sector is termed the area of economic shadow. Industrial interactance between a parent company and the area of economic shadow is seriously diminished because the primary regional market centre is an intervening opportunity.

Eastern Ontario's economic development is retarded because it lies in the area of economic shadow for all industrial centres except those in New England and adjacent

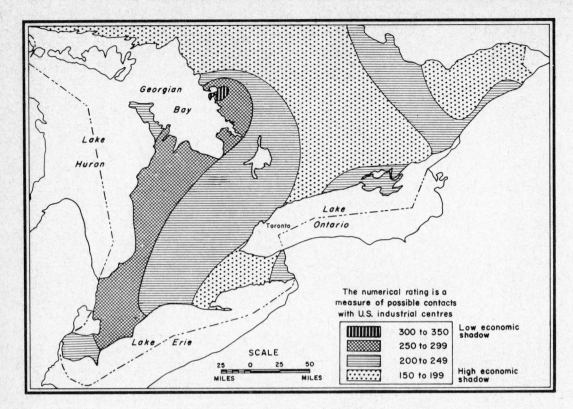

FIG. 10. Economic Shadow in Southern Ontario.

states. The regional contrasts also reflect Eastern Ontario's proximity to Upstate New York, itself a region of retarded development, compared with Southwestern Ontario's proximity to the United States Midwest, a rapidly growing industrial region. Ontario regions are most influenced by economic conditions in the closest parts of the United States because of the decline of interactance with increasing distance.

*

FOOTNOTES

1 Dominion Bureau of Statistics (DBS), *Canada's International Investment Position 1926–1954* (Ottawa: DBS, 1956), p. 21.

2 Canada, Royal Commission on Canada's Economic Prospects, *Canadian Secondary Manufacturing Industry,* by D. H. Fullerton and H. A. Hampson (Ottawa: Queen's Printer, 1957).

3 Hugh G. J. Aitken et al., *The American Economic Impact on Canada* (Durham, North Carolina: Duke University Press, 1959), p. 9.

4 Walter Isard, *Methods of Regional Analysis: An Introduction to Regional Science* (Cambridge: Massachusetts Institute of Technology Press, 1960), pp. 493–504.

5 Edward L. Ullman, *American Commodity Flow,*

A Geographical Interpretation of Rail and Water Traffic Based on Principles of Spatial Interchange (Seattle: University of Washington Press, 1957).

6 Distances from Toronto on Figures 2–9 equal the square root of the earth's surface distance. This projection is used because of the importance of United States industrial centres to Ontario declines as the square root of their distance from the province.

7 Donald Kerr and Jacob Spelt, "Some Aspects of Industrial Location in Southern Ontario," *Canadian Geographer* No. 15 (1960), pp. 12–25.

12

The Growth of Toronto*

DONALD KERR AND JACOB SPELT

* From The Changing Face of Toronto, Memoir 11, Geographical Branch Department of Mines and Technical Surveys (Ottawa, The Queen's Printer, 1965) Chapter V, "The Functions of the City," pp. 74–96. Reprinted by permission.

The economy of Toronto is indeed varied. Being a large metropolitan centre, the city produces goods and performs services of great diversity, not only for the local population but also for nearly all of southern Ontario and, in fact, for all Canadians, especially those in the West. In 1961, employment in the Metropolitan Toronto census area amounted to 789,651, which is about 43 per cent of the total population, an unusually high proportion compared with the national 35.5 per cent.[1]

First in employment is manufacturing, which is the livelihood of more than 234,500, or about 30 per cent of the labor force (Table 1B). Services constitute a broad category, which in recent years has assumed great importance in the economic structure of the Metropolitan Toronto census area, employing more than one quarter of the labor force. Trade, both wholesale and retail, accounts for 10.5 per cent of the employment, but finance for only 6.6 per cent. If the table showed the relative importance of the various groups in terms of income, some categories, such as finance, would assume much greater significance.

*

THE RISE OF MODERN MANUFACTURING

Industrialization in Toronto results from a number of complex and interrelated factors, of which the advantage of a head start and the benefit of increasing concentration of manufacturing are the two most important. Early in the nineteenth century, in response to its local market and its growing significance as a focal point for the transportation system of Upper Canada, York had already begun to acquire specialized craftsmen and manufacturing establishments. Thus, by 1830, Toronto had become the main silver-smithing centre in Upper Canada (Langdon). The government promoted the early development of printing for the publication of its own material and encouraged the printing of a weekly paper. Books, however, were not published until the late 1820's (Gundy). Steam engines were being manufactured in Toronto as early as 1833, and coaches for travel in Upper Canada in 1834 (Innis and Lower, pp. 296, 298 and 299).

It should not, however, be concluded that there was large-scale industrialization, for according to the 1851 census, only 2,600 persons could be considered as engaged in manufacturing. Many of these were artisans —including, for example, 204 tailors and 384

LABOR FORCE 14 YEARS OF AGE AND OVER
IN METROPOLITAN TORONTO, BY INDUSTRY AND SEX, 1951*

Industry	Male	Female	Total	Percentage
Primary	3,688	355	4,043	0.7
Manufacturing	138,812	50,459	189,271	35.9
Construction	35,701	968	36,669	7.0
Transport, storage, public utilities	40,996	7,989	48,985	9.3
Trade	66,859	34,247	101,106	19.2
Wholesale	24,437	7,611	32,048	6.1
Retail	42,422	26,636	69,058	13.1
Finance	16,823	14,902	31,725	6.1
Services	60,856	48,928	109,784	20.9
Not stated	3,798	1,447	5,245	0.9
Total	367,533	159,295	526,828	100.0
	69.7%	30.3%	100%	

TABLE IB
LABOR FORCE 15 YEARS OF AGE AND OVER
FOR CENSUS METROPOLITAN AREA OF TORONTO, 1961†

Industry	Male	Female	Total	Percentage
Primary	7,657	963	8,620	1.1
Manufacturing	170,615	63,896	234,511	29.7
Construction	49,174	1,881	51,055	6.5
Transport, storage, public utilities	56,115	12,586	68,701	8.7
Trade	96,400	50,096	146,496	18.5
Wholesale	37,667	11,927	49,594	6.3
Retail	58,733	38,169	96,902	·12.2
Finance	27,000	25,338	52,338	6.6
Services	108,458	102,222	210,680	26.7
Not stated	13,599	3,651	17,250	2.2
Total	529,018	260,633	789,651	100.0
	67.0%	33.0%	100%	

*Census of Canada 1951, v. 4   †Census of Canada 1961, v. 3, pt 2.

makers of boots and shoes. Besides, Toronto had only 6.5 per cent of the manufacturing workers of Upper Canada, most of this class being scattered through the colony and engaged in sawing timber and milling grain. In Toronto, industrial development was more varied than in other centres of south-central Ontario, but the number of employees per plant was proportionately no greater than in the other parts of the province (Spelt, pp. 67–72).

A general picture of manufacturing in Toronto on the eve of Confederation may be derived from the annual review of commerce that appeared in the Toronto *Globe* of February 12, 1866. It mentions, among other things, a rolling mill employing more than 300 men and producing a variety of goods including bolts, nuts and stoves; a cabinet factory employing 400 men and a meat-packing plant employing 300; and some textile- and tobacco-manufacturing as well as distilling and brewing (MacNab, pp. 59–80; Middleton, pp. 515–532). The 9,400 engaged in manufacturing in 1871, just before a depression, accounted for 10.8 per cent of those so employed in Upper Canada. During the 1880's and particularly during the 1890's, manufacturing grew rapidly in Toronto. The number of wage earners increased from 12,708 for 1881 to 25,242 for 1891 and 45,515 for 1901. Of great significance was the increasing geographical concentration of manufacturing that raised Toronto's percentage of the southern Ontario total to 25.5 per cent for 1891 and 34 per cent for 1901.

In assessing the growth of manufacturing in nineteenth-century Toronto, a number of factors must be considered. There was a striking lack of local natural resources, such powerful industrial attractions as coal and iron being entirely wanting. True, the rise of food-processing should be related, at least in part, to the increase in commercial agriculture, but the local market was probably of greater significance. Human factors, in particular that of personal initiative, played a dominant role in the expansion of industrialization; and it bears repetition that the choice of Toronto as capital was the most important factor in early industrial development. The maintenance of the city's lead in growth over its rivals, attracted new industry and thus caused a mushrooming that has persisted to the present day. Toronto's development as a focal point for railways further strengthened its position. The adoption of the National Policy, with its high tariffs, stimulated industry in the city, especially after 1896, when the opening of western Canada and the development of mineral resources on the Canadian Shield coincided with a general recovery in world economic conditions. In the 1890's Winnipeg was too distant to engage in large-scale manufacturing and could not duplicate the industrial growth of Chicago, its United States counterpart. Neither did the Shield present a suitable environment for the creation of a metropolitan rival. In many ways, Toronto played the role of a Canadian Chicago, functioning as a great supply centre for western as well as northern development while its local market was growing richer. The brisk economic development of the late nineteenth century, coinciding with the geographical and financial centralization of manufacturing operations, supported and strengthened the position of Toronto as one of the few major industrial centres in Canada.

A few auxiliary factors in nineteenth-century industrialization merit discussion. In some ways the emergence of the Canadian Manufacturers' Association in Toronto in the middle of the century and its consolidation in 1900, reflected the city's dominance in Canadian manufacturing (Clark, pp. 1–12). It is impossible to define precisely the part played by the C.M.A. in the introduction of new industry, but the occurrence of an organization devoted to sponsoring and promoting higher tariffs for manufacturers, undoubtedly made the city attractive for many firms, particularly those of United States origin. In the early years, the favorably situated Toronto members dominated the meetings of the council and committees. While the policy adopted in 1907, of holding some council meetings in Montreal, gave the members from that city a greater opportunity to participate in the activities of the C.M.A., the great body of members throughout the country remained without real representation (Clark, p. 80). Equally difficult to define was the work of the Board of Trade, which at various times led campaigns for the dissemination of electrical power, the strengthening of tariffs and the improvement of the harbor. The board played a part in bringing about more favorable freight rates for Toronto shippers. The board very early also took an active interest in the city's planning problems.

Now, at mid-century, manufacturing contributes substantially to the economic welfare of Metropolitan Toronto and is the dominant economic activity. Most striking is its tremendous variety, all major industrial groups except tobacco-manufacturing being well represented. The most important group, according to the Dominion Bureau of Statistics classification, is that of iron and steel products, which is led by agricultural implements, sheet-metal products, iron castings, many different types of household, office and store machinery, and heating and cooking apparatus. Most of the production in the food-and-beverage group is accounted for by industries oriented almost entrely to the local market. Only a few, such as those engaged in distilling or the manufacture of chocolates or special foods, have a wider market and a national reputation. The production of all sorts of electrical apparatus and supplies is important not only locally but nationally and amounts to more than 25 per cent of the national output. More than half the batteries produced in Canada, for example, are manufactured in Toronto. The city's contribution to the nation's printing and publishing exceeds 30 per cent, the most important elements within this group being trade composition (53 per cent) and engraving, stereotyping and electric typing (48 per cent). The diversity of Toronto's manufacturing is such that only 13 of the 172 subclassifications of manufacturing given in the census are not to be found in the metropolitan area. Among the various nationally significant subgroups not mentioned previously are inks (86 per cent of Canadian production), typewriter supplies (75 per cent), miscellaneous non-ferrous metal products (63 per cent), soaps and washing compounds (61 per cent), scientific instruments (53 per cent), adhesives (52 per cent), and toys and games (52 per cent).

Heavy industries requiring large tracts of land for successful operation are generally not found in Toronto; small to medium-sized plants producing for the consumer's market are dominant. More than 80 per cent of the manufacturing establishments have fewer than 50 employees each but account for only 22.7 per cent of all manufacturing employment. Some 22 plants employ more than 1,000 workers each, but these plants account for 18 per cent of those engaged in manufacturing. Clearly the city is not dominated by any type of industry, nor do a few large industries stand out. The average Toronto firm employs 44 workers, while its counterparts in Hamilton and Windsor, cities characterized by fewer and larger industries, employ 88 and 89 workers respectively.

Metropolitan Toronto accounts for just over 15 per cent of Canada's manufacturing and is exceeded only by Montreal, which accounts for 18 per cent. In number of production workers, Metropolitan Toronto ranks thirteenth among North American cities and Montreal tenth. According to a formula prepared by Rodgers (1957), Metropolitan Toronto has a diversification index of 075, which is exceeded in North America by Philadelphia only, with an index of 039.

*

THE EMERGENCE OF TORONTO AS A FINANCIAL CENTRE

The Banks

A study of the development of Toronto as a financial centre throws light on the growth of the city and, in particular, on the emergence of the distinctive financial district to be described later. Any discussion of this nature has to be rather superficial since very few detailed studies have been made of the history of financial institutions in Canada. Furthermore, the general lack of an organized body of statistical data by which to measure and describe changes in financial control, especially in Toronto and Montreal, precludes any searching analysis.

Toronto's emergence as a financial centre independent of Montreal dates from the early nineteenth century. Serious rivalry with Montreal, however, did not emerge until the late 1860's and early 1870's. On the eve of Confederation, although Toronto had spawned various banks and had established a stock exchange as early as 1852, Montreal dominated Canadian finance. Toronto was, at the most, only a regional centre, having won domination over Kingston, Hamilton and London.

By and large, banking operations in Upper Canada, including those of the Bank of Upper Canada, were on a very modest scale compared with those of Montreal.[2] Besides, between 1857 and 1873, when its policies were dictated by E. H. King, the Bank of Montreal attempted to reduce, if not eliminate, all competition in Upper Canada (Hague; Masters) and in 1864 this bank's prestige was greatly enhanced when the government's account was transferred to it. In addition, the wealth of the Bank of Montreal was substantially increased by remarkably successful speculations in gold in New York, where a branch had been opened in 1859 and the business of international exchange had been vigorously pursued. Such activities became dominant, and E. H. King was inclined to divert more and more of its funds (loanable capital) from the Canadian market. This dismayed and evoked the criticism of the banks of Upper Canada, which found it increasingly difficult to support the regular trade of the country (Breckenridge, pp. 175–176).

At the same time, two of the oldest banks in Upper Canada failed—the Bank of Upper Canada (Toronto) in 1866 and the Commercial Bank (Kingston) in 1867—and it was with some justification that the restrictive monetary policy of the Bank of Montreal was blamed. All in all, there was growing determination in Upper Canada, and particularly in Toronto, to break loose from the financial power of Montreal, just as the wholesale trade had done. It culminated in the formation of the Canadian Bank of Commerce by a group of Toronto business leaders. The new bank's first president was William McMaster, a former director of the Bank of Montreal, who strongly opposed that bank's policies (Ross, pp. 18–23).

It should not, however, be concluded that Toronto entirely lacked a stable local bank, for the Bank of Toronto, founded in 1855, had grown slowly, characterized by a cautious and reserved policy. Later, in 1869, its manager, George Hague, spearheaded a remarkable attack on E. H. King through the Banking Committee in Ottawa and, by mustering the support of McMaster and others, was able to arrest the growing power of the Bank of Montreal. In 1869, the new federal government, greatly influenced by King, introduced legislation for the first Canadian bank act. The main provisions of the bill were to abolish the note issues of banks and to replace them with government notes, which the banks would have to purchase. The banks were to hold specie equal to 20 per cent of the secured notes in circulation and to one seventh of their demand deposits not bearing interest. Most of the

banks, especially those in Upper Canada, would not have been able to buy the securities to be held by the government and still provide the necessary services for the various participants in the handling of grain and lumber, a trade long sustained by large seasonal loans. (For a discussion see Breckenridge and also Jamieson.)

If the bill had been passed, the system of branch banking in Canada would have collapsed and the United States system—the existence of small independent local banks providing local services and large banks in metropolitan centres dealing in the foreign and mercantile trade of the country—would have prevailed. There is little doubt that in Canada the role of the large metropolitan bank would have been inherited by the Bank of Montreal. Because of the activities of the Toronto group, particularly those of George Hague, who travelled far and wide over Ontario, Quebec and the Maritimes to gain support, strong opposition developed, obvious to the government the first day of the debate in the House, and the bill was withdrawn. Later, a more moderate bill favorable to the banks of Upper Canada, was passed. Not only was the system of branch banking preserved, but Toronto's role as regional financial capital was saved. A new and significant confidence was gained which helped to make Toronto a growing rival of Montreal and a leading partner in the development of western Canada.

While Montreal won control of railroad development in the West by gaining the Canadian Pacific Railway charter, Toronto interests participated in Western economic development by establishing branch banks. By 1906, 265 of these had been established in western Canada, of which 87 were of Toronto origin (including 21 branches of the banks of British Columbia absorbed a few years earlier by the Bank of Commerce) and 83 of Montreal origin (Table 2). Eight years later, by 1914, the number of branch banks had risen to 1,095, but the ratio of Toronto and Montreal interests remained the same. Furthermore, trust and loan companies, investment houses, and insurance companies with head offices in Toronto were engaged in the business of lending money for Western expansion. There is little doubt that this boom, brought about by the rise of the grain economy in the West, spawned many new financial institutions in Toronto and caused the expansion of the existing ones.

In the 1880's, the financial community of Toronto was stimulated by the development of trust and loan companies supported in large part by British capital. The rural communities in southern Ontario became increasingly interested in borrowing money to finance the building of schools, churches and other social facilities. Farmers no longer regarded mortgages as evil and began to take them out to build new houses and barns. Toronto provided most of the money to support these ventures in south-central and western Ontario, and the trust and loan companies grew accordingly.

The Stock Exchange

The growth of the Toronto Stock Exchange, to be one of the leading organizations of its kind in the world, is of special interest, for it reflects the broadening of financial institutions in Toronto in the twentieth century and their importance in the development of Canadian mineral and forest resources. Indeed, the ability of Toronto financiers to wrest control of the Canadian Shield, brought great wealth to the city and laid the basis for further striking growth, which was to reach a peak in the mid-1950's.

In the late nineteenth century, Toronto interests were engaged in promoting mining properties in the Kootenays of British Columbia and "Spokane was faced with the beginning of competition with Toronto" (Innis, 1936, p. 281). The promotion of the War Eagle mine, in southeastern British Columbia, in 1887, by W. G. Gooderham, T. G. Blackstock, the Hon. G. A. Cox and others, is an example of the activity of Toronto groups in Western mining development. In addition, strong demands for the building of the Crowsnest Pass line of the Canadian Pacific to check United States trade in the Kootenays and to facilitate mining expansion came from Toronto (Innis, 1939, p. 22).

In 1898, a group of Toronto financiers merged two small mining exchanges founded in 1895 to form the Standard Stock and Mining Exchange. The function of the new organization was to facilitate the promotion of mining ventures that the more conservative Toronto Stock Exchange would not handle.

The future of the new exchange seemed uncertain until 1903, when remarkably large deposits of silver were discovered at Cobalt, on the Shield about 300 miles north of the city. Mining promotion in Toronto was greatly stimulated, and the discovery of gold in northern Ontario—at Porcupine in 1911 and at Kirkland Lake in 1912—further increased the activity. From 1911 to 1914, shares traded on the Toronto Standard Stock and Mining Exchange averaged 25 million annually, exceeding the number traded on the Toronto and Montreal exchanges combined. Their value, of course, was much less.

It is true that much of the capital for development in northern Ontario came from various groups in different centres. The Timmins-McMartin-Dunlop Syndicate of Montreal, for example, provided capital for the Hollinger mine; Jules Bache and Associates of New York, after 1915, for the Dome mine; a group of Buffalo interests, for Wright-Hargreaves; and J. P. Bickle and Associates of Toronto, for the McIntyre mine. After the spectacular mineral discoveries in northern Ontario, however, especially the silver finds at Cobalt, which were unbelievably rich and made many fortunes in a matter of days, the public wanted to participate not so much by prospecting as by investing in speculative shares. Thus, the mining exchange in Toronto became the medium through which the public at large could invest its money and both honest and dishonest prospectors could raise caiptal. More and more of the prospectors who could not raise large sums privately turned to the Toronto mining exchange to float stock, and gradually the reputation of Toronto as a mining centre was built up. One of the most striking examples was the

TABLE II

BRANCH BANKS IN WESTERN CANADA, BY CITY OR REGION OF ORIGIN, 1906 AND 1914

1906	Montreal	Toronto	Quebec City	Hamilton	Ottawa	Eastern Townships	Other Origin	Total
British Columbia and Yukon Territory	34	27		3		4		68
Alberta	17	21	18					56
Saskatchewan	9	13	13	5	2			42
Manitoba	23	26	30	14	5	1		99
Total, Western Canada	83 (31%)	87 (33%)	61	22	7	5		265

1914	Montreal	Toronto	Winnipeg	Hamilton	Ottawa	Other origin	Total
British Columbia and Yukon Territory	110	79	32	10	2	14	247
Alberta	104	90	54	8	1	6	263
Saskatchewan	74	116	132	22	13	24	381
Manitoba	45	59	70	24	6		204
Total, Western Canada	333 (33%)	344 (34%)	288	64	22	44	1095

Note: The statistics used in this table have been compiled from the lists of Canadian branch banks in the 1906 and 1914 editions of the Canadian Almanac.

stock-floating done by Sir Harry Oakes, who in this way developed the property of Lake Shore Mines.

Another factor was the control Toronto wholesalers and distributors exercised from the beginning over most of the shipments of goods to the mining districts of northern Ontario. These dealers were undoubtedly favored by the fact that the Temiskaming and Northern Ontario Railway, the building of which stimulated mining exploration, constituted a direct link with Toronto via the Grand Trunk south of North Bay. Sponsored by the provincial government to open the north, the railroad ensured that the resultant trade would be handled by Toronto rather than by its rival, Montreal.

Statistics on freight traffic in northern Ontario show that, for the years 1909 and 1910, at least 90 per cent of the trade came from Ontario towns, mainly from Toronto, and that 10 per cent came from Quebec points, mainly from Montreal (Field, p. 73).

The influence of Toronto on Cobalt, the leading mining centre in the first decade of mining development in northern Ontario, may be measured by examining advertising in copies of the Cobalt *Daily Nugget*. It is true that most advertising was placed by local firms, but in that placed by the two competing metropolitan centres (primarily law firms and stock brokers), Toronto led by more than three to one. In a few issues of the *Daily Nugget*, hotel arrivals were listed, and they were five to one in favor of Toronto.

Increasingly, Toronto became the focal point of all mining developments on the Canadian Shield. By tabulating the locations of head offices of mining industries (exclusive of activities in sedimentary-rock formations) and by establishing places of residence of the members of the boards of directors of mining companies, it is possible to measure Toronto's growing importance in the mining industry of Canada. Twenty-five of the 52 mining companies listed in 1933 had head offices in Toronto (Table IV) and, of the 336 directors listed, 112 lived there (Table III). Personal factors undoubtedly had a profound influence on the growth of mining interests in Toronto and the association with the city of such well-known individuals as J. M. Murdoch, W. P. Bickle, W. H. Wright and Sir Harry Oakes.

TABLE III
NUMBER OF DIRECTORS OF MAJOR MINING COMPANIES*
ACCORDING TO PLACE OF RESIDENCE, 1933†

Toronto	Montreal	New York	Other Canadian	Other U.S.A.	U.K.	Province of mining operations
71	17	14	25	26	10	Ontario
18	17	4	9	2	0	Quebec
14	4	7	8	2		Prairies (mainly Manitoba)
9	12	22	33	7	5	British Columbia, Yukon Territory and Northwest Territories (mainly British Columbia)
112 (33%)	50 (15%)	47 (14%)	75 (22%)	37	15	Total 336

* Exclusive of companies operating only in sedimentary formations.
† Derived from descriptions of mining companies in the Financial Post survey of mines.

It is noteworthy that in 1922, when the New York syndicate of Chadbourne and Thomson came to Canada to develop the mining properties around Noranda, Que., they consulted John B. Holden, a prominent Toronto barrister, because of his close association with the Canadian mining industry (Roberts, pp. 49–50). Later J. Y. Murdoch, of Toronto, became president of Noranda Mines.

Most of the large and influential companies, such as International Nickel, chose Toronto for their Canadian offices in preference to Montreal. By 1959, the number of mining companies (exclusive of mining companies in sedimentary-rock formations) had increased to 255, of which 174 (68 per cent) had head offices in the Lake Ontario city. Of the 1,674 directors listed, 875 (52 per cent) lived in Toronto. According to their measures, only about 10 per cent of the mining industry was found in Montreal, Toronto being clearly the main centre (Table V).

It has been indicated that Toronto's growth as a national financial centre and rival of Montreal was influenced largely by land development on the Prairies and the discovery of minerals on the Shield. In short, Toronto's sphere of interest expanded greatly in the twentieth century, encompassing the Shield and overlapping with Montreal's in the West. Toronto's recent ascendance over Montreal in certain elements of finance and its exertion of greater influence in the Western hinterland during the last decade may be traced to the economic depression of the 1930's.

It is agreed that Montreal never fully recovered from the crash of 1929, which caused the bankruptcy of at least five prominent brokerage houses. Until that time, most of the high-value stocks (in banks, utilities, industrials, etc.) were traded on the Montreal exchange. In 1925, in fact, 86 per cent of all the trading by value in Canada was done on the Montreal Stock Exchange, and the volume remained consistently above 70 per cent

TABLE IV
LOCATION OF HEAD OFFICES OF MAJOR MINING COMPANIES,* 1933†

Toronto	Montreal	New York	Elsewhere	Province of mining operations
20		1	5	Ontario
2	4		1	Quebec
2			3	Prairies (mainly Manitoba)
1		3	10	British Columbia, Yukon Territory and Northwest Territories
25	4	4	19	Total 52

* Exclusive of companies operating only in sedimentary formations.
† Derived from descriptions of mining companies in the Financial Post survey of mines.

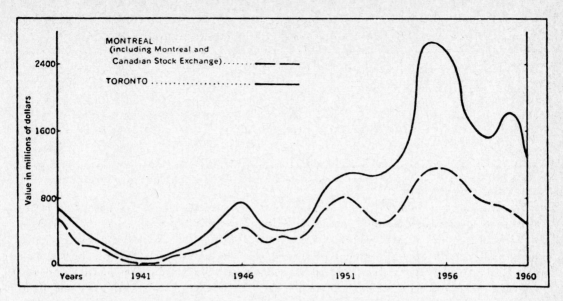

FIG. 1. Value of stock-exchange transactions, 1937-60. The greater value of stock-market transactions in Toronto compared with those in Montreal reached a maximum in the middle 50's.

until the depression. In 1933 Toronto's share of high-value securities on the market exceeded that of Montreal for the first time and has remained ahead ever since.[3]

The increase in the price of gold in the 30's, stimulated mining development on the Shield, most of the financing being done through the Toronto market. After World War II, development of mining properties increased greatly and the Toronto Stock Exchange grew accordingly. The oil industry of Alberta was heavily financed from Bay Street, as were the copper and uranium industries of the Shield; and Toronto tightened the hold on its northern and western hinterlands. This growth of the exchange, coupled with improvement in its trading facilities (the installation of high-speed electronic equipment and a data-processing centre) and the establishment of branches of Toronto brokerage houses throughout Canada, led to further acquisitions in the industrial market.

TABLE V

LOCATION OF HEAD OFFICES AND DIRECTORS OF MAJOR MINING COMPANIES* IN CANADA, 1959†

Province of mining operations	Toronto		Montreal		Other Canadian cities		New York City		Other U.S. cities		All other locations	
	H.O.	Directors	H.O.	Directors	H.O.	Directors	H.O.	Directors	H.O.	Directors	H.O.	Directors
Ontario	81	413	3	33	3	61	1	41	2	33		13
Quebec	44	228	18	110	4	56	1	35	2	26		3
Maritimes	4	20	2	9	3	10		11		10		3
Prairies	15	65		6	10	60	1	11		8		4
Y.T. and N.W.T.	9	46		5	3	10		7		4		1
B.C.	4	21	2	14	18	97		4	1	22		3
Miscellaneous	17	82		5	4	29	1	20	2	20		15
Total	174	875	25	182	45	323	4	129	7	123		42
Percentages	68	52	10	11	17	19	2	8	3	7		3

Directors (total) 1,674
Head offices (total) 255

* Exclusive of companies operating in sedimentary formations.
† Derived from company descriptions in the Financial Post survey of mines, 1959.

TABLE VI

BANK ASSETS AS PERCENTAGE OF CANADIAN TOTAL, BY CITY OF ORIGIN, 1890-1960

Year	Montreal	Toronto	Winnipeg	Quebec City	Hamiltion	Halifax	Other cities	Total
1890	44.5	28.3	0.6	5.9	2.4	8.3	10.0	100.0
1906	43.7	38.7	0.6	4.8	3.3	1.4	7.5	100.0
							(Weyburn, Sask.)	
1920	52.0	40.0	5.0	0.0	2.8	0.0	0.2	100.0
1932	58.5	41.5	0.0	0.0	0.0	0.0	0.0	100.0
1960	55.0	45.0	0.0	0.0	0.0	0.0	0.0	100.0

Note: This table has been compiled from various sources, mainly from the Journal of the Canadian Bankers' Association and the Monetary Times.

The importance of finance in the economic structure of present-day Toronto cannot be properly measured by employment, which makes up, at most, only 7 per cent of the labor force. What is really significant is the volume of money flowing through firms in the city for investment in all parts of Canada as well as in the city region. The fact that the stock exchange accounts for about two thirds of the value of Canadian sales of stock suggests the importance of Toronto in Canadian finance. No city-by-city statistics are available for over-the-counter bond transactions, but most authorities in Montreal and Toronto agree that at least three quarters of all Canadian sales are made in the latter city. The importance of bonds in the investment market cannot be exaggerated; in many ways they are the best indicator of the vigor of the Toronto financial community. Further, a little more than half the life insurance companies in Canada, accounting for 37 per cent of all life assets, and more than half the fire and casualty firms, with 52 per cent of all fire and casualty assets, have head offices in Toronto, as have trust and loan companies, which hold 35 per cent of all trust and loan assets. Finally, three chartered banks, with approximately 45 per cent of Canada's bank assets, have head offices in Toronto. In banking, however, Montreal remains ahead, with about 55 per cent of all bank assets (Table VI). Not necessarily a measure of financial function but an indication of the economic health of the city are statistics on bank clearings. In 1961, Toronto's share of bank clearings in Canada was 37.3 per cent as compared with 31 per cent in 1948. It is also worth noting that corporations with head offices in Toronto pay, on the average, 30 per cent of all the corporation taxes paid in Canada.

Those engaged in finance just exceed 52,000 (Metropolitan Toronto census area) and include such various types of employees as clerks, salesmen, economists and legal experts. The services most of them perform for the local population are in no way different from those of their counterparts in other towns and cities of Canada. The number engaged in financial activities within the financial district (stock-and-bond dealers, economists, brokers in foreign exchange, trust officers, etc.) and concerned in the main with the flow of capital has been estimated from different sources to be no more than 2,800.

*

TRADE

Retail Trade

Metropolitan Toronto is the leading retail centre in Canada, its sales constituting about 12 per cent of the national total. It is closely followed by Metropolitan Montreal. The relatively high purchasing power of the metropolitan area, combined with the shopping

TABLE VII

PER CAPITA RETAIL SALES IN METROPOLITAN TORONTO AND
METROPOLITAN HAMILTON, 1951

(IN DOLLARS)

	Metropolitan Toronto	Metropolitan Hamilton
All retail sales	1,114.70	922.30
Foods and beverages	349.19	326.74
General merchandise	191.63	114.14
Automobiles	249.49	231.20
Apparel	89.87	81.99
Building and hardware supplies	51.83	57.18
Furniture and appliances	41.00	41.09
Drug group	36.11	33.13
Other retail goods	108.22	94.12
Total value of retail sales	1,244,003,100	256,010,000
Median earnings of labor force	2,179	2,236

Source: Census of Canada, 1951 (Bulletin CT-13).

Note: Calculations based on 1961 data for the two census metropolitan areas do not reveal any significant change in the ratio of the per capita sales.

attraction the city holds for many residents of southern Ontario, provides a high volume of retail trade. In many ways, retailing in Toronto mirrors that of many large metropolitan centres in the United States, foods and beverages, general merchandise, and automobiles being the most important commodities. More than 80,000 persons find employment in various kinds of retailing throughout Metropolitan Toronto, general merchandising accounting for 36 per cent and foods for 22 per cent. The extent to which the city depends on outside buyers is difficult to measure. Some indication can be gained, however, by comparing statistics of the retail trade of Metropolitan Toronto with those of Metropolitan Hamilton, a medium-sized industrial city with a rather restricted trade area (Table VII). Retail sales per capita in Metropolitan Toronto exceed those of Hamilton in all categories except building and hardware supplies and furniture and appliances. Since the median earnings of the labor force in 1951 were lower in Toronto than in Hamilton, it could be argued that the proportionately higher volume is due to Toronto's relatively large number of wealthy people and the visits of outsiders for special shopping. Nearly all outside shoppers come from south-central Ontario, but every part of the province is represented. To buy certain products such as high-quality home furnishings or special jewelry, shoppers may come from as far away as the Prairie Provinces.

Wholesale Trade

Small in terms of employment but of great significance in the economy of the city is the wholesale trade. Many factors contributed to the emergence of Toronto in the nineteenth century as a point of distribution. Subsequent improvements in transportation and the general centralization of wholesaling that have occurred in the twentieth century have strengthened the position of the city as a national distribution centre surpassed only by Montreal. More than 2,600 firms are engaged in different types of wholesaling, employing about 50,000 persons and accounting for approximately 19 per cent of all sales made in Canada. It is impossible to know with absolute precision the relative values of local, regional, and national distribution, but it should be noted that several companies have national markets. Toronto, for example, is the distribution centre for more than 41 per cent of all the chemicals and drugs sold in Canada, 46 per cent of all the books and periodicals and 36 per cent of all jewelry. The city, on the other hand, accounts for only 11 per cent of the Canadian sales of hardware supplies.

Food products (including groceries) and tobacco make up 22 per cent of all the wholesale transactions in Toronto, most of this distribution being local and regional. Machinery (with equipment and supplies), automobiles, and construction supplies also rank high. As would be expected, all goods are represented in any wholesaling list, the city functioning as a great emporium through which passes the widest possible variety.

The Port

Significant at different times in the city's history, and now of increasing importance in its function as a trading centre, is the port. At present, Toronto ranks as the fifth port in Canada, its volume of trade in the last decade having averaged a little less than 5 million tons a year. More than three quarters of the trade handled is made up of imports. There are two main types of trade: that between Toronto and other Canadian and United States ports on the Great Lakes, which accounts for at least 85 per cent of the volume, and the direct overseas shipments, which have increased sharply since the opening of the enlarged seaway.

Great Lakes trade at the port of Toronto is mainly in heavy, bulky goods such as coal, grain and petroleum products. Coal has consistently been the most important cargo. In the early 30's, after the opening of the Welland Canal, it constituted almost half the trade. In the late 50's, coal shipments averaged 1 1/3 million tons, an increasing proportion of which was used to feed the furnaces of thermoelectric plants on the lakefront. The coal comes from the Appalachian fields in Pennsylvania and West Virginia and is shipped from Lake Erie ports, of which Toledo is the most important. Trade in petroleum products, including gasoline, has averaged more than 1 million tons over the last few years. About 170,000 tons come in from United States ports; some 400,000 tons arrive from Ontario ports, mostly from the refineries at Port Credit, only a few miles west of the city. Each year, about half a

million tons are shipped from Toronto, mainly to small ports farther east on Lake Ontario for further distribution. The grain trade at the port of Toronto is by no means insignificant; it averages more than 800,000 tons annually. So far it is entirely coastwise and involves only Canadian ports. Incoming shipments make up almost two thirds of the total, and wheat is dominant. Among the other major commodities shipped in the lakes trade are sand, gravel and crushed stone, cement, soya beans, and general cargo. Undoubtedly, general cargo has by far the highest value and comprises a great variety of products.

Comprising 15 per cent of the volume but very much more of the value, is the direct overseas trade. In 1963, foreign ships other than United States vessels, loaded and unloaded cargo totalling 1,045,262 tons, of which 658,763 tons were imports and 386,499 exports. Many different commodities including automobiles, specialty foods, steel products and chemicals made up the imports in 1963. Soyabean meal, oil, and scrap iron were the only important exports.

The influence of the port on the growth of Toronto at different times in the city's history is difficult to measure. The volume of trade reached a peak in the second half of the nineteenth century, when large quantities of grain and lumber were handled in the port. In the 1880's, however, trade began to fall off, and by 1912 only some 340,000 tons went through.

In 1911, however, the federal government passed the Toronto Harbor Commission Act, which ended a period of divided control of the harbor. During the period of efficient planning and administration thus inaugurated, trade slowly increased and in 1929, shipments through the port totaled 959,000 tons. Significant factors in the development of the port of Toronto were the opening of the new Welland Canal in 1931 and the more recent completion of the St. Lawrence Seaway.

The entrance of large lakers into Lake Ontario through the Welland Canal after 1931 greatly stimulated trade, and shipments of grain from the head of the lakes and coal from Lake Erie ports increased enormously. Total trade reached 2½ million tons in 1933, and never thereafter did it go below 3 million tons. After the Second World War, trade on the lakes continued to increase and was gradually augmented by direct overseas shipping. In the late 40's, small motor ships of Dutch, Swedish, British, and German origin, averaging 2,800 tons and able to navigate the small St. Lawrence canals of 14-foot draft, began to appear in the lakes with increasing frequency. Toronto became an attractive port of call, and the direct overseas trade increased from a little less than 20,000 tons for 1948 to more than 287,000 tons for 1958. The opening of the enlarged seaway in 1959 allowed the entrance of larger ocean vessels into the lakes and direct overseas trade in Toronto rose to 713,186 tons for 1959 and 1,045,262 tons for 1963.

*

TORONTO AS A SERVICE CENTRE

Reflecting the growing importance of Toronto as a metropolitan centre as well as the rising standard of living in Canadian society are the large numbers who find employment in what are broadly classed as services. To be more precise, 210,680 persons, or 26.7 per cent of those employed in the Metropolitan Toronto census area, fall into this category. Services, comprising education, health and welfare, religion, recreation, business services, personal services, etc., employ 167,722. Employment in the federal, provincial, and municipal governments is almost 43,000.

On a value basis, Metropolitan Toronto accounts for 13 per cent of all services in Canada. In 1951, furthermore, services per capita in York County were $139.16 while the average for all of Canada was $77.55.

It is also noteworthy that, on a value basis, Metropolitan Toronto provides one third of all Canadian business services and takes in just a little less than 40 per cent of all travel-bureau and ticket-agency receipts. In addition, 56.8 per cent of all the advertising-agency business done in Canada is transacted in Toronto.

The main characteristic of metropolitan status is the leading position a city occupies in the performance of a great variety of functions. In many fields, as already shown, Toronto is the most important centre in the nation, and in some, it even plays a leading part on the North American continent. So far the discussion has dealt mainly with economic functions, but in other aspects Toronto plays a leading, sometimes national, role and finds itself in healthy competition with Montreal. A few examples will illustrate.

As a primate city, Toronto attracts outstanding talent and skill in all fields of endeavor from all parts of English-speaking Canada. For the performing arts it is important as the headquarters of the English network of the Canadian Broadcasting Corporation. CBC Toronto has a permanent staff of 2,300 and hires some 7,000 performers annually. About two thirds of all English programming, exclusive of pick-ups from United States networks and relayed broadcasts, originates in Toronto. If, however, the French-language network and the International Service are taken into account, slightly less than a third of all CBC programs originate in Toronto. The city is thus the fourth-ranking television and radio production centre in North America, after New York, Hollywood and Montreal.

Finally, the city has a wide range of educational facilities, at the apex of which stands the University of Toronto, a provincial institution of national and international reputation. In the winter of 1960–61 it had an enrolment of 15,624 students. Its graduates of 1961 were awarded 25 Woodrow Wilson Fellowships, a total surpassed on the continent only by Harvard, Yale and Princeton.[4]

The University of Toronto Press and several commercial houses help to make Toronto a leading publishing centre. On the basis of value, according to the Dominion Bureau of Statistics, 79.2 per cent of all the Canadian books of 1960 were published in the Toronto area.

*

PRESENT ECONOMIC AND NON-ECONOMIC FORCES

A combination of historical forces has brought about the rise of a very diverse economic structure in Metropolitan Toronto. Viewed in terms of the contemporary environment, the continued growth of manufacturing, trade and finance can now be explained within the framework of the market, labor supply, and transportation facilities.

The Market

Of the various factors in the location of economic activity in Toronto, the market factor is most important. The local market, comprising a population of more than 1.8 million, is rich and varied; the regional market of southern Ontario and southern Quebec, made up of another 9.5 million, is readily accessible via truck and rail. Statistics on retail sales, a reliable measure of the consumers' market, show that York County, which has 95 per cent of its population and nearly all of its economic activity concentrated in Metropolitan Toronto, has the highest retail sales per household of all counties in Canada. In 1961, the value of retail sales in York County reached $2,023,812,400, or 32 per cent more than the per capita retail total for the whole country.

Statistics on wholesale trade also indicate the value of the market. When the concept of population potential is applied and wholesale sales are substituted for population figures and actual transport costs for distance, market-potential values can be computed. Thus, in Figure 2, Toronto's dominance in Ontario is apparent. Equally clear are the existence of two poles of market potential in Canada—at Montreal and Toronto—and the rapid diminution of values beyond their immediate vicinities (Kerr and Spelt, 1960).

Labor

Over the years the development of a diverse economic structure has created a remarkably varied supply of labor, which in turn has become increasingly important as a location factor in Toronto. A labor pool ranging greatly in skills and costs makes Toronto attractive to any prospective employer who may not find his special requirements in a small to medium-sized community. This applies particularly to the hiring of technical staff and very highly skilled labor for duties and tasks not to be found outside a metropolitan centre.

At the other end of the scale, the abundant reservoir of inexpensive unskilled labor forms the economic basis of many activities. Postwar immigration has brought to Canada, and particularly to metropolitan centres, thousands of European immigrants, many of whom are unfamiliar with the language and are forced to engage in menial jobs at low wages. The downtown female labor force has been greatly augmented by such immigration and innumerable small industries have thus been maintained (Kerr and Spelt, 1957).

Throughout Toronto, but mainly in the suburbs, housewives have been employed in increasing numbers especially in assembling and packaging. There are instances in which firms have investigated an area to discover the potential female labor supply and, once in operation, have arranged work schedules to meet housewives' requirements as far as possible.

By and large, female workers are in excellent supply in Toronto, their relatively high percentage being one of the striking characteristics of the labor force. In 1960, more

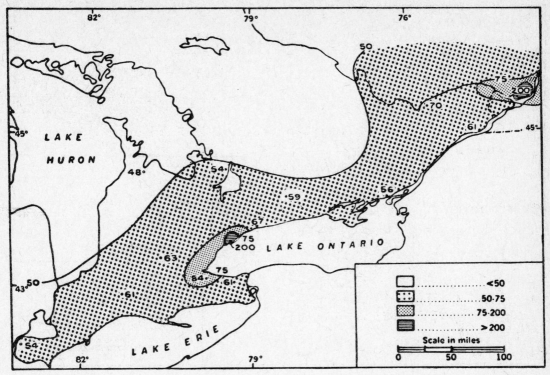

FIG. 2. Indices of market potential, which reach their highest values in Metropolitan Montreal. Toronto represents a second major concentration.

than 46 per cent of those employed in Metropolitan Toronto were females.

Labor costs in the metropolitan area vary greatly from one industry to another (Kerr and Spelt, 1960). Although in the category of skilled males, costs are above the provincial average, wage levels are below those of several medium-sized industrial communities, notably those of Hamilton and Windsor. In semi-skilled and unskilled labor, similar discrepancies exist. Unskilled female labor costs are very low in Toronto either because of the large pool of females or because of the employment of such large numbers, which in turn attracts more workers.

Transportation

For many manufacturers and wholesalers, location in Toronto has real advantages in terms of transportation facilities and costs (Figure 3). The city has functioned for many years as the main focal point for routes in

southern Ontario and, as such, has developed all the facilities and cost advantages of a major distribution centre. Frequent pick-ups and deliveries by rail and truck result in savings; and overnight services to Windsor and Montreal are common. Many firms importing parts from the United States find the air-freight facilities at Toronto International Airport indispensable to their operations. Deliveries ranging from small packages to heavy bulky materials made during the navigation season by direct overseas shipment through the St. Lawrence Seaway are increasing in quantity.

Other advantages include a large number of special competitive and commodity freight rates generally not found at other centres. Because of f.o.b. shipments, many manufacturers can avail themselves of the lower prices of materials not manufactured in Toronto. Small manufacturers, distributors and others can use the pool cars available for less-than-carload shipments, thereby low-

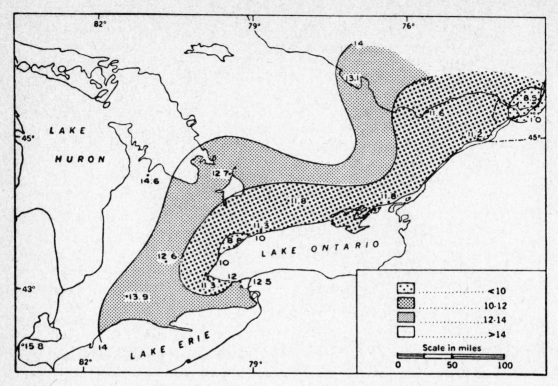

FIG. 3. *Indices of transportation costs are lowest in Metropolitan Toronto and Montreal and are almost uniform through the rest of the region.*

ering their shipping costs. Smaller centres obviously cannot offer these facilities.

Materials

The industrial and wholesale structure of Toronto does not depend to any great extent on the accessibility of raw materials. Only a few industries, such as the manufacture of bricks in the Don Valley and the processing or distribution of certain foods (dairy products or fresh vegetables) have any significant relation to the local natural environment.

Nearly all manufacturing in Toronto is concerned with the further processing of innumerable secondary materials such as steel, plastics and paper. Such products are assembled from far and wide, often by distributors whose facilities constitute one of the chief attractions to the host of small to medium-sized industries. The city is truly a storehouse of a remarkable variety of materials easily obtained by manufacturers who cannot afford

to maintain large inventories. Furthermore, spare parts for machines can be obtained quickly in Metropolitan Toronto, with the result that delays in production caused by the failure of equipment can be eliminated. All in all, by its very size the large metropolitan centre creates an environment in which it becomes profitable for a great number of distributors to store the widest possible variety of materials and parts. This variety, in turn, is advantageous, particularly to the small manufacturers engaged in the fabrication of consumer goods from substances of many kinds.

Other Factors

Although the local market and superb accessibility to other Canadian markets contribute most to economic activity in Toronto, other factors in combination with the aforementioned often influence decisions on location. To many European and United States

Industry and Cities

firms either Toronto or Montreal is the best place to establish a sales office. When the decision is made to begin manufacturing in Canada, the sales office is often changed into a small manufacturing plant, and the location in the large metropolitan centre thus becomes fixed, even though a smaller centre may be more economic. These initial decisions, undoubtedly favor one or the other of the two large metropolitan centres. Besides, because of the structure of the Canadian market, a company would want to maintain a sales office in one of the large centres even if it contemplated the development of its manufacturing facilities in a small community. For economy of operation, however, it would prefer to keep all its facilities under one roof.

Many companies prefer Toronto so as to be close to a large number of financial houses, such as investment firms, trust companies and banks, where capital can be raised. Banks are particularly influential in that many inquiries regarding a Canadian location come through their foreign service branches in Toronto or Montreal. To develop and hold an account, they will strongly suggest a location close to their facilities. To hold a client once

acquired or an account once developed, legal and chartered-accounting firms will emphasize the advantages of Toronto.

In building or leasing a plant, the prospective company finds advantages in Toronto that are lacking in smaller centres. It may buy land outright, employ an architect and builder and construct a plant. It may engage in one of several different types of package deals: the company may buy the land from a builder with the understanding that the latter will construct the plant; or it may lease a building that has already been built. The main advantage of the larger centre lies in the wide choice of purchases or contracts, although land costs are higher than elsewhere.

A number of personal factors influence the choice of Metropolitan Toronto, the preference for living in a large city being the most important. There are senior company representatives who admit that operations could be just as successful or even more so in a smaller centre but who, because of their preference for living in Toronto, make no move. This applies not only to local firms but also to many that have come from outside, particularly from the United States.

*

A METROPOLITAN CITY

In the twentieth century the primacy of Toronto steadily increased and the city's provincial rivals—they can hardly be described as such—fell farther and farther behind. In 1951 and 1961, for example, the population statistics for the major metropolitan centres of Ontario were as follows:

	1951	1961
Metropolitan Toronto	1,117,470	1,576,000*
Metropolitan Ottawa	292,476	429,750†
Metropolitan Hamilton	272,327	395,189†
Metropolitan London	128,977	181,283†

*Political unit The population of the census unit in 1961 was 1,824,481.
†Census unit.

The city became increasingly representative of the province and wide areas far beyond, attracting their talents and skills.

The primacy, important as it might be, had nevertheless to be shared with Montreal. In 1951, the population of the latter was 1,395,400 and by 1961 it had risen to 2,109,509. With these two primate cities, Canada is remarkably different from most other western nations. The causes of the difference are buried in the historical geography of the country and in the contrasts between Lower and Upper Canada, between French and Anglo-Saxon.

It should be noted, however, that in fulfilling its metropolitan functions, the city finds itself increasingly dependent upon the sub-urban communities, which provide space for the growing population and the expansion of industry, commerce, and transportation. In the 1950's, for the first time in its history the city proper began to decline in population, but it is expected that this trend will not continue. The increase to some 685,000 by 1980, allowed for in the Metropolitan Plan of 1959, would result from a rise in residential densities within the city.

At first, the population increase of the conurbation was absorbed by the nine inner suburbs. Several of these, however, are rapidly filling, and the greatest growth in Metropolitan Toronto is now taking place in the three outer suburbs—Etobicoke, North York, and Scarborough. These have a combined population of more than 638,000 and will, in the near future, contain more inhabitants than the city.

*

FOOTNOTES

1 The only data available refer to the census metropolitan area, which in 1961 had a population of 1,824,481 while the political unit of Metropolitan Toronto comprised 1,576,000 inhabitants.

2 "The Banks of Western Canada (Upper Canada) were at first almost entirely confined to the trade in agricultural exports and imports of manufactured goods. When the milling and railroad interests developed in the West (1850–60's) and received such liberal advances from the Banks, their business still depended almost entirely upon the agricultural interest. High prices for farm produce induced speculation in farm lands, country towns, mills and railroads, and furnished almost the whole of the rapidly expanding business of the Banks. The subsequent collapse, therefore, left the banks without any alternative resources. The Bank of Montreal, while heavily engaged in western business, was not so absolutely dependent upon it as the western banks. It had a large stake in the export timber trade of the country whose fluctuations were quite independent of agricultural prosperity; also in the shipping trade and in international exchange directly with New York City and Chicago, and through New York with Europe. Again the Bank of Montreal was not so heavily involved in land and railway speculation as the commercial and Upper Canada Banks" (Shortt, 1905, pp. 95–96).

3 In 1934 the Toronto Stock Exchange and the Toronto Standard Mining Exchange amalgamated to form the Toronto Stock Exchange, and innumerable low-value issues were listed on the T.S.E., with a corresponding distortion of the statistics. Since 1937 it has been possible to compare the value of all transactions on the two Montreal exchanges (combined) with those of the Toronto Stock Exchange. (Figure 1).

4 University of Toronto, 1961, President's Report.

*

BIBLIOGRAPHY

Breckenridge, R. M. *The Canadian Banking System, 1817–1890*. New York: Macmillan, 1895.

Clark, S. D. *The Canadian Manufacturers Association*. Toronto: University of Toronto Press, 1939.

Field, F. W. *The Resources and Trade Prospects of Northern Ontario*. Toronto Board of Trade, 1911.

Gundy, H. P. *Early Printers and Printing in Canada*. Toronto: Bibliographical Society of Canada, 1957.

Hague, George. *The Late Mr. King*. Jr. Canadian Bankers Association, 4, 1896.

Innis, H. A. *Settlement and the Mining Frontier*. Toronto: Macmillan, 1936.
"Toronto and the Toronto Board of Trade," *Comm. J.* 1939.

Innis, H. A. and Lower, A. R. M. *Selected Documents in Canadian Economic History, 1783–1885*. Toronto: University of Toronto Press, 1933.

Jamieson, A. B. *Chartered Banking in Canada* (revised edition). Toronto: Ryerson Press, 1957.

Kerr, D., and Spelt, J. "Manufacturing in Downtown Toronto," *Geographical Bulletin* No. 10, 1957.
"Manufacturing in Suburban Toronto," *Canadian Geographer* No. 12, 1958.
"Some Aspects of Industrial Location in South-ern Ontario," *Canadian Geographer* No. 15, 1960.
"Industry and Warehousing in the City of Toronto," *City of Toronto Planning Board Report,* April, 1961.

Langdon, J. E. *Canadian Silversmiths and their Marks, 1667–1867*. Lunenburg, Vt.: Stinehour Press, 1960.

MacNab, John E. "Toronto's Industrial Growth to 1891," *Ontario History* No. 47, 1955.

Masters, D. C. "Toronto Versus Montreal," *Canadian Historical Review* No. 22, 1941.
The Rise of Toronto, 1850–1890. Toronto: University of Toronto Press, 1947.

Middleton, J. E. *The Municipality of Toronto, 1*. Toronto: Dom. Pub. Co., 1923.

Roberts, Leslie. *Noranda*. Toronto: Clarke-Irwin, 1956.

Rodgers, A. "Some Aspects of Industrial Diversification in the United States," *Econ. Geog.*, 33.

Ross, Victor. *A History of the Canadian Bank of Commerce, 2*. Toronto, 1922.

Shortt, Adam. *The Early History of Canadian Banking: The First Banks in Upper Canada*. Jr. Canadian Bankers Association, No. 5, 1897.
The History of Canadian Currency, Banking and Exchange. Jr. Canadian Bankers Association, No. 13, 1905.

Spelt, J. *Urban Development in South-Central Ontario*. Assen, Van Gorcum, 1955.

13

Industrial Development in the Vancouver Area*

P. D. MCGOVERN

* *From* Economic Geography, *Vol. 37, (1961),* pp. *189-206. Reprinted by permission.*

The concentration of population and industry in a small part of the central provinces of Ontario and Quebec is a well-known feature of the geography of Canada, and one which has been given considerable study. Unfortunately, the effect has been to divert attention from the significant developments in other parts of the country, although, in one way or another, these are closely related to the trends in the central area. The neglect of these "other parts" is perhaps sufficient justification for this paper on the industrial development of the Vancouver area, but in addition, the nature of this development displays several features of particular interest to economic geographers. The Vancouver and other industrial areas outside the central concentration along the St. Lawrence are in the nature of subdominants which have persisted or become established in spite of the strong competition from the center. The reasons for their existence may, therefore, reveal some of the factors which counteract the attraction of the principal concentration of markets and suppliers.

The pace and direction of a region's industrial growth depend on its advantages and disadvantages compared with other regions. Fundamentally, these reflect the physical environment, but also various commercial and institutional policies, and from the point of view of an industrialist seeking a location for his plant, these may be the decisive factors in his choice of one region rather than another. Accordingly, in assessing the attractions of a region for industry, we have to think in terms of the economic environment —a concept which embodies all the influences, physical and otherwise, on the distribution of industry. It is further desirable to describe the economic environment in quantitative and comparative terms, and for this purpose we can use easily obtainable data on the costs of the various factors of production. Freight rates, wage rates, land values, etc., are the basis of most locational decisions even though in some instances the connection may be indirect and tenuous.

The Vancouver area has its quota of the latter; for example, there are firms which have been attracted to the region by such unique characteristics as (a) distance from competitors in eastern Canada, (b) proximity to parent companies on the west coast of the United States, and (c) the amenities of the region.[1] However, in the final analysis, even these firms were influenced by costs in one way or another, and, like the majority, they located here because they believed, rightly or wrongly, that this region offered a suitable economic environment. The features of this environment are, therefore, worthy of some discussion.

The location of Vancouver on the west coast of Canada and over 2000 miles from the nation's principal concentration of markets and suppliers, makes transportation costs a major influence on the course of industrial development. Three principal effects are discernible. Freight costs are a heavy burden on manufacturers of low value, bulky commodities in the Vancouver area who seek to compete in distant North American and world markets. The weight of this burden is, in fact, increasing due to the current tendency of the railway companies, in the face of increasing competition from the road haulage operators for the more remunerative traffic, to place a disproportionate share of their rapidly rising costs on the low value commodities. On the other hand, transportation costs do not discourage shipment of the more valuable items to distant markets, and by this criterion at any rate, peripheral locations such as Vancouver are not necessarily at a competitive disadvantage for this type of production.

Secondly, the very fact of distance from the principal industrial areas of Canada gives manufacturers of certain types of products in the Vancouver area a measure of protection from "outside" competition. The cost of sending relatively low value, perishable, bulky, heavy, or fragile goods from Ontario and more distant parts to western Canada is sufficiently high to encourage the establishment of plants in the "protected" market in the west. However, at the present time the areal extent of this is artificially reduced by the so-called bridge subsidy system. This has the effect of reducing the freight rate paid by manufacturers in the central prov-inces on shipments to the prairie provinces, in view of the large uninhabited part of the Shield which these have to cross. The result is to weaken the competitive position of Vancouver and other western firms in the prairie market and thus offset one of the natural incentives to establish plants in the west.

Thirdly, as a result of Vancouver's geographical situation close to the International Boundary, and on sheltered tidewater, local manufacturers have the opportunity of "exporting" their goods to eastern Canada by American as well as by Canadian railroads, or by sea via the Panama Canal instead of by rail across the continent. The port of Vancouver is undoubtedly one of the basic industries in the regional economy, and one which has encouraged several industries to locate here, but as a stimulus to industrial development the "Panama alternative" is an equally important consequence of the development of port facilities. The effect is to give firms in the Vancouver area lower freight rates on shipments of primary produce than those payable by the Edmonton and Calgary and other western industrial areas. The same advantage is obtained by Vancouver firms in their capacity as consumers of steel and other materials. Much of the local demand for such items is met by firms in eastern Canada, who invariably have obtained relatively low agreed charges from the railway companies. Because of the competition by ocean shipping, the freight charge to Vancouver is often considerably lower than to inland centers; for example, the rail rate on 100 pounds of steel from Hamilton to Edmonton is approximately $2.40 while to Vancouver it is only half as much.[2]

*

LAND COSTS

A feature of British Columbia is the very small part of the total land area which is inhabited or improved. Much of this is in the extreme southwest corner where the Lower Fraser Valley (Fig. 1) affords a relatively easy routeway through the coast batholith, and virtually the only part of the coast with a climate, topography, and soils conducive to intensive agricultural and urban development. This valley has a usable area of roughly 1000 square miles, little more than a quarter of one per cent of the land area of the province, but contains 60 per cent of the population, a large part of the agriculture, and nearly all the secondary manufacturing industry. The latter is in fact concentrated in the Vancouver Metropolitan Area at the extreme western end of the valley where the delta of the Fraser provides extensive waterfront sites for industrial and port development.

Some sections of the waterfront in the Vancouver area are expensive to develop because they either slope steeply down to sea level, or offer only low-lying peat deposits as a foundation for building, and in much of the remainder of the valley, a blanket of glacio-marine clays and tills gives rise to costly foundation problems.[3] However, these physical difficulties do not adequately explain why industrial land in the Vancouver area is, generally speaking, considerably more expensive than in other industrial areas in Canada. The extent of the difference is shown in Table 1. These prices pertain to serviced industrial land with good foundations within ten miles of the center of the metropolitan area; choice waterfront property on very central sites costs considerably more in all areas, and more distant sites with poor foundations and fewer services generally sell at lower prices.

Speculation is undoubtedly one of the major reasons for the high land values in the Vancouver area. The demand for land to hold has been extremely heavy in recent years because of the very fast pace of development, and because of a general belief that suitable land is very scarce. But, although the area of buildable land in British Columbia is limited, it is in fact very much more than is ever likely to be required for building purposes. However, up to the present at any rate, land is being bought for speculative and precautionary motives as much as for development, with the result that the Vancouver area is at a relative disadvantage in terms of land costs.

TABLE I

ESTIMATED COST OF SERVICED INDUSTRIAL LAND IN 1959

Metropolitan area	Dollars per acre
Vancouver	10,000–20,000
Calgary	4,000–10,000
Edmonton	6,000–15,000
Winnipeg	4,000–10,000
Toronto	6,000–15,000

Source: Industrial Development Commissions

A further reason for this is the sprawling pattern of urban growth. Figure 1 shows that Vancouver is hemmed in on the north by the southern edge of the Coast Range, and on the west by the Strait of Georgia, with the result that the southern and western fringes are having to accommodate a more than proportional share of the development. Excessive subdivision of land in these directions is forcing industry to pay high prices to reassemble parcels of adequate size, or alternatively to "leap-frog" far ahead of the fringe. As a result it is necessary to go much further out from the center in the Vancouver area than in other metropolitan areas to find cheap land in large parcels.

*

LOCAL MATERIALS

The hinterland of Vancouver contains several of the basic raw materials used by manufacturing industry. The outstanding feature is a huge and sustained yield of softwoods of various types, grades, and sizes. The coastal location of Vancouver enables mills and factories in the area to obtain logs easily and cheaply from all parts of the coast

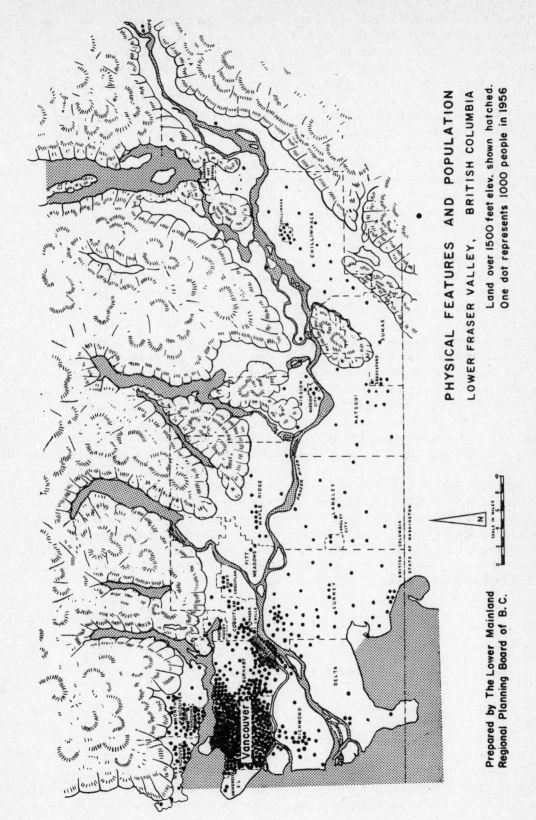

PHYSICAL FEATURES AND POPULATION

LOWER FRASER VALLEY, BRITISH COLUMBIA

Land over 1500 feet elev. shown hatched.
One dot represents 1000 people in 1956

Prepared by The Lower Mainland
Regional Planning Board of B.C.

FIG. 1

forest district of British Columbia, and the delta of the Fraser and its tributaries provide access and storage space far into the Lower Fraser Valley.

The climate and soils of the Valley provide the natural basis for a large output of dairy produce, vegetables, and small fruits, which represents input to the food processing industries. Great possibilities exist of increasing agricultural output by more intensive utilization of the better alluvial soils and by bringing into use a larger part of the boulder clays on the upland areas.[4] Obstacles to this are the increasing competition from other agricultural regions in Canada and the United States, and the loss of some of the best soils in the Vancouver area to urban development. Fortunately, in this area the usual conflict between agricultural land use and the extraction of gravel and other deposits is not likely to arise. Glacial, marine, and fluvial deposits of gravel, clays, and sand are found throughout the metropolitan area and the Lower Fraser Valley, the former offering the advantage of closeness to markets and the latter the attraction of cheap enough land for extensive industries producing relatively low valued non-metallic mineral products.

Oil and natural gas are available to industries in the Vancouver area via pipelines from northern Alberta and the Peace River district of British Columbia. Four refineries with huge built-in capacity for further expansion are now established in the area and producing petroleum and by-prod-ucts. In addition, mention has recently been made of a possible new pipeline to carry gas by-products from the northern fields to the Pacific coast to serve the growing markets in British Columbia and northwest United States. These developments are reducing the disadvantages of the Vancouver area compared with the Edmonton area in respect to the basic materials for certain chemical industries.

Many metals are mined in British Columbia, but at present the greater part of the output is exported either as raw ore or after primary smelting. The latter takes place at various locations in the interior of the province closer to the mines and where land, water, and power are cheaper than in the Vancouver area. Deposits of iron ore in the coastal part of the province are proven at 10 million tons and may possibly give rise to a small blast furnace unit in the next few years.[5] However, deposits of coking coal on Vancouver Island are of poor quality and virtually exhausted, and it would appear that, in regard to input at any rate, the Vancouver area is at a disadvantage compared with southeast British Columbia and southwest Alberta as a location for an integrated iron and steel plant. Vancouver has the advantage of large supplies of scrap metal from its port and existing industries, and this has provided the basis for an integrated operation comprising the production of steel ingots, and rolling mill and merchant mill products in the medium-size range.

*

WATER AND POWER

The Vancouver area is especially well endowed with the natural features basic to a good water supply. The principal source of this at the present time is the southern fringe of the Coast Range Mountains which line the north shore of Burrard Inlet (the Vancouver harbor); these mountains receive an annual rainfall of 125 inches at the intake points, and provide a large year-round source of supply. By their form they also provide suitable sites for storage reservoirs at elevations of 500 to 1500 feet above the main valley. As a result, virtually the whole of the Vancouver metropolitan area is supplied with water from a nearby source without any expenditure on pumping. This region starts off, therefore, with natural advantages in respect of water supplies.

However, there are undoubtedly certain disadvantages in the physical features of the area which partly offset the advantages. High costs were incurred in constructing the large dams which are required at the storage reservoirs in the mountains, and distribution mains had to be laid underwater to take the supply across Burrard Inlet to the main body of consumers, and across the Fraser River to meet the demand from the municipalities on the far side of the metropolitan area. In addition, the extensive sprawl development in that direction is particularly costly to supply, and as these areas are serviced at the common rate, the result is to raise the cost of water to more favorably situated users. The actual rates charged for water are compared with those of other metropolitan areas in Table II.

TABLE II

ESTIMATED COST OF INDUSTRIAL WATER SUPPLIES IN 1959

Metropolitan area	Consumption level per month	
	10,000 cu. ft.	100,000 cu. ft.
	cents per 100 cu. ft.	cents per 100 cu. ft.
Vancouver	18.0	10.0
Calgary	21.0	13.0
Winnipeg	19.0	12.5
Toronto	20.0	16.5

Source: Industrial Development Commissions.

In spite of the comparatively low cost of water in the Vancouver area, the rates are high enough to place a considerable burden on heavy water-using industries, with the result that industries of this type have been tending to rely on alternative sources of supply or else locate outside the metropolitan area altogether. Fortunately, alternative supplies of industrial water are readily available from the sea and rivers on the periphery of the area, and from the ground water found in the superficial deposits in the Lower Fraser Valley.

Water is also power in southern British Columbia, and in this regard the physical environment of the Vancouver area appears once again as something of a mixed blessing. Up to the present, practically all the electricity consumed in the Lower Fraser Valley has been generated by the harnessing of natural water power at various sites in the Coast Range. As demand has grown it has been necessary to develop the power potential of more distant parts up to 200 miles to the north, which has meant heavy transmission costs to bring the power across the very difficult terrain between the source of the supply and its consumers. Within the Valley, urban development has generally taken place at a much lower density than in the other metropolitan areas in Canada and power distribution costs are consequently higher. In addition, the Toronto area, for example, has the important further advantage of a much higher load factor due to the steady demand from the larger proportion of industrial customers and the lack of seasonal variation in industrial activity. The cost of providing electric power to the Vancouver area is, therefore, not as low as the physical endowment might lead one to expect.

In terms of the rates charged to industrial users of electric power, the Vancouver area is in a more favorable position, as shown in Table III. However, these rates are in part the result of the policies adopted by the various power companies, and any changes in these policies would change the relative position of the various areas. In the Winnipeg area the present practice is to charge on the basis of total connected load rather than on actual peak load incurred by the customer, which is the more usual system, and it appears that the Winnipeg rates might be even lower than they are at present if the rate structure were modernized. In the Toronto area, the rates charged to residential customers are susidized by increased charges on industry with the result that industrial rates are higher than they might otherwise be.[6]

TABLE III

INDUSTRIAL POWER RATES IN 1959 (AVERAGE PRICE IN CENTS PER KWH)

Operating system	3 shifts a day—5 days a week		Continuous-round-the-clock	
Demand level Consumption level	1000 KW 400,000KWH/Mo	3500 KW 1,400,000 KWH/Mo	3500 KW 2,100,000 KWH/Mo	6000 KW 3,900,000 KWH/Mo
Vancouver	1.01	0.87	0.70	0.64
Edmonton	0.95	0.95	0.89	0.88
Winnipeg	0.96	0.83	0.67	0.61
Toronto	0.90	0.90	0.71	0.68

Source: B C Electric Company Ltd., Vancouver, 1959.

*

LABOR COSTS

High labor costs and poor labor-management relations are a feature of British Columbia, and one which management representatives hold responsible for any setback in the fast rate of industrial growth which the province has come to regard as normal. This effect is far from proved, but it is undoubtedly true that, on the average, labor costs in manufacturing and also in the construction, transportation, and service industries have been consistently higher than in any other Canadian province throughout the fifties, without any apparent offset by higher productivity. Similarly, Vancouver has higher average labor costs than the other major metropolitan areas in Canada.[7]

The basis of labor conflict lies in the fact that the proportion of nonagricultural paid workers belonging to trade unions in 1957 was, in British Columbia, 55 per cent; Ontario, 33 per cent; Quebec, 25 per cent; and Canada as a whole, 34 per cent.[8] This in itself should not discourage industrial development, but Table IV shows that British Columbia has also had more than its share of labor-management disputes culminating in overt strikes.

The relatively unfavorable position of British Columbia and the Vancouver area in these respects is mainly due to the preponderance of strike-prone primary industries such as logging, saw-milling, and construction. The publicity afforded the frequent disputes and wage increases in these industries has encouraged other labor groups to aim high, and has also given rise to an exaggerated view of the labor situation and its retarding effects.

In view of the fast pace of industrial development in the Vancouver area in recent years, it is hard to believe that the relatively unfavorable labor costs and attitudes are a serious deterrent to development in this region at any rate. However,

TABLE IV

INDUSTRIAL CONFLICT IN B. C.

Year	Share of Canada's nonagricultural paid workers	1941 to 1954		
		Share of strikes	Share of strikers	Share of man-days lost
1941	8.0%			
1951	8.5%	11.0%	13.7%	17.5%
1956	9.0%			
Peak years of labor trouble:				
1946		29.2%	28.5%	29.0%
1952		16.2%	38.7%	43.0%

Source: Jamieson in B.C Natural Resources Conference 1958.

locational theory would suggest that they may in fact be exercising an important influence on the industrial structure of the region, and to check this, Table V has been prepared. This shows the relative importance of labor costs in the various major groups of manufacturing industry in the Vancouver area, and the rate of growth in employment in each group in recent years. A point of considerable interest is that, although growth has taken place in all industries, the highest rates of increase have been in those groups (other than food-stuffs) in which labor costs are a relatively small part of total costs.

*

LOCAL MARKETS

One of the principal factors which is offsetting, to some extent, the geographical isolation of the Vancouver area, is the rapid increase in the size of the local market for manufactured goods. This is the result of a fast rate of population growth combined with a high level of purchasing power and a high rate of spending. It has recently been shown that the British Columbia-Alberta market area has had higher per capita purchasing power than the other market areas in Canada over the past 30 years, and that by 1956 retail sales in British Columbia were higher than in any other western province.[9] The growth of population in the Vancouver area and in

TABLE V
LABOR COSTS AND RATES OF GROWTH, BY MANUFACTURING GROUPS, IN THE VANCOUVER AREA

Group	Labor costs as % of total costs in 1956*	Growth in employment 1951–1956
Transportation equipment	44%	21%
Printing	38	6
Textiles	28	15
Non-ferrous	28	0
Iron and steel	28	35
Wood products	27	0
Paper products	25	47
Non-metallic minerals	25	67
Electrical apparatus	22	60
Chemicals	15	150
Food-beverages	14	0

*Total wages and salaries as percentage of selling value of factory shipments
  Source: From Dominion Bureau of Statistics, *General Review of Manufacturing*, Ottawa, 1951 and 1956 editions.

British Columbia as a whole over the past 25 years is shown in Table VI. During this period, the proportion of the national population resident in British Columbia increased from 6.6 per cent to 8.7 per cent.

The increase in the population of British Columbia in recent years appears to have been mainly due to a large amount of immigration from other parts of Canada and from abroad rather than to any extraordinary rate of natural increase.[10] The majority of the immigrants to the province were no doubt attracted primarily by opportunities of employment and advancement but, although this cannot be proved at the present time, it seems likely that a large number of those who came to the Vancouver area were also attracted by the amenities of the southwest corner of British Columbia, just as many other people have been attracted to California in the United States. This is a region with what is generally recognized as a pleasant climate; average temperatures in the Lower Fraser Valley range from 35 degrees in January to 70 degrees in July, and annual rainfall from 35 inches in the western and southern parts of the Valley to 65 inches in the east and north.[11] In addition, Vancouver has natural surroundings of sea and mountain unsurpassed in natural beauty and recreational value by any other region in Canada. Factors such as these have been recognized as an important force in migration patterns in affluent societies.[12]

Thus, the amenities of the Vancouver

TABLE VI
POPULATION GROWTH IN BRITISH COLUMBIA AND THE VANCOUVER AREA, 1931–1956

	1931	1941	1951	1956
British Columbia	694.3 thous.	817.9	1165.2	1398.5
Vancouver area	379.8 thous.	449.3	649.2	767.2

Source: Census of Canada. Vancouver area figures are those for Census Division 4, B. C.

area constitute one of its most important advantages. It is attracting industry directly, as was shown at the beginning of this paper, and also indirectly by attracting people in their dual capacity as consumers and labor force. Population growth in the Vancouver area is, therefore, to some extent the spontaneous factor in the development process.

*

MANUFACTURING EMPLOYMENT

The place of manufacturing in the employment structure of the Vancouver area is illustrated in Figure 2. This shows that only about one quarter of the labor force is directly dependent on manufacturing, and that this is equalled by the service group and far exceeded by the combined total of all the tertiary sectors. Undoubtedly, part of the employment in the latter is "non-basic" in that it serves rather than stimulates regional growth, but in this region at any rate the tertiary sectors also provide a considerable part of the economic base. Transportation, wholesale distribution, and governmental, business, personal, and recreational services are important functions of the Vancouver area simply because it is the only major Canadian port on the Pacific coast, and the only major urban concentration in British Columbia. The result is a fairly diversified economy with consequent protection against widespread depression and an appeal to immigrants from a wide range of age and occupation groups.

Although not predominantly an industrial center, the Vancouver area is steadily increasing its share of Canadian manufacturing industry. Between 1931 and 1956, the proportion of national output of manufactured goods produced by firms in the Vancouver area increased from 2.6 per cent to 4.3 per cent, and the proportion of national employment in manufacturing from 2.4 per

cent to 4.2 per cent. Over this 25-year period, the number of people employed in manufacturing in the Vancouver area rose from 12,600 to 56,300 at a fairly constant rate, but with a slowing down during the depression and a speeding up during the war. The principal reasons for the increase are the expansion of the Canadian and international markets for wood and paper products, and the growth of a local market in western Canada for a multitude of other manufactured items.

STRUCTURE OF EMPLOYMENT IN THE VANCOUVER METROPOLITAN AREA IN 1956

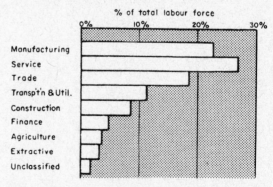

Source: Estimates for Census Div. 4 by the Bureau of Economics and Statistics, Victoria, B. C.

FIG. 2.

The changes which have taken place in the structure of manufacturing in the Vancouver area as a result of the developments since 1931, are evident from a comparison of the profiles in Figure 3. During this period the wood-based industries (wood products, pulp and paper) increased their share of the region's manufacturing employment from 27 per cent to 37 per cent. At the same time, the food and beverages group (the other large resource-based industry of the region) fell from 28 per cent to 20 per cent, mainly because of productivity increases in the canning and preserving of fish, fruit, and vegetables. The other major change, and a significant one, is the rise from 13 per cent to 20 per cent in the metals and machinery group (iron, steel, and non-ferrous products, and electrical apparatus). Its significance lies in the effect on the range and type of manufacturing carried on in the Vancouver area, because, although obviously this area is still highly specialized in wood products, important trends are discernible which are at once the outcome of the economic and geographical

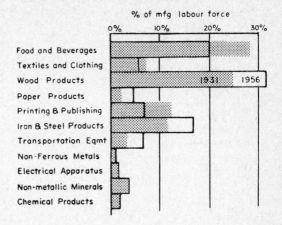

STRUCTURE OF MANUFACTURING IN THE VANCOUVER METROPOLITAN AREA,1931 & 1956

Source: Dominion Bureau of Statistics, General Review of the Manufacturing Industries of Canada, 1931 & 1956.

FIG. 3

characteristics of the area, and the foundation of the new economic environment facing future developers.

*

DIVERSIFICATION

The number and variety of the important and distinctive industries in a region provide a summary view of its diversification. In simple quantitative terms an important industry, in the Vancouver area at any rate, can be defined as one employing 1000 or more people, and a distinctive industry as an important industry with a location quotient of 1.5 or more.[13]

The important and distinctive industries in the Vancouver area in 1956 are shown in Table VII. Prominent in this list are the wood products, paper products, and foodstuffs groups; industries with a basis in the raw materials obtained from the coastal forests, the soils of the Lower Fraser Valley, and the rivers and the ocean. The shipbuilding industry is primarily concerned with building fishing vessels, and tugs and barges for the increasing volume of coastal traffic,

while industrial machinery is produced in response to the demand by the sawmills, pulp mills, and smelters scattered across British Columbia. On the other hand, the importance of printing, petroleum refining, bakery products, clothing, and sheet metal products is a reflection of the growth of the local market for consumer goods and Vancouver's position as the service center for the whole province.

Three of the industries in Table VII—namely, paper, petroleum and sheet metal products—grew to prominence between 1951 and 1956. Since then further diversification has taken place by the establishment in the region of several industries not previously represented here. The wood and paper groups have gained particle board plants and a fine paper mill. New metal industries include a steel pipe mill, a copper mill,

TABLE VII

PRINCIPAL MANUFACTURING INDUSTRIES IN THE VANCOUVER AREA, 1956

Industry	Regional employment		National employment		Location quotient
	-1- Thous.	-2- %	-3- Thous.	-4- %	-5- Col. 2 ÷ col. 4
Veneers and plywood	4.1	7.3	11.6	0.9	8.0
Sawmills	9.6	17.0	57.1	4.2	4.1
Shipbuilding	2.6	4.6	17.8	1.3	3.5
Fish processing	1.8	3.1	14.3	1.1	2.8
Machinery, industrial	2.1	3.8	26.6	2.0	1.9
Dairy products	1.4	2.5	20.1	1.5	1.7
Paper boxes and bags	1.0	1.9	15.5	1.1	1.7
Furniture	2.0	3.6	32.7	2.4	1.5
Meat packing	1.5	2.7	24.7	1.8	1.5
Fruit and vegetable preparation	1.0	1.8	16.8	1.2	1.5
Sash, door, and planing mills	1.2	2.1	19.9	1.5	1.4
Petroleum products	1.0	1.8	17.7	1.3	1.4
Printing and publishing	3.0	5.4	56.3	4.2	1.3
Bakery products	1.9	3.4	35.5	2.6	1.3
Sheet metal products	1.0	1.8	20.0	1.5	1.2
Clothing and knitwear	1.7	3.1	111.7	8.3	0.4

Source: Dominion Bureau of Statistics, *General Review of Manufacturing, 1956*, Ottawa, 1959.

aluminum extrusion and wire rod plants, and the production of copper and aluminum wire and cable. In the non-metallic minerals and chemicals groups, the last few years have brought into the region a large cement plant, plaster board manufacturing, and the production of phenol, chlorine, caustic soda, and sodium chlorate. The latter group is a direct response to the very rapid expansion of pulp and paper production in other parts of British Columbia.

Diversification can also be measured by the number of firms of various sizes in the region. In this case we need a typically diversified economy against which to compare the Vancouver area, and as the Toronto area is generally recognized as the most diversified secondary manufacturing region in Canada, it has been used for this purpose. Table VIII shows that in 1956 in the Toronto area, the number of employees in manufacturing industry was almost equally divided between small, medium, and large firms which suggests that a balance between the size groups is a feature of a diversified structure. By comparison the Vancouver area had a distribution heavily skewed towards small size of firm. It is significant that between 1946 and 1956, the proportion of employment in each of the three sizes of firm approached closer to the Toronto proportion, a fact which further reveals the trend towards more diversification in the Vancouver area. However, the latter will probably always have a preponderance of small firms because of the relatively small market for most of its products.[14].

*

PROCESSING

In 1956, 35 per cent of the manufacturing employment in the Vancouver area was in primary manufacturing, this being defined as the first-stage processing of raw materials received from the agricultural or extractive sectors. In the same year the figure for Canada as a whole was 23 per cent, and for the Toronto area only 8 per cent. The

TABLE VIII
DISTRIBUTION OF MANUFACTURING EMPLOYMENT BY SIZE OF FIRM
IN VANCOUVER AND TORONTO METROPOLITAN AREAS

Size of firm by number of employees	Percentage of manufacturing employment		
	Vancouver 1946	Vancouver 1956	Toronto 1956
Under 100	44	43	35
100 to 500	37	34	35
Over 500	19	23	30
Total manufacturing employment	42 thous.	56 thous.	209 thous.

Source: From D.B.S., *General Review of Manufacturing*, Ottawa, 1946 and 1956 editions.

high proportion in the Vancouver area reflects the predominance of such industries as fish canning and freezing, fruit and vegetable preparation, dairy products, and sawmilling.

These industries are engaged in the processing of the natural resources of the hinterland of Vancouver for direct sale to the consumer market and the construction industry. Their products do not generally constitute input to other manufacturing industries nor do the materials used offer much opportunity for more advanced processing. However, even in these industries, advances are taking place. For example, in recent years, the wood products industry in the Vancouver area has been developing plywood plants rather than new sawmill capacity, in response to the increasing tendency for plywood to displace sawn lumber in construction, and because the large diameter coniferous trees in the coastal forests give British Columbia an important advantage in plywood production. Changes such as these have been largely responsible for a reduction in the proportion of employment in the primary manufacturing group from 41 per cent to 35 per cent between 1951 and 1956.

Further information on the stage of manufacturing found in the Vancouver area is provided by statistics of the value added to materials by the processing which they receive in the transition from input to output[15] Table IX shows the major manufacturing groups in the Vancouver area, arranged in order of the proportion of value added in the gross value of production, with comparable figures for Canada as a whole. Some interesting points emerge from a comparison of the regional and national values for the various industries. The considerably larger proportion of value added in the transportation equipment group in the Vancouver area is due to the specialization in shipbuilding, an advanced type of manufacturing. On the other hand the higher percentage in the non-ferrous metals group is due to the *absence* here of primary metal refining for the reasons already given in the discussion of local materials.

In most groups (and particularly in electrical apparatus, chemicals, and paper products) Vancouver is mainly concerned with the production of the relatively low-value items which cannot easily carry the cost of shipment from factories in Ontario and the eastern United States. The more highly manufactured items, on which the burden of transportation costs weighs less heavily, are generally distributed from plants in the principal concentration of industries and markets. However, the growth of the industrial and the consumer markets in western Canada is encouraging the development of a more advanced type of manufacturing in the Vancouver area. This is shown by the fact that 75 per cent of the total increase in manufacturing employment between 1951 and 1956 took place in the first six industries in Table IX.

*

TABLE IX

COMPARISON OF VALUE ADDED BY MANUFACTURING
IN VANCOUVER AND CANADA IN 1956

| Industry | Percentage of "value added" in factory shipments | |
	Vancouver metropolitan area	Canada
Transportation equipment	75.3%	41.3%
Printing and publishing	69.3	66.7
Iron and steel products	50.4	51.9
Non-metallic mineral products	47.9	56.4
Chemical products	43.9	50.5
Rubber, leather, and textiles	43.7	46.7
Wood products	43.0	44.6
Petroleum and coal products	41.5	35.5
Non-ferrous metal products	40.4	35.9
Electrical apparatus	39.8	52.9
Paper products	37.2	48.1
Food and beverages	32.6	34.4

Source: From D.B.S., *General Review of Manufacturing, 1956*, Ottawa, 1959.

GROWTH POTENTIAL

Over the period 1951 to 1956, the number of people employed in manufacturing industry in Canada increased by 94,600. Each major group except textiles contributed to this total increase, but 75 per cent of it came from seven groups, namely, transportation equipment, electrical apparatus, iron and steel products, paper products, food and beverages, non-metallic mineral products, and chemicals. These may be called the "booming" industries to distinguish them from the groups with a less significant rate of expansion. In five of these seven groups, the rates of growth in the Vancouver area were three to nine times as great as those for the nation as a whole. In transportation equipment, the regional rate was slightly greater than the national rate in spite of stagnation in shipbuilding on the Pacific coast. Only in food and beverages did the region's rate of increase fall below the nation's, and here the national increase was also low at 6 per cent. Thus, the Vancouver area is sharing in the growth of the nationally booming industries, and developing an industrial structure with built-in growth potential.

Success in this respect is a measure of the buoyancy of a regional economy. In the case of Vancouver, this is primarily the result of the high rate of population growth and the more efficient utilization of local natural resources. These are the principal factors behind the development trends already described, but perhaps their most important effect has been to bring about notable changes in the traditional market distribution of Vancouver's manufactured products, and so to this we now turn.

*

INPUT-OUTPUT PATTERN

Until recent years the Vancouver area has been highly specialized in food processing and primary wood products, with the result that output of these items was far greater than the local market could absorb. On the other hand, production of many other manufactured goods was far below the level of local demand. Consequently, the regional economy was extremely dependent on exports to distant Canadian and world

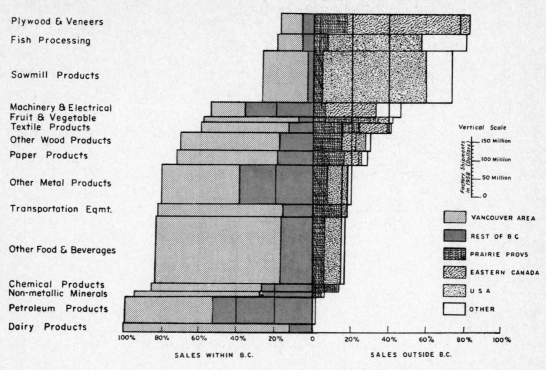

FIG. 4.

markets in order to pay for its many imports from equally distant producers. Unfortunately, as already stated, the low value, bulky commodities produced from the natural resources of the Vancouver area are subject to relatively heavy transportation costs which weakens the region's ability to compete against producers closer to principal markets. Thus, extreme specialization in primary manufacturing placed the Vancouver area in a very vulnerable position as well as limiting the opportunity, by way of industrial linkage, for the production of a wider range, and a more advanced type of product.

However, as a result of the changes in recent years, the region is developing a new input-output pattern. Some of the characteristics of this are evident from Figure 4, which provides a summary view of the markets for goods manufactured in the Vancouver area. Many points of interest emerge from this diagram, but the most significant from the

present point of view is the fact that the obviously heavy dependence on the traditional exporting of primary products is fairly well balanced by heavy sales of a wide variety of products in the western market. As already explained this is to some extent a protected market for Vancouver firms because of the much greater distance from plants in Ontario. Figure 4 also shows that considerable proportions of some of the more advanced products from the Vancouver area are sold in eastern and world markets. These are mainly items such as power saws, drilling equipment, etc., which have acquired an international reputation after having been developed for local extractive industries.

The market distribution diagram shows, as would be expected, a high proportion of sales within the Vancouver area. A large part of this represents inter-industry transactions, and a study of these shows how industrial linkage is stimulating the build-up

TABLE X

INTER-INDUSTRY TRANSACTIONS WITHIN THE MANUFACTURING SECTOR IN THE VANCOUVER METROPOLITAN AREA IN 1958

Read down columns for source of input
Read along rows for distribution of output

	Food and beverages	Clothing and textiles	Wood products	Paper products	Metal products	Transportation equipment	Electrical apparatus	Non-metallic mineral products	Chemical products	Miscellaneous manufacturing	Total buyers of output*	Number of firms in industry†	Interaction coefficient‡
Food and beverages	24								1		25	99	0.3
Clothing and textiles		7	10	4	1						22	50	0.4
Wood products	2	3	52	4	3	17	2	2		6	91	142	0.6
Paper products	12	1	1	10						17	41	17	2.4
Metal products	10	1	27	2	46	15	6	4	1	11	123	140	0.9
Transportation equipment												42	0.0
Electrical apparatus						1				3	4	14	0.3
Non-metallic mineral products	3		10	4	7	1		7	3	3	38	29	1.3
Chemical products	1	1	9	13	3	1	5	1	8	13	55	29	1.9
Miscellaneous manufacturing	18	2	9	1	8			7		2	47	50	0.9
Total suppliers of input*	70	15	118	38	68	35	13	21	13	55			
Number of firms in industry†	99	50	142	17	140	42	14	29	29	50			
Interaction coefficient‡	0.7	0.3	0.8	2.2	0.5	0.8	0.9	0.7	0.5	1.1			

* Totals of each row and column.
† Number of firms interviewed
‡ Totals of rows and columns divided by number of firms.

Source: Interviews by Lower Mainland Regional Planning Board of all firms with over ten employees.

of an industrial complex in this region. Some idea of the current linkage can be obtained from Table X. This shows input-output relationships for the manufacturing sector in the regional economy in terms of the number of transactions between firms in the industry groups which buy materials from or sell products to each other.[16] Obviously some industries have greater intra-regional linkage than others. Most of the differences can be explained by the nature of the input or output; firms using mainly imported materials (e.g., the textile group) or local primary produce (non-metallic mineral products) do not buy much from other manufacturing industries within the region, and firms that produce mainly finished goods (transportation equipment) or consumer goods (foodstuffs) do not provide much of the input used by other industries.

A rough measure of the extent of an industry's linkage is provided by the totals of each row and column in Table X. These show the importance of the industry to the manufacturing sector in terms of the number of inter-industry transactions performed by it. By this criterion the wood products group (as a purchaser of output) and the metal products group (as a supplier of input) have the most stimulating effect. However, some allowance should be made for the different number of firms in each industry, and the simple "interaction coefficients", shown in the last column and the last row of Table X, serve this purpose. These show that, per firm, the paper products group has, at the present time, the strongest linkage with other firms in the region, both as buyer and seller. The reasons for this bring us right

back to the characteristics of the economic environment in which the industry operates.

In recent years, a very large expansion of pulp and paper production has taken place on coastal sites on Vancouver Island and other parts of British Columbia. Although very little of this is located in the Vancouver area where land, water, and power are relatively expensive, and timber supplies relatively scarce, waterfront sites in Vancouver and on the delta of the Fraser have attracted several large chemical plants engaged in the manufacturing of products for use in the pulp and paper mills. The section of the paper products industry in which the Vancouver area is directly engaged is the paper converting group. Its basic input consists of paper rolls from the new mills, inks, wax, glues, and asphalt from local chemical plants, and felt and fibers from the textile group. Principal products are cartons and containers for the local food processing industries, bags for cement and fertilizer plants, roofing papers and paper board for the western construction industry, and a wide range of sanitary paper, wax papers, and labels for the western market.

The high rate of growth of the paper products industry in recent years provides a fine illustration of the importance to the industrial development of the Vancouver area, of an increased local supply of materials, and a growing local market for products. Growth in both respects has meant that the disadvantages of the region in respect to transportation costs and most of the other cost factors have had a less retarding effect on its industrial development than might otherwise have been the case.

*

FOOTNOTES

1 Much of the material in this paper was obtained by the Lower Mainland Regional Planning Board in the course of interviewing in 1958 all industrial firms in the Vancouver Metropolitan Area with over ten employees (a total of 1100 firms).

2 Information from General Freight Agent of the Canadian National Railways in Vancouver, July, 1959.

3 J. E. Armstrong, *Surficial Geology of Vancouver Area,* Department of Mines and Technical Surveys (Ottawa, 1956).

4 C. C. Kelly and R. H. Spilsbury, *Soil Survey of the Lower Fraser Valley,* B. C. Department of Agriculture (1939).

5 G. P. Contractor, *Some Aspects of the Canadian Iron and Steel Industry With Particular Reference to British Columbia,* Technical Bulletin No. 21, B. C. Research Council (Vancouver, 1954).

6 Brief by B. C. Electric Company to the Royal Commission on the B. C. Power Commission (Vancouver, 1959), p. 31.

7 Dominion Bureau of Statistics, *Review of Man-Hours and Hourly Earnings, 1946–57* (Ottawa, 1958).

8 S. M. Jamieson, "Cultural Factors Affecting Industrial Relations in B. C.," *Transactions of the Eleventh B. C. Natural Resources Conference* (Victoria, 1958), p. 13.

9 Western Development and Power Limited, *The B. C.-Alberta Market, 1925–1975* (Vancouver, 1959).

10 T. I. Matuszewski, "Population Trends in B. C.," *Transactions of the Eleventh B. C. Natural Resources Conference* (Victoria, 1958), pp. 7–12.

11 Lower Mainland Regional Planning Board, *The Lower Mainland Looks Ahead* (New Westminster, B. C., 1952).

12 E. L. Ullman, "Amenities as a Factor in Regional Growth," *Geographical Review,* Vol. 44 (1954), pp. 119–132.

13 The location quotient is calculated by the formula:

$$\frac{\text{No. of employees in the industry in the region}}{\text{No. of employees in all industries in the region}} \div \frac{\text{No. of employees in the industry in the nation}}{\text{No. of employees in all industries in the nation}}$$

14 This point is discussed by Gideon Rosenbluth in his recent book, *Concentration in Canadian Manufacturing Industries* (Princeton University Press, 1957).

15 "Value added," or the net value of production, is the difference between the gross value of production and the total cost of materials, fuel and power. Estimates of value added can be calculated for Canadian regions from the official annual reports on manufacturing, although these express value of output in terms of the value of factory shipments which may differ slightly from the gross value of production because of changes in inventories.

16 The input-output concept is a tool which economic geographers might use more freely in regional analysis, even though precise co-efficients are not easily obtainable from available statistics.

14

Large Urban Places in the Prairie Provinces– Their Development and Location*

* Translated from "Die Gross-Städte im Mittleren Westen Kanadas– ihre Entwicklung und Stellung innerhalb der Provinzen", Geographische Zeitschrift, 51 Jahrgang (October 1963), pp. 301–323, by permission. Revised by the author.

The economic growth of the Prairie Provinces during the last twenty years and the concomitant diversification of their economy through the extraction of mineral resources and the growth and development of industry, have resulted in a rapid growth of the larger cities. To this group belong the provincial capitals, Winnipeg, Edmonton and Regina, as well as Calgary and Saskatoon which are comparable in size and function. During the colonization of the West, these cities fulfilled important functions as centres of supply, commerce and transportation. In more recent time, because of their growing industry, they have become considerably important in the further economic development of the region.

Within Canada's populated area, Winnipeg occupies a particularly central position. To this favourable position as a collection and distribution point in Canada's continental transportation system, should be added the further advantage of Winnipeg's location on the eastern margin of the Prairie colonization region (Fig. 1). It became an important transfer point between the economically stabilized East and the Middle West, then on the verge of development. Two factors were relevant, the transfer of settlers and their supplies to the region, and the collection and shipment of agricultural goods from the region. Location with relation to the natural waterways must also be emphasized. These served as vital arteries of transportation during the early period of settlement and prior to the construction of the railway. Located at the confluence of the Assiniboine and the Red Rivers, the Winnipeg site has connections to the west and south and to Hudson Bay in the north. This locational advantage led to the development of a number of trading posts within and adjacent to the area which today is occupied by metropolitan Winnipeg. The first of these centres, Fort Rouge, was established in 1738 by La Verendrye. Prior to 1821, at which time the consolidation of the two formerly economically and politically opposed groups—the Hudson's Bay Company and the North West Company— took place, the region was the scene of much bitter rivalry. In 1835, Fort Garry was founded near the confluence of the Assiniboine and the Red Rivers, as a mutual undertaking of the two companies. This was also the administrative centre of the Red River Colony, founded in 1811–1812 by Lord Selkirk and several hundred

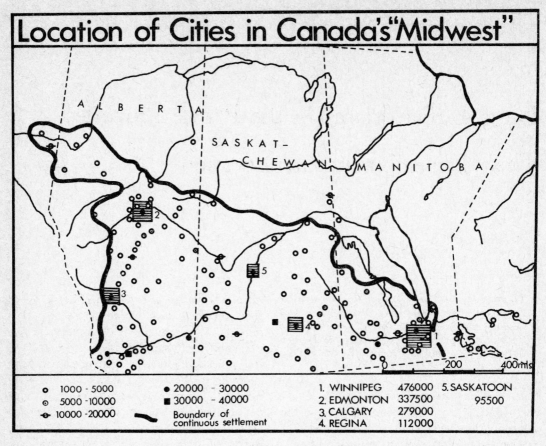

Location of Cities in Canada's "Midwest"

○	1000 - 5000	●	20000 - 30000	1. WINNIPEG 476000
◉	5000 -10000	■	30000 - 40000	2. EDMONTON 337500
✦	10000 -20000	▬	Boundary of continuous settlement	3. CALGARY 279000
				4. REGINA 112000

5. SASKATOON 95500

FIG. 1.

Scottish settlers. However, because of a lack of a new influx of immigrants, this early settlement developed very slowly and can hardly be regarded as the basis for the growth of the city. It was not until the 1860's that any significant development took place in that area. During this period a small commercial centre named Winnipeg emerged near Fort Garry at the intersection of the roads from the west and south, which together with Fort Garry forms the centre of modern Winnipeg. In 1871 the settlement consisted of a few frame structures and had some 241 inhabitants. Although the founding of the province of Manitoba in 1870 with Winnipeg as its capital, the settlement of the surrounding area, particularly by Mennonites, and the railway connection with St. Paul in 1878, brought about some expansion of the community, the most important factor inducing

growth did not come until the construction of the transcontinental railroad between 1881 and 1885 (Fig. 2). Shortly after 1881, a marked increase in population took place. The basis for a commercial and financial centre for the opening of the prairies and for the development of industry (mainly flour milling and iron works) was created. It is readily apparent that the further development of the city was dependent upon the success of the colonization of her vast hinterland. Winnipeg's dynamic growth and expansion was largely determined by the production of wheat and the availability of good export markets. Special rail privileges and preferential freight rates further enhanced its position as the leading city of Canada's Middle West, a position which was dominant until the beginning of World War I. As early as 1908, Winnipeg's population had risen to over 100,000.

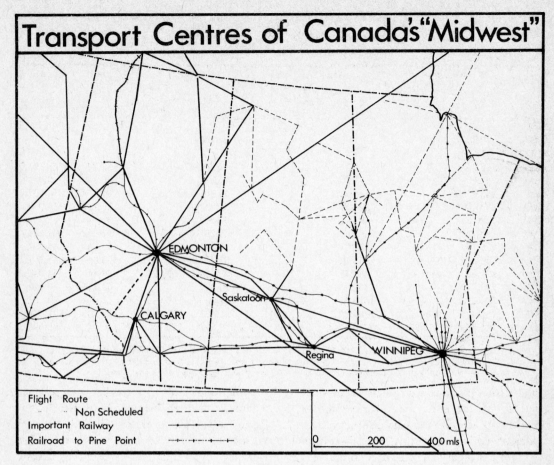

Transport Centres of Canada's "Midwest"

Flight Route —
·· ·· Non Scheduled — — — — —
Important Railway —•—•—•—
Railroad to Pine Point —+—+—+—

0   200   400 mls

FIG. 2.

Many analogies with Winnipeg exist in the development of the four other prairie cities, although they are overshadowed by the development of Winnipeg itself. Since Winnipeg was able to develop the important functions for the entire prairie region, the growth of these other cities as regional centres was determined by the settlement of their immediate surroundings. Proximity to the railroad and the land use potential of the nearby area proved to be the most important factors.

The Edmonton area, much like Winnipeg, was characterized by a particularly favourable transportation position during the period of the fur trade. Connections to the east and west existed via the North Saskatchewan River, as well as to the north over a land route to the Athabasca River, from which, access to the Mackenzie territory was possible. This favourable location led as early as 1794–95 to the establishment of Fort Augustus and Fort Edmonton, somewhat south of the present city. At the beginning of the 19th century both of these forts were relocated, and, in 1821, united to form a larger Fort Edmonton. This was soon to develop into one of the most important centres along the northern trade route. In 1858 it had 120 inhabitants who, apart from trading, were also occupied with the construction of boats. Settlement in the immediate vicinity of the fort began during the seventies, and by 1880 the place had a population of 300. The change in the original plans for a railroad going through Edmonton, to a position favouring a more southern route, was a considerable disadvantage to Edmonton. In addition, the wide valley of the North Saskatchewan River,

TABLE I
THE DEVELOPMENT OF POPULATION OF THE
LARGER CITIES OF CANADA'S MIDDLE WEST*

| | Winnipeg | | Edmonton | | Calgary | | Regina | Saskatoon |
	City	Metropolitan Area	City	Metropolitan Area	City	Metropolitan Area	City	City
1871	241							
1881	7,985		ca. 300		1884: ca. 500			
1891	25,639		?		3,876		?	?
1901	42,340		4,176		4,392		2,249	113
1906	90,153		11,126		11,967		6,169	3,011
1911	136,035		31,064		43,704		30,213	12,004
1916	163,000		53,846		56,514		26,127	12,048
1921	179,087		58,821		63,305		34,432	25,739
1926	189,708		65,163		65,291		37,329	31,234
1931	218,785		79,197		83,761		53,209	43,291
1936	215,814		85,774		83,407		53,354	41,734
1941	221,960	290,540	93,817	97,842	88,904	93,021	58,245	43,027
1946	229,045		113,116		100,044		60,246	46,028
1951	235,710	354,069	159,631	173,748	129,060	140,645	71,319	53,268
1956	255,093	409,121	226,002	251,004	181,780	200,449	89,755	72,858
1961	265,429	475,989	281,027	337,568	249,641	279,062	112,141	95,526

*Census of Canada - A small proportion of the population increase may be ascribed to an increase of the census area, particularly with respect to Metropolitan areas. —The "Metropolitan Area" according to the definition given in the Census of Canada, consists of a group of communities which have close geographic, economic, and social relations.

which formerly was a strategic factor in the defense of the fort, now proved to be a serious obstacle for the establishment of connections with the south. The first branch line from Calgary, which was completed in 1891, did not reach the settlement north of the river, but rather induced the development of the competing community of Strathcona, which was not annexed by Edmonton until 1912. In the meantime, this railroad, as well as the two lines constructed between 1906 and 1911 which connected Edmonton with the east (Fig. 2), brought about a rapid settlement of central Alberta. Good soil and climatic conditions favoured the development of an intensive and stable mixed farming economy, with a fairly dense network of farms.[1] Edmonton gained in importance as a centre of supply for this region, by attracting commercial firms and the first basic manufacturing industries (flour milling and meat packing). In addition, Edmonton gained the function of provincial capital when Alberta became a province in 1905, and became a university city with the establishment of the University of Alberta in 1906. These developments encouraged

construction and a further population increase. Although Edmonton's sphere of influence was thus greatly widened, the expansion of its service area was nevertheless restricted by a relatively limited expansion of settlement to the north and the growth of Calgary to the south. However, by the beginning of World War I, Edmonton had a population of 50,000, and could anticipate further expansion and growth because of its ideal location as a potential point of transfer with relation to the still undeveloped north-west.

Calgary had its beginning in 1875, with the establishment of a fort by the Royal North West Mounted Police, under the leadership of Colonel J. F. Macleod. Its location at the confluence of the Elbow and Bow Rivers was wisely chosen, especially since an important mountain pass, the Kicking Horse Pass, may be reached through the upper valley of the Bow River. The distances to Winnipeg and Vancouver by rail or highway are approximately the same (780 miles), and Edmonton lies roughly 190 miles to the north. Location in uninhabited territory at first delayed development. The impetus to settlement came with the railroad which reached Calgary in 1883; one year later a community of 500 people had been formed. At the same time, the federal government allotted large tracts of pasture land in southern Alberta to ranchers, who marketed their products in Calgary. Thus, its function as a centre for the trade of beef cattle and for meat processing was determined. Less important was its function as a supply centre because of a relatively small umland population. However, this situation was partly changed when, from the turn of the last century onward, more settlers came into the area to take up wheat farming. In comparison with Edmonton, the hinterland of Calgary has remained less populated, partly because the immediate foothills zone to the west was mainly pasture land and not conducive to intensive settlement. The beginnings of irrigation, in the late 1880's by the Mormons, and the exploitation of coal in nearby mines, gave the city new functions and stimulated further growth. A sustained impetus to rapid growth came with the discovery of natural gas and oil. As early as 1904, certain gas wells near Medicine Hat, south-east of Calgary, could be utilized successfully (Hanson, p. 40). Further discoveries in Southern Alberta led, in 1905, to the founding of the Calgary Natural Gas Company, which promoted further explorations. The greatest success was achieved by the Calgary Petroleum Products Company which, in 1913-14, discovered rich oil and natural gas deposits in the Turner Valley, south-west of Calgary. These discoveries, as well as preceding and subsequent speculation, encouraged a rapid increase in the city's population, which, until the thirties, was larger than that of Edmonton.

Compared to Edmonton and Calgary, the early development of Regina and Saskatoon was much slower. The beginnings of Regina go back as far as 1882 (see Drake). In connection with the construction of the railway and the colonization expected in the area, the Federal government sought a location for the administrative centre of its newly

obtained Northwest Territories. The decision was made in favour of a place in the midst of the expansive grassland area on the small Wascana Creek, and close to half the distance between Winnipeg and Calgary. Also important was its central location within the territory of Assiniboia, which was laid out in 1882, and was earmarked for provincial status. In the same year, the railroad reached the site, and a few buildings were erected, of which the governor's residence and the headquarters of the North West Mounted Police were the most important. The administrative functions, however, were not sufficient to sustain the development and growth of a settlement. Not until 1900, with the colonization of the umland, one of the richest wheat regions of the West, did Regina obtain its economic basis as a supply centre. This function was facilitated by the presence of a branch line to the north, constructed in 1870, which gradually brought about the colonization of central Saskatchewan. With the establishment of the province, Regina was made the provincial capital, which gave it an important administrative function. Population growth followed, as well as the modification of the outward morphology of the city. How sensitive the young settlement remained to the influence of external factors is reflected in the decline of the population between 1911 and 1916. A tornado destroyed parts of the city in 1912, and unfavourable economic conditions such as those of 1913, were the primary reasons for this decline.

Saskatoon on the South Saskatchewan River, occupies within the Prairie Provinces a particularly favourable central position (Fig. 1). However, during the early development of the city, this was not an effective advantage because the western cities were too far from one another, and communication between them was minimal. Saskatoon was established in 1883 by the Ontario Temperance Society, which acquired land in this unsettled district for the purpose of colonization (see Peel). The provisioning of the settlers and the few inhabitants of the town was at first carried out from Medicine Hat, via the South Saskatchewan River. The hopes of the Society to develop a strong and rapidly growing community, however, did not materialize. Not until after the completion of the railway connection to Regina and the connecting lines to Winnipeg and Edmonton, which were completed between 1906 and 1911, did the rate of settlement of the umland increase. With these changes, Saskatoon increased in importance as the supply centre of a region characterized by mixed as well as wheat farming. The status of the city was further enhanced with the establishment of the University of Saskatchewan (in 1907), which brought Saskatoon into closer contact with functions on the provincial level.

A comparative study of the early development of these five larger cities of Canada's Middle West very clearly reveals the considerably more advanced stage of Winnipeg. Here the lines of a hinterland extending hundreds of miles westward came together; from here, trade and export (especially of wheat) and the supplying of the entire region were directed. This concentration of trade, capital and industry within four decades brought about the development of a large metropolitan centre. In contrast, the other cities were primary supply centres for their immediate umlands; their growth depended to a very large extent upon regional intensification of the economy and regional expansion of their population. Edmonton and Regina received additional functions as provincial capitals, while Calgary's potential for growth was enhanced through the development of the oil and natural gas industry within its region.

During the next period of about 30 years (until 1940), Winnipeg's locational advantages deteriorated. With the opening of the Panama Canal (1914), a great deal of Alberta's trade moved to Vancouver. At the same time, the special rail privileges and preferential freight rates held by Winnipeg expired. Gradually a decentralization took place, resulting in the gradual take-over by the other cities of some of the commercial and supply functions formerly centred upon Winnipeg. Through these changes the various regions became increasingly independent and the economic position of their centres was strengthened. For Winnipeg, these changes resulted in a slower growth, increasing somewhat towards the end of the twenties, but never again reaching the phenomenal pace characteristic of the period between 1900 and 1914. However, industry, which in the meantime had become stabilized, gave the city a secure economic basis. The peripheral location of its industry, as well as the relocation of urban dwellings from the centre to the edge of the city and to suburban areas, led to the development of Metropolitan Winnipeg, which expanded far beyond the actual borders of the city.

Despite this economic decentralization, the growth of these other cities compared to Winnipeg, was relatively slow. The boom which began with the early discoveries of oil and natural gas petered out, until further discoveries in the Turner Valley secured a steady and more substantial supply.[2] However, the position of Calgary as an administrative centre for the oil and gas companies of Western Canada was made secure, and with the construction of a refinery in 1921, the basis for a petro-chemical industry was established. At that time Edmonton played no special role in the oil business of the province, although by 1925 other fields were also in production. Edmonton's growing industry was predominantly based on the processing of cereal and livestock products. The fertile soils and the relatively dense settlement of its umland, secured Edmonton's position as a commercial and supply centre. In addition, its hinterland was greatly expanded through the settlement of the Peace River country, northwest of Edmonton, after 1911.[3]

The stabilization of the cities and their slow but steady growth, was interrupted by the world economic crisis of 1929–30 and the relatively small wheat harvests prior to 1937.[4] The disadvantages of a one-sided economy, based primarily upon the production of wheat, now became evident. Although most of the weight of the depression was borne by the rural population, the

| | Increase between 1941 and 1961 | |
	Absolute Increase	%
Greater Winnipeg	185,449	63.8
City of Winnipeg	43,469	19.6
Greater Edmonton	239,726	245.0
City of Edmonton	187,210	199.5
Greater Calgary	186,041	200.0
City of Calgary	160,737	180.8
Regina	53,896	92.5
Saskatoon	52,499	122.0
Metropolitan Areas of:		
Montreal	969,588	85.1 (1961: 2,109,509 pop.)
Toronto	923,990	102.6 (1961: 1,824,481 pop.)
Vancouver	438,674	124.8 (1961: 790,165 pop.)
Ottawa	214,728	99.9 (1961: 429,750 pop.)
Hamilton	219,079	124.4 (1961: 395,189 pop.)
Quebec	156,754	78.1 (1961: 357,568 pop.)

*Census of Canada 1941, 1961 A small part of the population increase must be ascribed to the increase in the size of the census area.

close relationship between the cities and their umlands resulted in heavy losses for the cities as well. Immigration, which formerly contributed significantly to an increase in population, decreased sharply. The populations of Winnipeg, Calgary, and Saskatoon declined, while that of Regina remained stationary. Edmonton also registered a loss but it was made up within a short time after 1933. In this respect its location within a region of mixed farming was of some importance.

Out of this crisis arose an appreciation of the urgent need to diversify the economy of the Prairie Provinces and to make it less dependent upon the production of wheat. The extension of irrigation districts in southern Alberta and Saskatchewan, the further development of the livestock industry, and especially the mechanization of farms and use of better farming methods which greatly increased the size and profitability of operations, were some of the important measures taken in agriculture. In mining, the rapid increase in the exploitation of resources, particularly metal ores, oil and natural gas were important in stimulating economic growth. Together they provided the basis for a more diversified development of in-

dustry, and the local market for their products was enlarged.

The larger cities figured prominently in these changes, and this is reflected in their population increases since the thirties. Population changes were brought about by a high rate of natural increase, by a renewed and larger post-war influx of immigrants, who for the most part settled in the cities, and finally, by migrations from the rural areas of the provinces to the cities. These were attracted by urban opportunity, and freed by increasing mechanization on the farms. Once this trend had begun the various economic sectors of the cities, such as manufacturing, construction, commerce, and administration, experienced mutually dependent expansion. The leading position among Canada's large cities in the percentage of growth over the last 20 years has been occupied by Edmonton and Calgary.

The important factors in Edmonton's rapid rise to prosperity were its location on the southern margin of the Northland, and its proximity to new oilfields. As the only large city of the Northwest and because of its transportation links with other large centres of North America (Fig. 2), Edmonton became an important wartime supply base between the United States and Alaska. Its role in the construction of the Alaska Highway which begins at Dawson Creek, north-west of Edmonton, derived from its location. Edmonton was given further responsibility in the construction of an oil pipeline between Norman Wells, west of Great Bear Lake, and Whitehorse, which was vital to transportation (Canol Project). The measures by which the city became the headquarters for a number of military functions as well as for some private companies, especially during 1942–43, greatly facilitated and encouraged the development of the Northwest, for which Edmonton is the natural gateway. Today, numerous air routes lead from Edmonton to the important northern settlements. Along these routes lie smaller, normally inaccessible places, which are supplied from Edmonton as well. The combination of regular transit routes and non-scheduled routes have made Edmonton an important air transport centre, with a position comparable to Winnipeg's as a rail transfer point at the beginning of Western colonization. Other transport connections with the North are important as well; the Mackenzie Highway, completed in 1947–48, connecting the Peace River settlements and Hay River on the Great Slave Lake and a railroad following the same route, provide access to the extensive lead and zinc deposits at Pine Point, east of Hay River.

As a gateway to the north, Edmonton's functions as an important supply centre greatly expanded, especially after 1947 with the opening up of extensive oil deposits. Edmonton's location close to rich oilfields, particularly those of Leduc-Woodbend, Redwater, and Pembina, has been extremely important. About 70 per cent of Alberta's total petroleum production is produced within a radius of less than 100 miles of Edmonton.[5] Thus, the city became the centre of an extensive network of oil and natural gas pipelines, and the point of origin of many of the pipelines to the east and west. As the site of important oil processing and petro-chemical industries, as well as iron and steel processing, manufacturing of construc-

tion materials, and production of synthetics, Edmonton has diversified and considerably expanded her industry. If the selling value of factory shipments is used as an index, food-products and beverages are still the most important products, even though they have declined in relative importance from 80 per cent in 1948 to about 40 per cent in 1959 (Wonders, 1957, p. 12). A particularly important position is occupied by the meat processing and packing industry which expanded considerably during the last war.

With an ever growing industry, Edmonton takes on a new function besides its dominating role as a centre of commerce and transportation. It also carries the administrative functions of the province, is a university city, and serves as a cultural centre. These changes and the increase in population have brought about the expansion of the city's area to 42 sq. miles. City planners anticipate an extension of the city's territory to 108 sq. miles, and a consolidation of some of the loosely connected parts of the metropolitan area (Dant, p. 19; Davies, p. 31). The optimum size of the city has been estimated to be one with a population of between 350,000 to 400,000 people[6]; once this level has been reached, satellite cities will be developed. To improve the transportation system and the appearance of the inner part of the city, some ambitious projects are planned.

The rapid development in the extraction of oil and natural gas in Alberta, since 1947, has also been an important factor in the growth of Calgary. Nearly 400 companies, which, in one way or another, are directly connected with the exploration and production of oil and natural gas, have located their offices in metropolitan Calgary. Much like Edmonton, Calgary has become the site of an industry which is still dominated by meat packing and processing as well as flour milling, but whose leading role is gradually being modified by that sector of the industry which depends upon oil, natural gas and coal as raw materials. In addition, there are a fair number of small light manufacturing companies which have excellent opportunities for growth because of a growing market. Besides these functions, Calgary continues to be the important commercial and supply centre for southern Alberta, whose agriculture has been diversified through the development of irrigation districts and will be diversified even more in the future as new districts are set up. The cities of Lethbridge and Medicine Hat, however, assume part of the supply function for this region. Finally, mention must be made of an increasing tourist traffic, which is encouraged by the annual Calgary Stampede and the city's proximity to the mountains and particularly to Banff National Park. Various constantly growing industrial areas near the outer margins of the city, as well as the rapid urban expansion in the suburbs of single family houses, have allowed Calgary's area to grow to 150 square miles. The necessity of enlarging the city's territory, only very recently, would indicate that this rapid growth is expected to continue, and a population of 500,000 for the metropolitan area is anticipated by 1975. As in Edmonton, the appearance of the central part of the city has been changed greatly through the construction of high rise buildings; plans for future developments indicate that the changes will continue.

Regina and Saskatoon were able to double their populations over the past 20 years; however, their development, compared with that of Edmonton and Calgary, has been much less spectacular. Both cities have remained, essentially, supply and administrative centres for the southern and central Saskatchewan region; the formation of an industrial base is only slowly taking place. Some of the reasons for this are to be found in the economic structure of the province which is still dominated by agriculture and particularly the production of wheat. It is significant that between 1936 and 1951 Saskatchewan was characterized by negative population trends; not until 1962 was the population figure of the mid-thirties (930,000) reached again. The change in 1951 may be ascribed to an increase in the production of copper and zinc, oil and natural gas.[7] In both cities this made possible the

growth of industry, which consists of the processing of agricultural products (mainly flour milling), two oil refineries in Regina, iron and steel processing and production of cement; thus, since 1951 the value of factory shipments has doubled. The recently discovered potassium salt deposits in the Saskatoon area and the completion of the South Saskatchewan irrigation project are likely to bring about further growth.

The population increase of Winnipeg since 1941 has taken place primarily in the suburbs of the metropolitan area. This is indicated by the decrease in the area available for expansion, as well as by the formation of various city districts which are economically, socially, and culturally connected and interdependent.[8] The expansion of the city complex took place radially around the nearly 100 year old core. The various economic phases through which the city has passed are reflected in this pattern of growth. Within these rings, the various cities which developed independently are now functionally a part of Greater Winnipeg. This form of development is also evident from the city's land use pattern, which is typified by a central business district consisting of the wheat exchange, banks, commercial and administrative buildings and the larger retail stores, and a long, well-developed belt reaching to the northern edge of the city, where active growth is taking place; in this band we find near the Central Business District the wholesaling centres and some light manufacturing plants, as well as the old and compressed residential part; in the outer circles near the fringe of the city single family houses dominate the scene. Furthermore, the structure of the city becomes clearer in the distribution of daytime population showing that over 500 people per acre are concentrated within the inner circles about the core of the city.

In addition to the functions indicated above, Winnipeg contains a well developed industry and extensive rail and freight yards. Its industry is extremely diversified.[9] In addition to the processing of agricultural products, the city contains iron and steel

TABLE III

PROPORTION OF CITY POPULATION TO TOTAL PRAIRIE PROVINCES' POPULATION*

	1901	1921	1941	1961
Manitoba	255,211 pop.	610,118 pop.	729,744 pop.	921,686 pop.
Winnipeg	16.6 %	29.4 %	41.1 %	51.6 %
Cities over 5,000 population	(1) 2.2 %	(3) 5.7 %	(2) 3.4 %	(5) 7.3 %
Cities between 1 and 5,000 population	(9) 6.2 %	(10) 3.3 %	(13) 3.7 %	(28) 6.2 %
Saskatchewan	91,279 pop.	757,510 pop.	895,992 pop.	925,181 pop.
Regina	2.5 %	4.5 %	6.5 %	12.1 %
Saskatoon	0.1 %	3.4 %	4.8 %	10.3 %
Cities over 5,000 population		(3) 4.2 %	(5) 5.6 %	(9) 12.8 %
Cities between 1 and 5,000 population	(2) 3.7 %	(17) 3.7 %	(23) 4.4 %	(41) 8.1 %
Alberta	73,022 pop.	588,454 pop.	796,169 pop.	1,331,944 pop.
Edmonton	5.7 %	10.0 %	12.3 %	25.3 %
Calgary	6.9 %	10.8 %	11.7 %	21.0 %
Cities over 5,000 population		(2) 3.5 %	(2) 3.2 %	(6) 7.5 %
Cities between 1 and 5,000 population	(2) 5.0%	(20) 5.2 %	(25) 5.3 %	(65) 10.2 %

*Census of Canada—In the case of Winnipeg, Edmonton and Calgary, the figures are for the total metropolitan area since 1941; the affected municipalities have been omitted from the columns 'cities over 5,000 people' and 'cities between 1,000 and 5,000 people,' for Manitoba and Alberta. The numbers in brackets indicate the number of cities involved. For 1961 unincorporated places are included in the group 1-5000 inhabitants (For Manitoba 5 places, for Saskatchewan 2 and for Alberta 3)

processing plants, a machine and rolling stock industry, textile plants, printing, publishing, forest industries, oil refineries and chemical plants. Apart from the food processing and forest industry, which are based upon the raw materials of the umland,[10] the relatively early concentration of industry may be ascribed to good market conditions and a constantly growing labour force. The natural market is provided by northwestern Ontario, and by the entire area of the Middle West. Recently, this has been increasingly limited by the rapid industrialization of other cities. Winnipeg's position as a rail transportation centre has facilitated the marketing of its products, while at the same time making it an important transfer point for goods coming from the east. Industry, commerce, and transportation provide employment for the larger percentage of the city's labour force. Finally, Winnipeg's position as an important economic and commercial regional centre is accentuated by the presence of the Canadian Wheat Board, the Wheat Exchange, and numerous finance and insurance companies.

With the growth of the cities and the stabilization and expansion of their functions since the end of the thirties, their position as centres of population and commerce within the prairie region has steadily grown (Table III). The share of the total prairie population held by these cities has risen from 13 per cent in 1901, to 24 per cent in 1942, to 41 per cent in 1961. A similar concentration is evident from the large part of the province's industrial potential held by these cities, (Table IV).

Because of their favourable location, Winnipeg, Edmonton, and Calgary, stand out as cities supporting strong industrial development. The concentration and important role of the food processing industry indicates that agriculture and its export products form the economic basis of the Middle West. The development of this important sector of the economy and, later, the extraction of mineral resources made possible the growth of the cities. This brought with it an increased income to the individual and increased revenue to the provincial treasury, facilitating the expansion of markets. At the same time, the cities were able to employ and utilize the excess labour force from rural

TABLE IV

THE CITIES' SHARE OF THE INDUSTRIAL POTENTIAL OF THE PRAIRIE PROVINCES*

	Number of Industries		Number of Employees		Value of Factory Shipments (in $1000)	
	Total	%	Total	%	Total	%
Manitoba	1,592	100	42,339	100	738,457	100
Metro Winnipeg	1,017	66.5	36,307	85.8	600,226	81.4
Brandon	41	2.7	778	1.8	14,131	1.9
Saskatchewan	887	100	12,918	100	344,773	100
Regina	133	15.0	3,671	28.4	99,200	28.8
Saskatoon	141	15.9	3,555	27.5	94,417	27.4
Moose Jaw	47	5.3	1,347	10.4	48,077	13.9
Prince Albert	31	3.5	880	6.8	22,236	6.4
Alberta	1,848	100	39,157	100	889,658	100
Metro Edmonton	489	26.5	17,127	43.7	414,915	46.6
Metro Calgary	404	21.9	12,054	30.8	267,997	30.1
Lethbridge	62	3.4	1,338	3.4	24,523	2.8
Medicine Hat	43	2.3	1,277	3.3	32,973	3.7

*The Manufacturing Industries of Canada 1960, Section G, Geographical Distribution, Ottawa (D.B.S.), 1962—Other cities listed rank next in importance and emphasize the contrasts.

areas. This is particularly significant, since one of the vital functions of cities is to supply their umland regions. Reflecting all of these new relationships, the growth of cities epitomizes the economic progress of the Prairie Provinces, since the beginning of colonization and over the past 20 years.

*

SUMMARY

The development of the large cities of the Middle West of Canada—Winnipeg, Edmonton, Calgary, Regina and Saskatoon—has been summarized in three periods.

From its foundation between 1865 and 1885 up to about 1914-15, Winnipeg held a supreme position. Being the gateway of the colonization area of the Middle West, it had every qualification concerning a concentration of traffic, trade, capital, and industry of a hinterland stretching far towards the west. In contrast to Winnipeg, the other cities were supply centres of their immediate surroundings. Edmonton and Regina, from 1905 on, received additional responsibilities as provincial capitals.

In a second period, until 1940, decentralization gradually gained ground. The Middle West having become an independent settlement area and economic region, the several districts became more independent and the economic position of their centres strengthened. After an interruption, caused by an agricultural crisis in the thirties, the development of the cities received an extraordinary impetus after the second world war. The basic reasons for this development were especially a better adaptation and mechanization of agriculture as well as the successful extraction of mineral resources. Thus, apart from Winnipeg with its many-sided industries, the other cities also gained an additional function as industrial centres.

At present, the five large cities mentioned above contain the preponderant part of the industrial potential as well as 41 per cent of the population of the three prairie provinces. As a starting-point for opening up the North West in the future, Edmonton has a position similar to that of Winnipeg when the Middle West was opened up.

FOOTNOTES

1 The umland population (excluding city population) within a radius of 100 miles was: 1921, Edmonton: 175,000; Calgary: 126,000 1956, Edmonton: 263,000; Calgary: 155,000

2 Particularly successful drilling operations were achieved in 1924 and again in 1936. Until 1926 the Turner Valley oil field was the only oil field in Alberta. An all time high production was achieved in 1943, 9.8 million barrels (95% of Canada's total production). By 1949 the area had produced a total of 94.9 million barrels. See Hanson, p. 50; Alberta Oil and Gas Industry 1959, Oil and Gas Conservation Board, Calgary, p. 56.

3 The population of the area increased from about 4,000 in 1911 to 20,000 in 1921, and 49,000 in 1931; the 1961 figure was about 73,000.

4 Wheat production for Southwestern Saskatchewan in bushels per acre was: 1928: 27.1; 1933: 4.1; 1936: 3.5; 1937: 0.5; yearly average for the period 1929–1938: 8. (Reports of the Department of Agriculture, Province of Saskatchewan, Regina).

5 Petroleum production in Alberta rose from 10.1 million barrels (1942) to 6.8 million barrels (1947) to 171.4 million barrels (1963). The production of natural gas increased from 34.5 million cubic feet (1942) to 895 million cubic feet (1963). (Canadian Mineral Statistics, D.B.S., Reference Paper 68 (Ottawa, 1957); Canada Year Book, 1965, p. 589.

6 According to several calculations, this upper limit may be reached between 1965 and 1975.

7 Crude oil production by 1963 reached 70 million barrels; natural gas production 39.0 million cubic feet. Canada Year Book, 1965.

8 This development led in 1960 to the formation of a central city council, which makes possible the centralized direction of planning, water supply, taxation, etc. This necessary and widely demanded institution has until now not been adopted by Edmonton or Calgary.

9 Of the 159 different types of industry of Canada, about 75% are represented in Metropolitan Winnipeg. Atlas of Manitoba (1960), p. 78.

10 Emphasis must also be given to the extraction of mineral resources, notably copper, zinc, nickel, as well as petroleum (1963: 3.8 million barrels), however, this production lags considerably behind that of Alberta and Saskatchewan.

*

BIBLIOGRAPHY

For other sources see the bibliographies issued by the Department of Mines and Technical Surveys, Geographical Branch, Ottawa; also, Peel, B. B. A Bibliography of the Prairie Provinces to 1953. Toronto: 1956.

Bellan, R. C. Relief in Winnipeg: The Economic Background. Unpublished University of Toronto M. A. Thesis, 1941.
The Development of Winnipeg as a Metropolitan Centre. Unpublished Columbia University Ph. D. Thesis, 1958.

Britnell, G. E. "Perspective on Change in the Prairie Economy," The Canadian Journal of Economics and Political Science. Vol. 19, No. 4, 1953, pp. 437–454.

Bussard, L. H. "The Establishment of Fort Calgary," Alberta Historical Review, Vol. 3, No. 1, 1955, pp. 34–41.

Dant, N. "Edmonton: Practical Results of Planning Measures Since 1950," Community Planning Review, Vol. 4, 1954, pp. 31–40.

Davies, P. G. "The McNally Blue Print for Edmonton and Calgary," Planning in Alberta Series, 1955–56. Edmonton, 1956, pp. 19–36.

Drake, E. G. Regina, The Queen City. Toronto, 1955.

"Regina 1882–1955," Canadian Geographical Journal. Vol. 50, No. 1, 1955, pp. 2–17.

England, R. The Colonization of Western Canada: A Study of Contemporary Land Settlement (1896–1934). London, 1936.

Gislason, I. Prairie Panorama, a Brief Study of the Prairie Provinces. Calgary, 1948.

Halliwell, H. M. "The next Chapter in the Prairie Economy," New Commonwealth, Vol 33, No. 8, 1957, pp. 369–372.

Hanson, E. J. Dynamic Decade: The Evolution and Effects of the Oil Industry in Alberta. Toronto, 1958.

Hedges, J. B. Building the Canadian West: The Land and Colonization Policies of the Canadian Pacific Railway. New York, 1939.

Innis, H. A. History of the Canadian Pacific Railway. Toronto, 1923.

Jordan, M. E. "Edmonton—Old and New," Canadian Geographical Journal. Vol. 51, No. 6, 1955, pp. 244–247.

Lenz, K. "Neuere wirtschaftliche Entwicklungen in den Prärieprovinzen Kanadas," Geographische Rundschau. Jg. 14, 1962, pp. 1–9.
"Die Prärieprovinzen Kanadas. Der Wandel der Kulturlandschaft von der Kolonisation bis zur

Gegenwart unter dem Einfluss der Industrie," *Marburger Geographische Schriften*. Heft 21, 1965.

McConnell, R. S. "Planning in Edmonton, Alberta," *Journal of the Town Planning Institute*. Vol. 44, No. 2, 1958, pp. 39–43.

McCrimmon, E. R. "The Impact of Alberta's Growth on its Market Centres,' *Community Planning Association of Canada, Alberta Division, Planning in Alberta Series*. Edmonton, 1957–58, pp. 14–18.

MacDonald, G. H. *Ft. Augustus-Edmonton*. Edmonton, 1954.
Edmonton, Fort–House–Factory. Edmonton, 1959.

Macintosh, W. A. and Joerg, W. L. G., eds. *Canadian Frontiers of Settlement*. 8 vols, Toronto, 1934–40.

Marlyn, F. and Lash, H. N. "The Edmonton District: A City Centered Multiple Resource Region," *Resources for Tomorrow, Conference Background Papers*. Vol. 1, Ottawa, 1961, pp. 455–468.

Morton, W. L. *Manitoba, a History*. Toronto, 1957.

Oliver, F. "The Founding of Edmonton," *Queen's Quarterly*. Vol. 37, 1930, pp. 78–94.

Peach, J. S. "Calgary–The Foothills City," *Canadian Geographical Journal*. Vol. 53, 1956, pp. 168–181.

Peel, B. B. *The Saskatoon Story 1882–1952*. Saskatoon, 1952.

Putnam, D. F. *Canadian Regions: A Geography of Canada*. (5th edition). Toronto, 1961.

Robertson, T. B. "Winnipeg–The Prairie Capital," *Canadian Geographical Journal*. Vol. 7, 1933, pp. 132–142.

Robinson, I. M. "Peace River Region," *Resources for Tomorrow, Conference Background Papers*. Vol. 1, Ottawa, 1961, pp. 505–525.

Rosenbluth, G. *Concentration in Canadian Manufacturing Industries*. Princeton, 1957.

Schott, C. "Wandlungen der Landwirtschaft in den Kanadischen Prärieprovinzen," *Deutscher Geographentag Essen 1953, Tagungsberichte und Wissenschaftliche Abhandlungen*. Wiesbaden, 1955, pp. 83–95.
"Die Industrialisierung der Landwirtschaft am Beispiel Kanadas," *Beiträge zur Geographie der Neuen Welt*. (Festschr. O. Schmieder), herausgegeben von W. Lauer, Schriften des Geographischen Instituts der Universität Kiel, Bd. 20, 1961, pp. 23–54.

Shortt, A., ed. *Canada and its Provinces*. 23 vols. Toronto, 1914–17.

Slater, D. W. "Decentralization of Urban Peoples and Manufacturing Activity in Canada," *Canadian Journal of Economics and Political Science*. Vol. 27, No. 1, 1961, pp. 72–84.
"The Political Economy of Urban Changes in Canada," *Queen's Quarterly*. Vol. 67, No. 4, 1961, pp. 586–604.

Smith, P. J. "Calgary: A Study in Urban Pattern," *Economic Geography*. Vol. 38, No. 4, 1962, pp. 315–329.

Spry, G. "Economic Changes in the Canadian Prairie Provinces," *International Affairs*. Vol. 29, No. 3, 1953, pp. 309–315.

Stead, R. J. C. "Calgary–City of the Foothills," *Canadian Geographical Journal*. Vol. 36, 1948, pp. 154–171.

Thompson, N. and Edger J. H. *Canadian Railway Development From the Earliest Times*. Toronto, 1933.

Thrift, E. W. "Greater Winnipeg, Manitoba," *Journal of the Royal Architectural Institute of Canada*. Vol. 23, No. 11, 1946, pp. 272–275.
"Metropolitan Plan, Greater Winnipeg," *Journal of the Royal Architectural Institute of Canada*. Vol. 25, No. 7, 1948, pp. 219–252.
"The Progress of Planning in the Winnipeg Area, 1953–54," *Community Planning Review*. Vol. 4, 1954, pp. 76–78.

Watt, A. B. "Edmonton," *Canadian Geographical Journal*. Vol. 33, 1946, pp. 242–251.

Weir, Th. R. "Relation of Daytime Population to the Functional Areas of Metropolitan Winnipeg," (Abstract). *Annals of the Association of American Geographers*. Vol. 45, No. 3, 1955, pp. 304–305.
"Land Use and Population Characteristics of Central Winnipeg," *Geographical Bulletin No. 9*. 1956, pp. 5–21.
Economic Atlas of Manitoba. Winnipeg (Department of Industry and Commerce, Province of Manitoba), 1960.
"A Survey of the Daytime Population of Winnipeg," *Queen's Quarterly*. Vol. 67, No. 4, 1961, pp. 654–662.

Winkler, E. "Die Kanadischen Prärieprovinzen im Industriellen Umbruch," *Geographica Helvetica*. Vol. 7, 1952, pp. 235–249.

Wood, L. A. *The Red River Colony: A Chronicle of the Beginnings of Manitoba*. Toronto, 1920.

Wonders, W. C. "Edmonton, Alberta: Some Current Aspects of its Urban Geography," *The Canadian Geographer*. No. 9, 1957, pp. 7–20.
"River Valley City—Edmonton on the North Saskatchewan," *The Canadian Geographer*. No. 14, 1959, pp. 8–16.
"Repercussions of War and Oil on Edmonton," *Cahiers de Géographie de Québec*. 3e année, No. 6, 1959, pp. 343–351.

Atlas of Canada. Department of Mines and Technical Surveys, Geographical Branch, Ottawa, 1957.

Reports from *The Financial Post* (Toronto); *The Monetary Times* (Toronto); *Trade and Commerce* (Winnipeg); *Western Business and Industry* (Vancouver).

PART

V

CANADIAN REGIONALISM

15

Canadian Regionalism in Life and Letters[*]

J. WREFORD WATSON

[*] *From* The Geographical Journal, *Vol. 131, Part I,(1965), pp. 21–33. Reprinted by permission.*

Regionalism is well marked in Canada since, from the beginning, Canada grew up as a series of separate colonies, some of which, like Newfoundland, Nova Scotia, New Brunswick, Prince Edward Island and Quebec, had a longer existence as individual entities than as parts of a united realm. Separation has been more long standing than togetherness; difference has had a longer sway than unity. In a sense unity grew from without rather than within. Fear of absorption into the United States and impatience at dependence on Britain did as much to bring regions together as the need for trade between the colonies, the opportunity of forging transcontinental communication links, or the fact of sharing the same environment. Whenever the United States tried to induce Canadians to join with them, they aroused a sense of national distinctness in Canada that dispelled any idea of continental fusion. The British and French first got over their rivalry with each other in Canada when they banded themselves together against the Americans. In Lower and Upper Canada, for example, both British and French resisted America in the American War of Independence, in the War of 1812, in the

threatened invasions of 1837 and 1846 and in the Fenian raids of the 1860's. But when the fear of absorption by America finally abated, and when the need to be free of Britain was acknowledged, then the pressures that made the Canadian colonies unite were greatly relaxed, and the old, underlying regional differences sprang up again.

During the twentieth century, Canada has had to generate internal forces to replace the external pressures promoting national unity. And great strides have been taken through the building of transcontinental railways, roads, airways, telegraph and telephone systems, through the setting up of national broadcasting and television networks, the emergence of national church synods, national scientific and academic councils, great national industries, nationwide economic and social policies, and the increased range of power of the Federal Government. Nevertheless, a growing sense of Canadian nationhood has not prevented a lively feeling of regional individuality. The separate problems and opportunities of the individual regions of Canada have bred regional modes of thought, made all the more distinctive by the way in which artists and writers have picked out the unique features at the expense of features held in common. Many people have feared and are still afraid of regionalism, because they equate it with separatism. And this has some-

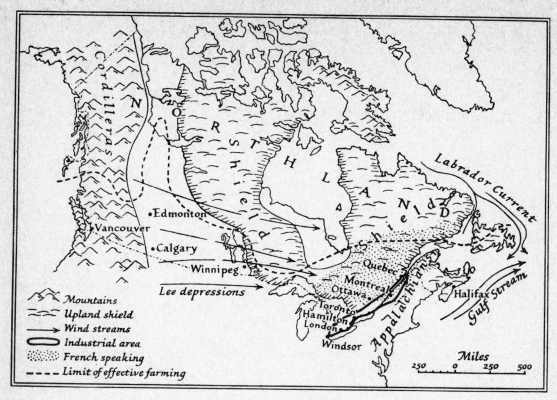

FIG. 1. Factors in Canadian Regionalism

times been the case. To permit regionalism to develop may involve internal tension. But then, as the Abbé Maheux has shown, such tension is a challenge and a spur to new understanding and a richer harmony. Of course, there are Canadians who find it difficult to meet this challenge and who try to resolve the tension by increasing separation. Those authors whose attachments are to all that the "Loyalists" stood for, glory in the British connection; those who honour the French past, look to France; those who have no particular ties with Britain or France, and they are becoming an ever greater portion of the Canadian people, ape the American. If they were allowed to have it their way the country would disintegrate, and a great and noble experiment in multi-cultural development would fall to the ground.

But regionalism need not mean disintegration. It may mean diversification. And as long as all the diversities involved recognize their dependence upon each other,

they can actually add to the idea of unity. Certainly they can enrich that unity by giving it many ways of expression. And this is what most Canadians are ready to do. Aware of their diverse origins and interests, they are willing to make room for their regional differences. At the same time, they are anxious to use these differences to fill out and enrich their experience as a people in themselves, sharing North America with the United States (and yet being more than Americans), and acknowledging a common heritage from Britain and France (yet growing beyond either of their motherlands). If this is so, we must ask, to what extent do the regions of Canada differ from each other, what are their special characteristics, how have they been expressed and how have they helped to round out the Canadian character as a whole?

Let us begin with the Atlantic Provinces which were the first to be discovered and settled by the British and French—Newfoundland, Nova Scotia, Prince Edward

Island and New Brunswick. They form a rugged and broken region, mountainous, storm-beaten and sea-infested. They have no large plain, no gathering place for a large population and no great node or crossroads of routes. They tend to be cut off from the rest of the country and have no easy access to markets. Agriculture and industry are limited and people have relied to a greater extent than elsewhere on the mines and forests of the hills and on the fish of the ever-present seas. The sea is of special importance. As in most maritime regions, it forms the great link between the landward parts. But here it is of particular value because the landward parts are difficult, and often hostile. Men, therefore, look to the sea and depend on it to an unusual degree. Running as it does through the Belle Isle and Cabot straits into the Gulf of St. Lawrence and so to the very heart of the region, it forms the great highway, even though it is blocked by ice for part of the year. The sea's presence is everywhere—not only in bay, sound and gulf, but in the maritime airs that sweep over the region, modifying its climate, its flora and its fauna. And it is not merely the geographical interpenetration of land and sea, it is the economy of their mutual dependence that counts. This is a "gateway" region, handling many of the imports and exports of Canada, especially during the long winter when the St. Lawrence estuary is frozen over. Then, Halifax and Saint John become the outlets for all Canada east of the Rockies. Coastwise traffic, between parts of the region itself, is also of tremendous value. It is the coalfield by the sea, the iron mine by the sea, or the lumber camp by the sea that have long been the chief centres of activity. Farming is also affected, being most favoured where nearness to sea ameliorates the severity of winter and lessens the danger from autumn frost.

Yet the sea is something more than a maritime economy. It is part of the thought and sentiment of the people. The sea as a *felt* reality, more than tides, capes, coastal meadows or little settlements pinned to the shore, more than the call of the sea in fishing and whaling and carrying and trading; the sea as man's battle with storm and disaster and, indeed, with life itself—all these are in the heart and mind of a people who, because of these things, think of themselves as different from dwellers in the Canadian interior.

Charles Bruce, writing of his fellow Nova Scotians, says:

> These are fellows who smell of salt
>   to the prairie
> Forever mindful that something wet
>   and wild
> Creeps and loafs and marches round
>   the continent.

The Maritimers cannot get the sea out of their blood. As another Nova Scotian poet, Kenneth Leslie, writes, their hopes and ideals, their memories and stories are not

> ". . . mouthed from a book
> But taken alive and terrible from
>   the sea."

Leslie's best-known work, *By Stubborn Stars,* is full of the sea's testing and the sea's reward, and he says of his life:

> The silver herring throbbed thick
>   in my seine,
> Silver of life, life's silver sheen of
>   glory.

Sea, tide, wind and crag, then, are part of the human struggle; they have entered into the character of the people. Thus, E. J. Pratt, the greatest of all the Atlantic poets, writes of his home, *Newfoundland:*

> Here the tides flow,
> And here they ebb;
> Not with that dull, unsinewed tread
>   of waters
> Held under bonds to move
> Around unpeopled shores—
> Moon-driven through a timeless
>   circuit
> Of invasion and retreat,
> But with a lusty stroke of life

Pounding at stubborn gates,
That they might run
Within the sluices of men's hearts.

Pratt is taken up with the struggle of life against the sea, or rather of the struggle for life within the sea, and the part the sea can play in the achievement of power, or maturity or greatness. His most successful poems are those about *The Cachalot,* the fight for the mastery of the seas between the saurian strength of the beast and the will and cunning of man; or the sinking of the *Titanic* with all that it revealed in the character of men; or the *Roosevelt and the Antinoe,* an epic of courage and mercy as one ship rescued another in the perils of the deep. Struggles of this kind stress individual reaction and put an unusually high premium on individual initiative and judgement, will-power and skill. The late Dr. Innis makes much of this. Writing in his preface to Grant's *The Atlantic Fishery* he says:

The [fishing] industry depended ultimately for its efficiency on the individual fisherman. The scattered character of the fishing grounds, the importance of individual initiative...[led] to the growth of a strong sense of local importance. Whereas the fur trade [in the interior] was characterized by centralization, the fishing industry was characterized by decentralization. The Maritimes have continued, as a result of the dominance of fishing and of their geographical background, to emphasize individualism and flexibility.

These traits are by no means confined to the fishing communities but have spread throughout the region and become quite general. For example, they characterized *Sam Slick,* Haliburton's lovable Yankee, who, though no fisherman, believed in "free trade and sailors' rights", and whose shrewdness, address and individuality, as he peddled his clocks amongst the Nova Scotians, have become a byword not only in Nova Scotia but throughout Canada.

In the next major Canadian region—Quebec—ingenuity and resourcefulness are not lacking, and the individual still has his importance. Yet there is a difference. He tends to gain that importance through the group, and it is his work for the group and the strength he derives from the group that are significant. This is partly due to his cultural heritage, but in part it evolves from his environment—from the struggle with the *land* where everyone has been committed in the task of conquering the wilderness. In Quebec, the sea is virtually ignored and the lessons man has to learn are the lessons of the land. Indeed, no people in Canada have shown such a passionate love of the land as the dwellers of Quebec. There is a long shore and much sea in Quebec, but somehow the high mountains of the Gaspé and of the Canadian Shield tend to shut the sea out. These same mountains look into, and focus life upon, the St. Lawrence plain. This plain is much narrower and more enclosed than anywhere else in the whole length of the river, and, shut in as it is between wall-like mountains, has drawn the people of Quebec together. It has made them an inward- and not an outward-looking folk. They have concentrated most of their effort and devotion within a restricted hearthland, reaching out into the uplands or towards the coast or to the interior only to draw these remoter areas back to the essential home. If ship and wave are emblems of the Atlantic, plough and soil characterize Quebec. Arthur Bourinot sings of the "plough's bright spade", that "bites straight and true", and of soil that is "quick with the dust of men." We have moved into a different world.

Part of this love for the land was that the land had to be *made;* it was not there for the taking, like the sea; and it had to be made by each individual, from his own strength and skill, *though coupled with the will and work of wife and family,* and supported by village and church. And what a difficult land it was to make, heavy with boulder clay, stony from the long shingle beaches left by the receding post glacial seas and obstructed by a thick growth of maple and pine. An immense amount of work was required to make it habitable—more than was asked from men in the Annapolis Valley or by the shores of the Lower Great Lakes where both soil and climate were more agreeable.

In Louis Hémon's classic of French-Canadian life, *Maria Chapdelaine*, he has the mother of the heroine say:

If there is anything which could reconcile me to living in the woods, it is seeing my men make a nice bit of land—a nice bit of land that was full of trees and stumps and roots which one beholds in a fortnight as bare as the back of your hand, ready for the plough: surely nothing in the world can be more pleasing or better worth doing.

Again Hémon writes,

While waiting upon [her men-folk] Madame Chapdelaine asked a hundred questions about the day's work, and when the vision rose before her of this patch of land they had cleared, superbly bare, lying ready for the plough, her spirit was possessed with something of a mystic's rapture.

With hands upon her hips...she extolled the beauty of the world as it existed for her: not the beauty wherein human beings have no hand, which the townsman makes such an ado about with his unreal ecstasies— but the quiet unaffected loveliness of the level champaign, finding its charm in the regularity of the long furrow...

It might be asked, why should this be the vision of Quebec? Surely *all* pioneers shared in this dream and experienced this joy, whether they "made land" in the Maritimes or the Prairies? That is true, yet none showed such a deep love for the land; such a tremendous attachment to the soil as the *habitant* of Quebec. As Michael Brunet claims, there was a sort of "messianic" faith in the French peasant's move to the new land and this, coupled with his deep suspicion if not hostility of the State, made him love his own plot in his own parish in a way that no British-Canadian could match. To the latter, land was real-estate, it was something to speculate with and, if it could show a higher value by using it for road development, city growth, or the expansion of recreational facilities, then it was withdrawn from the plough and put to work in more profitable ways. Love of the soil, of owning it and working it and living on it and dying on it, is basic to Quebec, and it arouses everywhere in Canada a real and deep sympathy for the rural virtues that have become associated with Quebec. Canadians who know the French-Canadian *habitant* are somehow strengthened against the temptations of an almost too-affluent American society by the recognition that thrift and foresight, frugality and simplicity, patience and endurance and, above all, work and a belief in work, are assets in the nation's character not lightly to be ignored. Yet the suprising thing is that over 80 per cent of the people in Quebec no longer live on the soil. The vast majority of French-Canadians today live in town and city. Indeed, almost 40 per cent of them live in Montreal alone. Yet many of them still preserve the rural virtues of loyalty to family and love of work even when they have become townsmen.

None the less, the fact that they *are* townsmen is beginning to tell. It is making them more like townsmen in Toronto or Winnipeg or Vancouver. They are more aware of the commercial and industrial ties that bind them to the town-centred areas of the head of Lake Ontario and the Niagara and Windsor peninsulas. They are becoming more cosmopolitan. This is expressed in a new school of thought which Guy Sylvestre in his essay on French-Canadian literature calls the "literary" school to distinguish it from the older "patriotic" school. The "literary" movement is sophisticated, cosmopolitan, liberal and forward-looking. It is centred in Montreal. The "patriotic" movement, promoted by writers and artists in Quebec city, is conservative, nationalistic and backward looking.

In the thirties, a third school arose: the school of realism, and these realists began to describe the French-Canadian in terms of the same difficulties and problems faced by English-Canadians. Emphasis was placed on poverty, unemployment, crime, over-crowding, juvenile delinquency, urbanization and industrialization. As Gerard Tougas says, instead of trying to reconstruct an Eden that no longer existed, contemporary French-Canadian novelists began to shake the pillars of their society, namely religion and family. Jean Simard became openly critical and Roger Lemelin, ironic if not sarcastic, exposing the hypocrisy of those who maintained the old modes in the new conditions. Langevin was frankly anti-clerical, and Filiatrault anti-filial. Other writers dwelt on the changing social pressures that brought about the great new changes in personal relationships. Thus, Gabrielle Roy's *Alexandre Chenevert* describes the sufferings of men caught up in the complications of modern life, large in heart but confused in mind and restricted in circumstance. In other words, the new writing reflected a growing awareness that Quebec was linked with the modern forces in Canada by the increasing commercialization and secularization of life. It could not escape what was happening in the rest of the St. Lawrence basin, and especially what had revolutionized its immediate neighbour, Ontario.

It was at this stage that English-speaking writers in Montreal such as Hugh MacLennan, Morley Callaghan, A. M. Klein, F. R. Scott, Patrick Anderson and Louis Dudek began to have a great impact on the life of the Province. MacLennan's *Two Solitudes* is full of the tensions which the sharp juxtaposition of race, religion and culture in the cosmopolitan city has produced. Callaghan wrote about Montreal as though it were any one of the St. Lawrence-Great Lakes towns. When criticized for doing so, he replied, "But it was!" It was far more like Detroit or Chicago than French-Canadian towns such as Trois Rivières or even Quebec City.

A. M. Klein finds all Canada in Montreal. It is its inclusiveness, its representativeness, its cosmopolitan nature that he sings:

> Grand port of navigations, multiple
> The lexicons uncargoed at your
> quays,
> Sonnant though strange to me; but
> chiefest I,
> Auditor of your music, cherish the
> Joined double-melodied vocabulaire
> Where English vocable and roll
> Ecossic
> Mollified by the parle of French
> Bilinguefact your air.

Frank Scott goes further, delighting not so much in the presence of many races and creeds but in the idea that man will someday subsume all races and creeds, since social and economic forces in the great centres of life like Montreal and Toronto are one with each other and make a new kind of unity. In his *Villanelle For Our Time* he writes:

> The lesser loyalties depart
> And neither race nor creed remain
> From bitter searching of the heart.

Obviously, this kind of writing is expressive of a spirit that sees beyond the boundaries of French or English speech, British or Roman Law, the Protestant or the Catholic faith, to a sense of interdependence that must bring and keep people together.

It is out of this togetherness that a feeling of unity has been and is growing up in Ontario and Quebec, in spite of what the "separatists" say. The two Provinces are closely and inextricably linked. Together they form the linch-pin of Canadian unity. They dominate Canadian life. They control the economy. Ontario and Quebec produce 81 per cent of all the manufactured goods in Canada; in fact, within the Commonwealth, this region ranks second only to the United Kingdom in manufacturing. This great concentration of power, accompanied by a shift of population from country to town and by a change in occupation from primary to secondary production, has resulted in a new landscape, full of double-line railway tracks, multiple-lane highways, great strings of telephone and electricity cables, cities sprawling over the countryside and land use geared to the city. In Ontario, as in Quebec, many writers tried to ignore this and held on to their love of the countryside, describing an Ontario that was passing with the days. Others admitted the change but still went to the countryside for rest and inspiration. But most of them took part in the change and helped it along by writing about the new industrialized, commercialized and urbanized way of life. Two poems of Alan Creighton's come to mind. In the first he is full of nostalgia for the beauty of the countryside; in the second he sees the promise in the towns:

Spring Burning

Beyond the twirling wood smoke
The fixed town lies with factories,
    railroads, and steeples
Wearying one with its static grip,
    its subterranean deadness.
Even the motor traffic is a robot
    monotony of conventional transfer.
But this spring-burning close by,
    breaking away, bloody and rapid
Bewilders me into an entranced
    acceptance of misty hills,
Making me husky and excited,
    affronted by houses...
After years, my obeisance to birds,
    trees and brooks
As I feel in my hand a fluff of
    burnt grass.

The second poem is entitled *Woodman's Return,* and after describing the isolated and confining life of the forest-worker, concludes with the following lines:

He stumbled on
Toward a firm horizon
Till, below clear hills,
Lay his town, black and unspring-like.
But in it would be no loneliness of
    cloud
Of dawn and sundown.
For in it were lives—
Lives strong in knowing him
Of the same curves and texture.

The younger poets and writers hardly ever get out of the city. It is their life. And they find enough in it to give them hope, even though they see its dangers and sorrows. A writer like Raymond Souster is typical:

Search

Not another bite, not another cigarette
Nor a final coffee from the shining
    coffee-urn before you leave
The warmth steaming at the windows of
    the hamburger joint where the Wurlitzer
Booms all night without a stop...
Wrap yourself well in that cheap coat that
    holds back the wind like a sieve
You have a long way to go and the streets
    are dark
You may have to walk all night before
    you find
Another heart as lonely, so nearly mad
    with boredom, so filled with such strength,
    such tenderness...

Layton, soliloquizing on the nature of things, cries:

God, when you speak, out of your
    mouth drop the great hungry cities.

The word "hungry" is tremendously significant. It signifies communities growing so roughly, strongly and rapidly as to prey upon human nerves, human sensibilities, and human decencies; it means an urban sprawl that is so great it swallows up some of Canada's loveliest and most productive countryside—such as the Niagara Fruit Belt; it portrays centres of power that reach right out into farming and lumbering and mining areas to make them subservient to urban interests and modes of living; and yet it bodies forth the vital entities of a region hungry for new ideas, new ideals, new techniques, new plans and all the best that is in people. Urban renewal, town planning, landscape design, regional development—these are the living issues of industrialized Ontario and Quebec; issues born of the city. The way in which these problems are being tackled in Toronto and Montreal is influencing the approach to urban problems and the outlook on city life throughout the Dominion, and so is making a tremendous contribution from Halifax to Vancouver.

When one turns west to the open prairies, the cities and towns fade into the background and life concerns itself with the fortunes of the elements. True there are great cities like Winnipeg, but their greatness rests on wheat and cattle and all that is involved in raising these. Roy Daniells, who lived and taught in Winnipeg for many years, is urbane in style, but his quest, like the title of his book, leads him *Deeper Into The Forest,* into the realms of being where man has to come to grips not only with his nature but with the nature of things.

> Lonely, lovely, in the midmost wood
> The hidden flowers translucent
>   petals spread.
> But I am a man, grown and filled
>   with trouble
> Double I am and daily conflict
>   rends me...
>   O inaccessible country
> Heard of, beheld, but ever remotely
>   folded
> Coldly in skies, floating, moated
>   of entrance
> When shall I press to your shore
>   past the unseen sentry?
> When shall I know what hands
>   your contour moulded?
> Or if the heart its own dark dream
>   fulfilled?

Here all the remoteness of the western lands, their vastness, the difficulty of ever grasping them, their openness, their surprising secrecies and above all their huge enigmatic skies challenge men to rethink their ideals and indeed rethink themselves.

One interesting thing that comes out in so much Prairie art and writing is the role of the skies and of their winds and rains, their hailstorms and droughts, their short hot summers ablaze with light and their long, dark, bitter winters, and all the rich part they have in the life of the people. Whereas with the Maritimes it is the sea, with Quebec the land and Ontario the street, here in the Prairies it is the sky that counts.

This is not only because there are few cities, hills or trees to block out the heavens and, consequently, there is a far greater stretch of sky, but because the skies hold the promise of help or threat of disaster to the Prairie dweller. If, in autumn and spring, day passes into day with nothing but high thin cirrus, if winds are northerly and keen, if continental airs settle over the land, then the peril of frost will stalk abroad; if in summer, clouds start up only to fade away week after week and dry warm airs from above the arid plateaus to the west descend and in doing so become a scorching blast, the spectre of drought haunts every community. The Prairies are on a knife-edge of hope between the despairs of frost and the terrors of drought. Hence, their tremendous preoccupation with the heavens from which help or destruction comes. Two pieces of writing bring this out: Frederick Grove's *Over Prairie Trails,* and Anne Marriott's *The Wind Our Enemy.* Grove's little book tells of his journey between his place of work and his home across stretches of prairie that included forest, bog and tall-grass meadows. Altogether, seven trips are recorded, and of these, four deal not so much with the landscape as with the land held in the grip of the sky. Thus, his second trip was made through all the eeriness of an atmosphere swirling and dripping with marsh-fog. His fourth and fifth journeys were through bitter storm. "I still remember," he writes, "the foreboding that I had challenged a force in Nature which might defy all tireless effort and the most fearless heart." Intense cold coupled with a whip-lash wind stung him to the bone, drifting the snow up over his path until he was all but lost and desperate and done. Yet he endured and came to his goal. And, symbolic of this success, the last trip is full of the calms and beauties of the great night skies that make so little of man's struggles and yet urge him to struggle on to their eventual peace.

Anne Marriott is less optimistic, more realistic. She knows that in the last resort the heavens have nothing to offer man that is not in himself. On the contrary they are constantly testing him and trying him out with tribulations and terrors that take everything in him to overcome. In the thirties, during the Great Drought, there seemed very little prospect that man ever would overcome, and the best that could be done against the implacable hostility of the heavens was to hold on and keep holding on. Anne Marriott's poem *The Wind Our Enemy* is one of the great expressions of the Canadian experience. It could only have been written of and from the Prairies. It could not have been true of any other region, and yet because all Canada shuddered at the trail of woe and destruction that swept over the Prairies, the experience was shared by all and became part of the national story. The opening lines of the poem are redolent of the anguish that had to be endured and the strength of will with which it was faced:

> Wind
> flattening its gaunt furious self
>   against
> the naked siding, knifing in the
>   wounds
> of time, pausing to tear aside
>   the last
> old scab of paint.
>
> Wind
> surging down the cocoa-coloured
>   seams
> of summer-fallow, darting in
>   about
> white hoofs and brown, snatching
>   the sweaty cap
> shielding red eyes.
>
> Wind
> filling the dry mouth with
>   bitter dust
> whipping the shoulders worry-bowed
>   too soon,
> soiling the water pail, and in
>   grim prophecy
> graying the hair.

Leaving the Prairie scene we come next to the Far West where mountain and rivers dominate the land, plunging into a coast made one of the most beautiful in the world by headland and fjord. There is no other area in which the relief of the land is so strong or matters so much.

The late Griffith Taylor had an article entitled *British Columbia, An Example of Topographical Control,* and his description of how relief affected vegetation and soil, land use and settlement showed that he used the term topographical "control" advisedly. While in other parts of Canada, relief may *influence* development, in British Columbia it virtually *dictates.* Even in the Maritimes, crossed by the Appalachians, relief is not nearly as significant—perhaps because the sea, which has no relief, penetrates into almost every part and dominates affairs. Certainly relief has played a much less significant role in Ontario and Quebec, and in the Prairies, although that is not to say that it has not been important. But in British Columbia and the Yukon it is supreme.

Hence, it should occasion no surprise to say that the supreme poem about this mountainous west is Earle Birney's *David,* which is a tense, vivid, dramatic description of an attempt to climb an all but unassailable peak in the Rockies. Here is the mountainous west at its best. For here is the challenge of the heights to men who insist on getting still higher, on being, in fact, the highest. Two friends make the attempt to climb an unknown peak with a bad overhang which they named "The Finger". All goes well till they reach the top when one of them relaxes and in doing so has a moment of incaution that makes his foot slip and stumble. The other, forgetting the austerity of peaks (carved out of the fury of the elements from the fierceness of livid rock), throws out a helping hand and, because of this human softness, himself slips, falls, hurtles over the cliff and breaks his back on a spur of rock below:

> *David*
> (vii)
> But always we talked of the Finger
>   on Sawback, unknown
> And hooked, till the first afternoon
>   in September we slogged
> Through the musky woods, past a

swamp that quivered with frog
And camped by a bottle-green lake...
At the base of the Finger we tried
  once and failed. Then David
Edged to the west and discovered
  the chimney; the last
Hundred feet we fought the rock
  and shouldered and kneed
Our way for an hour and made it.
  Unroping we formed
A cairn on the rotting tip. Then
  I turned to look north
At the glistening wedge of giant
  Assiniboine, heedless
Of handhold. And one foot gave.
  I swayed and shouted.
David turned sharp and reached out
  his arm and steadied me
Turning again with a grin and his
  lips ready
To jest. But the strain crumbled
  his foothold. Without
A gasp he was gone. I froze to the
  sound of grating
Edge-nails and fingers, the slither
  of stones, the lone
Second of silence, the nightmare
  thud. Then only
The wind and the muted beat of
  unknowing cascades...

Yet in this terrible failure, there is the human glory—the instinctive urge to help out against the pitiless power of nature—that somehow rises higher than the peaks themselves. In this sense, topographical control fails of its effect because it rouses in man the need to offset the power of the environment with powers suddenly released within himself. He is, in the ultimate, the maker of his own geography.

And that has, in fact, been the case. Anyone who has journeyed down the Fraser Canyon by train or by car must have been amazed at the way in which, while acknowledging the general control of this tremendous gorge, man has neverthless mastered all its terraces and its narrow places to fling bridge upon bridge over the river's awesome gorge and tunnel through spur upon spur, conquering one of the worst hazards Canada has to offer.

And this is because something of the strength and grandeur, the toughness and turbulence of mountain and river have entered into the people and made them exceptionally venturesome and determined. There is a vigour, a grimness, a courage, a conviction about West Coast painting and writing. Emily Carr's magnificent landscapes are full of height and light, harshness, destruction and conflict with, out of it all, a ringing transcendent beauty. The same kind of forcefulness and power is heard in L. A. MacKay's writing, except that here it is presented in finely-worked, highly-controlled beauty, as though chiselled out of granite. And no wonder, because in a sense he feels that he himself is hewn out of the rock. In his poem *Nunc Scio, Quid Sit Amor* he writes:

I know him now, not now to know
  demanding,
No goddess-mother bore a child
  so grim,
So only terrible, though he were
  standing
Swordless, among the sworded
  seraphim.
The hard rock was his mother;
  he retains
Only her kind, nor answers any sire.
His hand is the black basalt, and
  his veins
Are rocky veins, ablaze with gold
  and fire.

Doubtless it was because of this "gold and fire", this hardness and splendour, this challenge and magnificence, that the West long gripped the imagination of Canada and became the main goal of the bold and adventuresome.

However, the North tends to displace the West in the Canadian image of the frontier today, and it is in the North that men have at last found something distinctively Canadian such as no American region can rival. The North means an emptiness to be filled, a potential to be realized, a wealth to be discovered and unlocked, a future to be staked and deeds to be done that are uniquely Canada's chance and challenge. The vast structure of the Laurentian Shield, which is the very core of the continent, lies almost entirely in Canada. Quite narrow at the west end of Lake Superior it widens out in an immense embrace to take in most of Canada from Labrador to the Mackenzie delta. Long considered barren and intractable, it was thought to be a hopeless barrier, a cross to be born; it separated eastern from western Canada, driving a great wedge of virtually uninhabited land in between. Then it came to be seen as veined with mineral wealth and as an unmatched source of hydro-electric power. Though it had few agricultural possibilities it had great forestry reserves. Consequently, it called out for exploration and exploitation, and, as its mines, power dams and forestry camps attracted ever more capital and labour, as they demanded tools and machines of the manufacturing East, and wheat and meat from the food-producing West, the Shield began to be recognized as the great bridge uniting east and west; as indeed the keystone of the arch of Canadian character and identity.

Hence, many of Canada's painters and poets have turned to the North for today's inspiration. They have sought in its vastness, and stoniness, and loneliness and power the source of a new belief in Canada, of new hope in its future, and new faith in its being. Their work has brought a quietness, a clarity, a simplicity, a dignity and a sense of purpose that have immensely heartened and strengthened Canadians. Undoubtedly, it was the School of Seven who directed the nation to the North, and painters like Tom Thompson came with a new grace and a fresh point of view to their fellows. Writers were not slow to follow. In A. J. M. Smith's *The Lonely Land* we catch something of the stillness and clearness and loveliness of the loon-loud lake locked in its stony fastness far from man, and yet of immense significance to man. For, from this quiet strength a new firmness and conviction are borne home to the people and they can go back into the turmoil of existence not only re-freshed but somehow refurbished in mind and spirit:

> ...This is a beauty
> of dissonance,
> this resonance
> of stony strand,
> this smoky cry
> curled over a black pine
> like a broken
> and wind-battered branch
> when the wind
> bends the tips of the pines
> and curdles the sky
> from the north.

> This is the beauty
> of strength
> broken by strength
> and still strong.

The poets before the war saw the North largely in these terms, that is, as *inspiration*. To the poets after the war it was even more, it was a *dedication*. Here, Canada could dedicate its will and energy, its imagination and skills, its courage and faith to capturing its real future and fulfilling its own unique destiny. This is what comes out of Patrick Anderson's magnificent poem on Canada, which reaches its climax in the vision of the North. For it is in the North that Canada at last finds herself, and finds an answer alike to the challenge of America and the appeal of Europe; since the North is something to put against the American pull to the south, and is more than Britain and France can offer.

It is perhaps fitting, therefore, to end this paper on the regions of Canada with lines about a region so eminently Canadian as the North—a region which may do so much for Canada if its tremendous potential can be captured and used. As Anderson writes:

> ...And the North was. With winter
>   the snow came.
> Whole folios of it. Yet nothing written
> except one thing, a bleak
>   expectancy—
> the possible with its strenuous shade

of whiteness,
where an intuition almost without
equipment
could trek into the faint wind of
the future...

What are you? They ask, in
wonder
What are you? They ask.
And she replies: I am the wind that
wants a flag
I am the mirror of your picture
until you make me the marvel of
your life...
America's attic, an empty room
a something possible, a chance, a
dance
that is not danced. A cold kingdom.

The aura of the future irradiates the whole North, and through that gives a glow to the nation at large, since each major region of the nation has its portion of the North. It is this belief in a greatness still to come and in a destiny still to be fulfilled that gives Canada one of its most distinctive features and makes it a land whose future must rouse an ever greater interest, especially among its neighbours and friends.

To conclude, then, Canada, is divided into regions, each with old associations of its own, each with very real differences in tradition, way of life, outlook and interest, and each with a belief in itself and its ideals. Regionalism, which is so deeply entrenched in geography and so strongly etched in history, could divide a country and might even lead to its disintegration. Yet regionalism, developed with a view to helping each part of the country help the country as a whole can greatly strengthen and enrich national unity. Canada has a tremendous problem to face, yet a wonderful opportunity to exploit, in the wealth of its regional differences. With the vision and the will to use these differences to its own advantage the Canadian nation can afford not only to tolerate but to welcome Canadian regionalism.

*

BIBLIOGRAPHY

Poems or novels quoted in the text may be read in the following anthologies. Their authors are discussed in the literary or cultural histories listed.

Birney, E. *Twentieth Century Canadian Poetry*. Toronto: Ryerson, 1953.

Carman, B., *et al. Canadian Poetry in English*. Toronto: Ryerson, 1954.

Dudek, L. and I. Layton. *Canadian Poems, 1850–1952*. Toronto: Contact Press, 1952.

Gustafson, R. *Anthology of Canadian Poetry*. London: Pelican Books, 1942.

————*Canadian Accent*. London: Pelican Books, 1944.

Klinck, C. F. and R. E. Watters, *Canadian Anthology*. Toronto: Gage, 1955.

Lortie, L. et A. Plouffe. *Aux Sources du Présent*. Toronto: University of Toronto Press, 1960.

Pacey, D. *Creative Writing in Canada*. Toronto: Ryerson, 1961.

Park, J. *The Culture of Contemporary Canada*. Ithaca: Cornell University Press, 1957.

Rhodenizer, V. B. *A Handbook of Canadian Literature*. Ottawa, 1930.

Robins, J. D. *A Pocketful of Canada*. Toronto: Collins, 1948.

Roy, C. *Manuel d'Histoire de la Littérature Canadienne-Française*. Montreal, 1927.

Smith, A. J. M. *The Book of Canadian Poetry*. Toronto: Gage, 1943.

————*Oxford Book of Canadian Verse in English and French*. Oxford University Press, 1961.

Tougas, G. *L'Histoire de la Littérature Canadienne-Française*. Paris: Presses Universitaires de France, 1960.